W9-CKF-956

# Rural Land Tenure in the United States

# Rural Land Tenure in the United States

## A SOCIO-ECONOMIC APPROACH
## TO PROBLEMS, PROGRAMS, AND TRENDS

**ALVIN L. BERTRAND, Editor**
Professor of Sociology and Rural Sociology
Louisiana State University

**FLOYD L. CORTY, Assistant Editor**
Associate Professor of Agricultural Economics
and Agribusiness
Louisiana State University

**and Associates**

**Louisiana State University Press**
**Baton Rouge**

" I have often thought that if heaven had given me choice of my position and calling, it should have been on a rich spot of earth, well watered, and near a good market for the productions of the garden. No occupation is so delightful to me as the culture of the earth."

THOMAS JEFFERSON

# Preface

THE PREOCCUPATION OF agricultural economists, rural sociologists and others with land tenure research during the last fifty years predestined this book. It is the logical outgrowth of two major concerns of specialists in the field. The first stems from the lack of a volume which pulls together, in succinct and systematically organized fashion, the information contained in the many fine studies in the field. The second major concern is related to the need for presenting tenure problems in their total social aspect and not separately from the economic or sociological point of view. The importance of the latter is reflected in numerous recent discussions and formal papers relating to land tenure.

A clue to the features of this book which set it apart from previously published works on land tenure is found in the above. Specifically, four features make it a unique contribution to the field. First, it is an attempt at a systematic presentation of the voluminous current research knowledge in the field of land tenure. The first-hand information and wide acquaintance with tenure research agencies by the specialists writing each chapter will be readily apparent to the reader.

In this regard, many tenure publications treating specialized problems have not been widely publicized and consequently have escaped the attention of potentially interested persons.

A second feature of this book which stands out is its interdisciplinary approach, combining sociological and economic understandings. Although various chapters have been written by professionals in one or the other field, all chapters have been reviewed by persons representing the second discipline. As a matter of fact, chapter outlines were reviewed and revised by a joint committee before work was started on the individual chapters.

The third feature which makes this book distinctive is its emphasis on change. It was recognized that tenure relations, as rural-social relations in general, were dynamic and transitional. Technological innovations, government programs, population changes, and other factors constantly impinge upon farm people, causing them to change their behavior. The reader will see that the focus in each instance is on process, with static connotations carefully tied down as to time and space characteristics.

The fourth and final feature which characterizes this volume is a section devoted to the conceptual framework of sociology and economics and to the research approaches used in the study of land tenure. In this way the student can visualize how tenure studies fit into the broad theoretical framework of the separate social sciences as well as appreciate the specific application of statistical and other methods to tenure study.

It is well known that symposiums present problems of organization, content, and style. Cognizant of these problems, the Southwest Land Tenure Research Committee (sponsor of this volume) moved to minimize them by giving primary editorial responsibility to two of its members. Alvin L. Bertrand, Rural Sociologist, was elected editor-in-chief, and Floyd L. Corty, Agricultural Economist, was elected assistant editor. The editors in turn asked for and received full permission of the contributing authors in coordinating, standardizing, and integrating, the various chapters. They, therefore, assume full responsibility for shortcomings in organization and style which may be apparent.

The Southwest Land Tenure Research Committee, no longer active, was jointly sponsored by the Farm Foundation, the agricultural experiment stations of Arkansas, Mississippi, Louisiana, Texas, and Oklahoma, and the Economic Research Service of the United States Department of Agriculture. The committee was active in tenure research from 1939 to 1961 and it is not inappropriate to say that it included among its members some of the foremost tenure specialists in the nation. While the sponsoring agencies of the tenure committee were apprised of this project, it is not an official document of the agencies, and the views expressed are those of the writers alone. However, all participants gratefully acknowledge the opportunity provided by the committee's sponsors for undertaking this project.

ALVIN L. BERTRAND
FLOYD L. CORTY

# List of Contributors

ALVIN L. BERTRAND: 1 and 3; coauthor, 2, 15, 16, and 17
Departments of Sociology and Rural Sociology
Louisiana State University

LAWRENCE CHARLTON: coauthor, 16
Department of Agricultural Economics and Sociology
University of Arkansas

FLOYD L. CORTY: 11 and 12; coauthor, 2, 15, and 17
Department of Agricultural Economics
Louisiana State University

NELSON L. LERAY: 13
Economic Research Service
Farm Economics Division
United States Department of Agriculture

FRANK H. MAIER: 4, 5, and 6
Economics Research Service
Farm Economics Division
United States Department of Agriculture

HENRY J. MEENEN: 8
Department of Agricultural Economics and Rural Sociology
University of Arkansas

L. A. PARCHER: 10
Department of Agricultural Economics
Oklahoma State University

FREDERIC O. SARGENT: 9
Department of Agricultural Economics
Ontario Agricultural College

ROBERT L. SKRABANEK: 7
Department of Agricultural Economics and Sociology
Texas Agricultural and Mechanical College

JAMES D. TARVER: coauthor, 15
Department of Sociology and Rural Life
Oklahoma State University

GEORGE L. WILBER: 14
Division of Sociology and Rural Life
Mississippi State University

GENE WUNDERLICH: 18
Economics Research Service
Farm Economics Division
United States Department of Agriculture

# Table of Contents

# List of Figures

# Rural Land Tenure in the United States

# Part 1: Introduction

AGRICULTURAL RESOURCES ARE held and used under certain "tenure" arrangements which specify the relationship of people to the land. These arrangements are all important in terms of the production of agricultural commodities and the well-being of the persons who till the soil. Part I is a general and theoretical introduction to the subject of land tenure. In Chapter 1 the interdisciplinary nature of land tenure is discussed, land tenure is defined, and a conceptual model—the social system—is presented for the study and understanding of this subject.

Chapter 2 is a summary presentation of the important concepts in sociology and economics and is designed to provide the reader with an understanding of technical terms used throughout the volume. Something of an innovation insofar as land tenure works are concerned is offered in Chapter 3. A description of the major tenure systems found the world over is presented along with the social and economic organization characteristics of each system.

# CHAPTER ONE

# Land Tenure: Definition and Conceptual Frame of Reference

THERE HAS BEEN a growing concern over land tenure problems in national and world agriculture within recent years. This concern stems from the realization that social and economic development everywhere is dependent on wise and equitable practices and policies regarding the use of the land.[1] In the United States much time and considerable resources have been spent studying tenure patterns and problems. This volume presumes to be an interdisciplinary approach, bringing together sociological and economic understandings relative to land tenure in this country. It is predicated on the belief that the subject of land tenure cannot be fully understood from the standpoint of one discipline alone.[2] The hope is that the synthesized approach will be a contribution to the study of land tenure in and of itself.[3]

Two aims were foremost in the writing of this chapter. First, in keeping with an integrated approach to the study of land tenure, it was necessary to make explicit those particular aspects of the relation of man to land which were to be considered. Also, it was necessary to lay the groundwork for a socio-economic understanding of land tenure theory and research.

---

[1] This is the central theme of a recent volume. See *Modern Land Policy, Papers of the Land Economics Institute* (Urbana: University of Illinois Press, 1960).

[2] For a succinct and scholarly treatment of the unity of the social sciences see George Simpson, *Man in Society* (New York: Doubleday & Co., Inc., 1954).

[3] A comprehensive discussion of the interdisciplinary approach appears in Wilbert E. Moore, *Economy and Society* (New York: Doubleday & Co., Inc. 1955).

## Definition of Land Tenure

Perhaps the best way to present a comprehensive definition of land tenure is to review certain key concepts which are an integral part of the definition. The first term which is basic to the definition of land tenure is *property*, or more precisely *property in land*. One must go back to the ancient Romans to find the origin of the word property. It was used by them as " propter," a Latin adverb meaning " according to custom." The word gradually spread to France and from there followed the Norman conquerors into England. Here it was anglicized as " proportie," " propriete," etc. and understood to mean a feudal privilege or relationship. About the time of the Industrial Revolution (the late eighteenth and early nineteenth centuries) " liberties " (as feudal privileges or relationships) were disassociated from the term, and it began to assume its present connotation.[4]

Today there is common agreement that property is " the system of rights of persons or other social units in ' scarce ' values." [5] Property rights, as Black's Law Dictionary points out, are guaranteed and protected by government. In a general sense, property may be viewed as defining the relations between persons which relate to scarce values. As Wilbert E. Moore states, " A right is meaningless unless there are potential challenges to that right." [6] In other words, the concept of property must include more than the idea of control over scarce values and productive wealth. It must be understood to mean the power relations, real or protential, between persons holding property rights and those persons who do not. This is how property will be used in defining land tenure.

The second term to be considered is *division of labor*. From the time of Adam Smith to the present, this concept has been a recognized one in social science analysis. Economists point out that such things as how the allocation of useful work is accomplished, what is causally involved in specialization, and the origin and function of particular labor systems, among other things, must be considered if one is to understand productivity in its total sense. To the sociologist labor is only one basis for the social differentiation of society. It is understood by them in terms of statuses and roles; that is, the association of occupation and work with age, sex, race, education, etc. In this

---

[4] The writings of Locke, Adam Smith, Hume, and Blackstone played an important part in bringing about the change in definition.

[5] Moore, *Economy and Society*, 12.                    [6] *Ibid.*

way they can explain certain restrictions to the response of a labor supply to a market demand and aid the economist in his predictions. The important point is that the combining of the labor and wage theory of economists with the status and role theory of sociologists makes for a more adequate understanding of the institutional aspects of division of labor and for a more workable definition of land tenure.

The third term which is basic to land tenure theory and which helps to explain the usefulness of the interdisciplinary approach is *exchange* (or *distribution*). According to economic theory, laying aside all qualifying statements for the sake of simplicity, the impersonal market distributes economic rewards according to merit. Merit (or economic contribution), however, is too narrow a concept to explain fully the distribution principle even in a " free " market. The sociological concept of " values " (ideas as to whether objects or behavior are good, bad, desirable, etc.) is one of use here. It helps explain such things as government intervention (in the form of subsidy measures, for example), preferences of tenants, motivational factors, etc. All of these factors enter into the broad concept of tenure.

It is now possible to attempt a definition of land tenure. As understood here, *land tenure means the customary and codified rights which individuals and groups have to land and the behavior characteristics which directly result from these rights.* The reader will readily see that the above definition denotes social relationships manifest in the property rights which individuals and groups have to the land.[7]

*The bundle of rights concept:* The conceptual scheme which has been used most often to illustrate the varying rights of individuals to land is that of the " bundle of rights." According to this concept, a part or all the rights to the land may be contracted by the owner to others. The idea is that there are many kinds of rights to land as property and that these may be shared with a tenant or others. Roland Renne points out that property rights may be split between various owners, between owner and occupier, between owner and occupier and creditor, and between private and public owners.[8]

[7] T. Lynn Smith, *The Sociology of Rural Life* (3d ed.; New York:  Harper & Bros., 1953), 274. Marshall Harris summarizes the important considerations for understanding land tenure as a concept in *Land Tenure Workshop Report* (Chicago:  Interregional Land Tenure Research Committee, Farm Foundation, December, 1956), 1–13.

[8] Roland R. Renne, *Land Economics* (New York:  Harper & Bros., 1947), 429.

The bundle of rights idea is portrayed graphically by the *fasces* which was used as a symbol of authority in the Roman Empire. The fasces consists of a bundle of sticks tied around an ax. The sticks are symbolic of the varying rights in land, while the ax represents the supreme authority and superior rights of the state. The rights of the sovereign state include that of *eminent domain* (use of the land for a public good) and of *escheat* (reversion of property to the state for want of a competent inheritor).

The larger bundle of rights may be conceptually divided into three smaller bundles to represent special classes of rights: the right to use, the right to lease, and the right to sell. These broad classes are further subdivided into many specific rights pertaining to use, lease, or transfer of a particular piece of property.

### A Model for the Study of Land Tenure—The Social System [9]

Scholars are continually searching for analytical devices to make their studies more meaningful. From the social science point of view, the model of the social system provides a sound theoretical frame of reference for understanding tenure relations.

Although this model has been used more extensively by sociologists than economists, it lends itself well to economic conceptualization. For example, there is little difficulty in adopting the economic model of the " firm " to a specific farm operation conceived in a somewhat broader sense as a social system. The latter is the more inclusive term, and this is why it has been selected as more appropriate for an interdisciplinary approach. The person who may have difficulty in reconciling economic terminology and concepts to the social system model may profit by referring to the discussion of the farm firm in Chapter 2. The point to remember is that an interdisciplinary model must be adaptable enough to provide a theoretical frame of reference for explaining social relationships relating to economic goals and other goals as well. The social system model is designed as an analytical tool for studying human relationships per se and thus may be used by all social scientists. It is described in detail below.

The term social system is used generally to refer to a complex web of social relations beyond primary groups. More specifically, the term

[9] The discussion in this section is part of a report prepared by the writer for a land tenure workshop. See Alvin L. Bertrand, " The Social System as a Conceptual and Analytical Device in the Study of Land Tenure," *Land Tenure Workshop Report*, Chap. VII.

refers to integrated social interaction at various levels. For example, in concrete social systems the members interact more with other members than with nonmembers when participating in the system as an ongoing concern. A tenure or family group would be identified as a concrete social system.[10] An abstract social system is one in which the patterns of relationship prevail from one generation to the next and from one geographic area to another. Systems of religion, such as Roman Catholicism, exemplify such systems.

Social systems are also characterized by subsystems. Thus, the American social system may be thought of as a going whole, while certain aspects of American life such as the family, education, religion, etc., represent systems within the systems. The central core of a family system would be in the immediate conjugal group, father, mother, and children, whereas subsystem relationships would be evident in the interaction with close relatives such as grandparents, aunts, uncles, etc.

Regardless of type, tenure group, family, or church congregation, social systems are characterized by two common elements—social structure and value orientation. The reader must be aware of both if he is to understand the behavior of individual members.

The social structure of social systems may be explained as follows: In given societies an individual learns quite early in life that certain members of the society are expected to do different things, according to their positions or status in the community. If he has high status, the individual has more or less authority—the privilege of influencing the action of others. If he has low status, he is more subject to the influence of others. Behavior according to role and status is assured, because a person in a given system is compelled by the folkways, mores, or legal codes to conform.[11] At this point it may be noted that territoriality or location in space is important. Thus, in one locality a given set of rules for behavior will apply, while in another an entirely different set of rules will exist. Regardless of behavior requirements, structure is apparent and is an important part of the system.

[10] Charles P. Loomis and J. Allan Beegle, *Rural Sociology, The Strategy of Change* (Englewood Cliffs, N. J.: Prentice Hall, Inc., 1957), 1–3. The elements, processes, and patterns of social systems are discussed in detail in Charles P. Loomis, *Social Systems: Essays on Their Persistence and Change* (New York: D. Van Nostrand Co., Inc., 1960), 1–56.

[11] For an operational definition of Rural Social Organization, including the concepts of folkways, mores, etc., see Chap. 2. See also Alvin L. Bertrand *et al., Rural Sociology* (New York: McGraw-Hill Book Co., 1958), Chap. II.

The second component of social systems is value orientation or the nonpurposive behavior which persists in interpersonal relations. This may be illustrated by reference to the intangible factors which bind groups together such as loyalty, affection, etc. Charles Loomis and Allan Beegle state, " For purposes of empirical procedure, we consider value orientation as including the *ends* or *objectives* and *norms*." [12] In other words, value orientation not only accounts for the " rules of the game " but for the things, ideas, or goals considered worthwhile. Generally, greater harmony (morale) will result when all members of a system are in accord with the value orientation and conform to group expectations.

*Tenure groups as concrete social systems:* The conceptual scheme of the rural social system has been developed most intensively by Loomis and Beegle. They quite logically place tenure groups under the general designation of social strata systems. In defense of their classification these scholars state, " In all agricultural societies there are designations for roles; the chief differences among which are tenure variations of the respective rights to the use of and the control over land." [13]

From the discussion in the preceding section it is clear that social systems are made up of unique networks of social relationships. Therefore, to speak of a tenure-social system one must have in mind, clearly, two things: the specific actors and their pertinent behavior. Both may be identified easily and quickly, if the reader accepts the explanation that a tenure-social system includes only those persons or groups interacting meaningfully in terms of their rights to, and use of, a particular parcel of land. In other words, the term applies to the persons and groups involved in a single operation only. This definition places no size limitation on either the number of persons or amount of land. For example, tenure systems can range from small family farm operations to huge plantation or hacienda-type operations. With the above definition in mind, one can readily verify that tenure systems are true social systems.

The fact that there are differentials in status, role, and authority in tenure systems and that one can place or rank individuals quite easily in given systems is the first clue that such systems are bona fide social systems. The validity of this statement is made clear, if the previous illustrations are further pursued. In a family farm operation, for example, there is a definite pattern of authority and decision-

[12] Loomis and Beegle, *Rural Sociology*, 33.                    [13] *Ibid.*, 309.

making and definite roles and statuses. The father, mother, siblings, and others in the household, as well as occasional hired hands, know fully well their privileges and duties. On a plantation operation, the groups and individuals involved are just as cognizant of their rights and responsibilities. Here, however, the scope of operation is such as to introduce the further understanding of the subsocial system. For instance, a particular tenant may operate under the general direction of an overseer or supervisor but may in turn be specifically responsible for the successful operation of his particular allotted acreage.

The above provides the primary criteria for delineating tenure systems, although other tests remain before they can be finally classified as social systems. First, it must be clear that there are definite objectives which members hope to achieve through operation of the system. This is a simple matter of logic. The most obvious end-goal of agriculturists is economic sustainment or betterment through the production of agricultural products. Other goals might be apparent in unique instances but would be relatively minor.

The next test is whether or not meaningful interaction between persons within tenure systems is greater than with outsiders in the attainment of the goals of the system. This, too, seems a question with an obvious answer.

In terms of the objective mentioned above, persons in a tenure system cannot help interacting more meaningfully with others in the system.

The final test is found in the question of whether or not there are norms within the system which apply specifically to the system and govern action of all kinds within the system. In applying this test, one can think of the folkways, mores, and laws associated with the roles and statuses in given tenure systems. This contemplation immediately brings home the realization that certain norms or standards of behavior apply especially to these specific relationships and are responsible for the behavior patterns.

The fundamental attributes of social systems listed below provide an adequate yardstick for classification of behavior traits in tenure systems.[14] Social groups or systems are commonly classified according to the nature of the ties or bonds which hold individual members together. The terms used by Ferdinand Toennies, *Gemeinschaft* and *Gesellschaft*, are utilized in the remainder of this discussion. (See

[14] *Ibid.*, 18–25.

Chapter 2.) *Gemeinschaft* refers to group relationships that develop
unconsciously or subconsciously while *Gesellschaft* refers to those
groups entered into deliberately for the achievement of recognized
ends. The latter would generally be more applicable to the achievement of economic goals.

*(1) Nonrational vs. rational action:* The wholly rational act is one
in which the interpersonal relationships of the members of a system
in no sense are identified as ends or goals in and of themselves. In
contrast, the nonrational act is recognized as one in which the relationships and interpersonal bonds are the only significant ends. To illustrate, in a tenure system characterized by *Gemeinschaft* relations the
aged, unproductive tenant will not be cast off by the landlord merely
because he may not produce as efficiently as a younger person. Nor
will a close relative, such as a son, be discharged because of economic
considerations. In contrast, in a system characterized by *Gesellschaft*
or rational relations, efficiency might be the sole key to the security
of the tenant or relative.

*(2) Functional specificity vs. functional diffuseness:* The activities
of members of a social system may be general or specific in nature.
Thus the rights and responsibilities of a plantation owner-operator
over his sharecroppers may be quite paternalistic, including a wide
range of "responsibilities" to his subordinates. Such responsibilities
may go so far as to include getting them out of jail on occasions. This,
of course, would be an extremely *Gemeinschaft* type relationship. In
contrast, the relationship may be very specifically limited to certain
contractual obligations as in certain lease or rental agreements. In
the latter, the landlord's obligations are limited to what is specifically
written down. Here we see the *Gesellschaft* relationships.

*(3) Community of fate vs. limited responsibility:* One characteristic
which will help the social scientist classify a particular tenure system
is whether or not the hardships and gains are shared in proportion by
all members in the system. In a *Gemeinschaft* situation, such as the
family farm, this would be true; whereas in a more or less impersonal
*Gesellschaft* situation the landlord and/or tenant would feel little
responsibility to share his fortune or misfortune with the other.

*(4) Integration of roles within and outside the system:* Some social
systems jealously guard their prerogatives and do not allow their
members to play roles outside the system which conflict with their
roles in the system. In the *Gemeinschaft* system a landlord, for ex-

ample, might prevent a tenant from assuming a position of authority outside the farm situation which would give him additional status before his peers. In a *Gesellschaft* situation the landlord would not have the authority or inclination to interfere with the personal life of his tenant.

In summary, one can readily see that behavior characteristics in tenure situations must be known and understood before they can be classified. Admittedly the tools and techniques for measuring these relationships have not been refined as much as they might be. It is certain, however, that enough refinements have been made along these lines to provide sociologists and economists with fundamental insights into human relationships in the rural land tenure setting.

# The Conceptual Framework
# of Sociology and Economics

THE FOLLOWING CHAPTER is a brief introduction to the conceptual framework of sociology and economics for those readers not especially familiar with these disciplines. To endeavor to condense the basic theory of a major discipline into a few pages is difficult. Perhaps this task is best approached by pointing out certain basic facts, defining several key terms, and introducing the reader to conceptual models used in the two disciplines.

## The Sociological Approach

Two basic facts provide a *raison d'être* for sociology. The first is that *human behavior is patterned* or *ordered* similar to the patterning of natural phenomena. The second factual basis for sociology is that *man is a social creature*.

One has but to observe the everyday activities of men to see that certain acts are performed in a more or less standardized way. One may further convince himself that behavior can be anticipated by describing beforehand the eating and dressing habits of his associates.

The simple test outlined above brings out an important facet of sociological prediction. A member of a group is able to predict the behavior of his associates because he knows how they *should* act in given situations. It is thus that the four general concepts or ideas of the so-called " exact " sciences—regularity, structure, function, and change—do not suffice for sociological analysis. A fifth general concept or idea—*meaning*—must be added.[1] This concept refers to the fact that individuals behave according to their interpretation of a situation in the light of their cultural experience.

---

[1] John W. Bennett and Melvin M. Tumin, *Social Life* (New York: Alfred A. Knopf, Inc., 1948), 82.

14

Many writers, beginning with Aristotle, have pointed out a natural tendency for men to associate themselves in groups. Indeed, group association holds the answer to human behavior, since the latter cannot be explained in terms of instinct. The examples of " feral " men of " isolates " demonstrate that it is necessary to look for explanations of behavior in the realm of learning and experience.

The above remarks set the stage for a definition of sociology. In simplest terms, sociology is the *scientific study of human relationships*. More elaborately, sociology may be defined as the *generalizing science and theory of social action systems*. The basic concepts in the field, defined below, provide a further understanding of the nature of sociology.

## Basic Sociological Concepts

The concepts of sociology, like those of other disciplines, are terms of general reference. They are used to refer to types or classes of events, persons, or relationships and are not concerned with the nonrecurrent or unique. When defined precisely, sociological terms are devoid of moral connotations. Many of the concepts of sociology are used popularly in a different sense—such as status, society, race, etc.— and must be defined with extreme care for professional usage. Sociological concepts generally have a higher level of abstraction than the same words do in ordinary discourse.

The first basic sociological term to be defined is *social interaction*. This is the key concept in sociology. It refers to the reciprocal contact (interstimulation and response) between individuals and groups. The study of interaction may take many forms, but it has two aspects which are commonly analyzed. The first aspect is termed *social structure*. The understanding here is that society (as a complex structure of groups and individuals) is held together in a web of social relationships. Sociological inquiry of this nature is directed toward discovering and understanding the arrangement of persons in their culturally defined relationships. The second aspect of interaction which is usually analyzed is *social function*. This concept includes the contribution one part of society makes to the larger social system of which it is a part. Ely Chinoy makes the point that, on the most general level, " function refers to the contribution of any social or cultural item to the survival, persistence, integration, or stability of society as a whole." [2]

[2] Ely Chinoy, *Sociological Perspective* (New York: Doubleday & Co., Inc., 1954), 38.

The structural-functional aspects of sociology provide a conceptual framework for understanding much about human behavior. However, there is another term which helps understand social interaction. Those types of interaction which occur over and over with great uniformity are designated *social processes*. The latter may be identified as " solidary " if they involve behavior such as cooperation, accommodation, or assimilation. Antagonistic processes are indicated by behavior which is competitive or conflicting. It may be noted that in actual life almost all situations contain behavior which represents more than one interactional process.

With the concept of interaction in mind, we turn logically to the concept of *social differentiation*. It is clear even to the most unsophisticated observer that no two individuals are alike. One person differs from another in age, sex, race, education, marital status, occupation, skills, intelligence, wealth, and power, among other things. These differences are recognizable by members of the society and are the basis for the assignment of various duties and responsibilities to individuals and groups. In sociological parlance the differential participation of individuals in their groups and the greater society, which is related to their varying characteristics, is termed social differentiation. The concept of social differentiation is not only a device for relating the differences among individuals to differential social participation but, in another sense, is useful in evaluating the desirability of various human attributes in a given society.

Social differentiation within a society is best understood in terms of *roles* and *statuses*. Everyone is familiar with the fact that individuals fill a number of positions in society. For example, one person may be a landlord, parent, male, president of the Farm Bureau, and many other things at one and the same time. The sociological name for a social position relative to other positions is *status*. A person's status determines the nature and amount of his responsibilities and obligations as well as his superior-inferior relations to other members of the group. Individuals come to occupy statuses in two entirely separate ways. One group of statuses (ascribed status) is acquired at birth without effort or choice—such as race, sex, and social class. Other status positions are thrown open to competition and are known as achieved status—such as occupation, education, elected political office, etc.

Each status carries with it certain rules of conduct which guide the social relationships of the occupier with others. The patterns of be-

havior expected of those who occupy given statuses are defined as
*roles*. Social roles are prescribed for every status, and interaction
becomes predictable to the extent that individuals behave in accordance with the norms of their roles. Social roles fit together in a given
society as a rule, with reciprocal relations such as that between landlord and tenant and husband and wife calling for reciprocal obligations.

*Social organization* is the term used to describe the everchanging,
complex network of patterned human behavior within a given society.
Social organization is more meaningful if one understands the technical
usage of the term *society*. To the sociologist, a society is " that group
within which men share a total common life." [3] In simpler language,
a society is a collection of people, characterized by a sense of belonging
together, who are sufficiently organized to carry out all the necessary
conditions for living together. Used in this sense, aggregates of individuals such as the crowd at a baseball game or attending a concert
would not be societies, whereas tribal or national groups would be
societies.

Another concept basic to sociological inquiry is *culture*. This concept is a complicated one and is used in two senses by sociologists.
The first or generic sense is used to refer to all man-made environment,
whether material or nonmaterial. The second and more specific meaning of the term is the " social heredity " of particular groups of people.

The study of culture is significant in the prediction of human behavior as follows: Persons behave, as a rule, in accordance with what
they have learned is acceptable in their groups. Thus a knowledge of
the culture of any group goes a long way toward explaining the
behavior of individual members of the group. The term *subculture* is
employed to designate the unique cultural heritage of smaller groups
within a greater society and explains local variations in behavior.

At this point it is possible to answer the question as to why human
behavior is orderly. The answer is found in the nature of culture.
Orderliness arises out of culture because of certain universal elements
found in all cultures. These include: (1) *folkways* or commonly accepted rules of conduct which do not carry compulsive status, (2)
*mores* or " must-behaviors," and (3) *laws* which codify and reinforce
the mores and control behavior outside the scope of the mores. The
reader will recall in Chapter 1 how the elements of culture were discussed as an important part of social systems. Conformity to the
folkways, mores, and laws is assured because of societal sanctions to

[3] *Ibid.*, 21.

the point of force. Cultural requirements of the above nature are transmitted to the oncoming generations through the process of socialization.

In the context of culture there are certain important human needs or values around which folkways, mores, and laws tend to cluster. For example, many cultural traits are clustered around the biologically determined need for reproduction. These complexes or clusters of cultural norms and usages and the resultant controls for enforcing them can be identified as *systems of social relationships*. In sociological parlance they are customarily termed *social institutions*.

The terms *group* and *system* have been used in connection with the above discussion without having been made explicit. These concepts are central to the understanding of social organization but must logically be defined after the concepts of social differentiation and social interaction are in mind. They are used in much the same way by different schools of sociology. Social groups or systems come into existence when various statuses and roles interlock in a pattern of interaction within a society. The prerequisites for a group or system are two or more people in definable interaction directed toward attaining a common goal and oriented through a pattern of structured and shared symbols and expectations. Relationships among group or system members normally will persist over some time. Groups or systems are classified according to their characteristics in too many different ways to list here. However, it may serve a purpose to note their most common elements.

According to Loomis, there are nine elements which are characteristically found in all concrete social systems. These are: (1) belief (knowledge); (2) sentiment; (3) end, goal, or objective; (4) norm; (5) status-role (position); (6) rank; (7) power; (8) sanction; (9) facility. Each element is articulated by certain social processes. Specialized elemental processes articulate the separate elements, and comprehensive or master processes articulate several or all of the elements of a system.

In concluding this discussion, it may be noted that group or system relationships are normally differentiated according to their nature. The terms *Gemeinschaft* and *Gesellschaft*, defined in Chapter I, are commonly used to classify broadly the relationships predominant in given systems. By way of review, the former refers to group relationships which develop unconsciously or subconsciously, and the latter designates group relationships which are entered into deliberately for the achievement of recognized ends.

## The Economic Approach

Economics is a discipline concerned with the allocation of scarce resources for the purpose of satisfying human wants.[4] The stage for describing our economic system may be set by visualizing the need and desires of people for various goods and services. They want bread, milk, meat, automobiles, clothing, housing, haircuts, etc. At the same time the resources used in production of goods and services—for example, land, cattle, oil, timber, minerals, machines, etc.—are scarce. How the people obtain and share these resources provide the drama of a complex and dynamic economic system.

### Households and Business Firms

First, let us consider how people of all ages—that is, babies, teen-agers, husbands, wives, and widows—give economic expression to their wants. Many are grouped together as families. Others act as individuals but, in either case, we may say they represent household units. Thus, households are the decision-making units for consumers.[5] They decide what, when, where, and how much to buy. Their purchases will depend to a great extent on level of household income plus willingness to buy.

Why are goods and services supplied? When entrepreneurs recognize an existing market for certain goods or services, as well as an opportunity to make a profit, they soon establish a business to supply the needed goods and services. Farmers, for example, will produce wheat to make bread and raise cattle to provide milk and meat. Ford and General Motors will manufacture automobiles. Textile mills will make clothing. Contractors will build houses. Barber shops will give haircuts. All of these are business firms engaged in the production of goods and services. It is obvious, then, that there are two principal decision-making units in our economic system—households and business firms.

### The Role of Money

Just as a catalyst is needed to encourage certain chemical reactions, money in our economic system serves as a catalyst to facilitate trading.

[4] John G. Evans, Jr., *Basic Economics* (Chapel Hill, N. C.: University of North Carolina Press, 1935), 5–8.
[5] George J. Stigler, *The Theory of Price* (Rev. ed.; New York: Macmillan Co., 1957), 42–43.

Instead of trading corn for eggs, shoes for bread, autos for houses, or beans for watermelons, the consumer will normally buy the desired items with money.

Initially, the money supply is controlled by the Federal Reserve System.[6] It exercises control over the lending operations of commercial banks by requiring that commercial banks maintain a certain level of reserves against their deposit liabilities. If the Federal Reserve Board (supervisory board of the Federal Reserve System) decides that the amount of money should be decreased, it can order the member banks to raise the reserve ratio by requiring larger reserve deposits. If the object is to increase the money supply, the reserve requirements are made more lenient. In addition to control of reserve ratios, the Federal Reserve System can manifest two other controls over the money supply: (1) It can change the actual volume of reserves held by member banks by buying or selling government securities in the open market, and (2) it can raise or lower the interest rate charged by the reserve banks for money borrowed by commercial banks.

By the exercise of control over member bank reserves, the lending policies of member banks are controlled. As long as member banks have adequate reserves, they may create additional money by lending funds to borrowers, thus creating demand deposits. Similarly, a reduction in reserves will lead to reduced bank loans and investments and a reduction in money supply. Bank loans and investments generally stimulate business activity and lead to increased employment. Employment provides wages and salaries. In addition to wages and salaries there may be other sources of income such as rents, dividends, interest, inheritance, gifts, or piracy.

Money as part of consumer income may be totally expended for goods and services, as would be true for low-income groups, or only partially expended by higher income groups, and the balance put into savings or investment. In either case the money flows back to business firms. In the first instance, the money normally defrays cost of production, and in the second, the money is used to develop or expand businesses. If saving takes the form of hoarding, money is removed from circulation and investment is curtailed.

[6] *The Federal Reserve System, Purposes and Functions* (Washington: Board of Governors of the Federal Reserve System, 1954), 31–55.

## The Economic Flow Model

It should now be evident that individuals and business firms serve dual roles. They are both buyers and sellers. Individuals buy goods and services and sell their labor and capital. Business firms buy labor and capital and sell goods and services. This leads to a circular flow model of our economic system [7] consisting of an interrelationship between the two principal decision-making units of our economic system.

## Price Determination Model

Demand for goods and services may increase because of an increase in income, an increase in population, an increase in need and desires, or a combination of the three. An increase in demand means that larger quantities will be taken without a change in price, or the same quantity will be taken at higher prices. How much the price will change, incident to the change in demand, will depend on how easily the supply can be adjusted to meet the new demand. If supply can be changed in like proportion, then it is likely that price will not fluctuate appreciably. On the other hand, when there is a sudden change in demand, there is usually a lag in the adjustment of supply. This is especially true for farm products because production is a time-consuming process requiring planting, growing, maturing and harvesting. Likewise, once the production cycle is started, it must run its course; hence the flow of agricultural products does not respond to price changes as readily as industrial-type products.

The theory of the interaction of supply and demand to arrive at equilibrium price is found in the cobweb model included in many economic texts.[8] How effectively equilibrium price is attained depends on the relative elasticities of the demand and supply curves.

Many variations may be introduced to explain the price determining process for individual commodities, but the principle of supply and demand remains the same. In the real world we recognize that price may not be the only criteria affecting supply and demand.[9] There can be many interruptions to theoretical adjustment. In agriculture, for example, weather may influence supply even more than price. Further-

[7] Richard H. Leftwich, *The Price System and Resource Allocation* (Rev. ed.; New York: Holt, Rinehart and Winston, 1960), 11–13.

[8] Walter W. Wilcox, and Willard W. Cochrane, *Economics of American Agriculture* (2d ed.; Englewood Cliffs, N. J.: Prentice Hall, Inc., 1960), 266.

[9] Walter Eucken, *The Foundations of Economics* (London: William Hodge and Co., Ltd., 1950), 134.

more, to reduce losses on committed capital a low price is better than no price at all, and in the short run, supplies may continue to flow despite falling prices.

If it is agreed that the interaction of supply and demand determines price, then it should logically follow that price prescribes the use of resources. A higher price encourages the commitment of more resources into production of the scarce good or service. A falling price will discourage the use of resources in a given enterprise and will divert resources into a more profitable use. Price, therefore, prescribes what, when, and where goods will be produced. Price also rations the goods to those who can afford to buy.

The price system within our economy functions most efficiently under conditions of perfect competition. But we recognize more and more that conditions of perfect competition rarely prevail. Imperfect competition and monopoly are increasingly prevalent, and institutional restrictions have impaired normal competitive pricing. Under these circumstances we find it necessary to have more and more government intervention and control. Monopolies, or partial monopolies, result from large capital structures, control of secret processes and patents, and control of raw material supplies or market supplies. These imperfect conditions are symbolic of institutional restrictions in our economy and give rise to additional institutional regulations and controls.

### Types of Business Firms

Business firms in our economic system are permitted the choice of four possible types of organization: single proprietor, partnership, corporation, or co-operative. The farm business is most frequently a private enterprise in which the farm operator is the owner. In many instances the farmer and his son may join forces and form a partnership.

There is a growing tendency, also, for farms to incorporate, particularly the larger farms. Incorporation permits accumulation of capital by selling stock in the business. It may reduce individual liability by increasing the number of owners. It may also provide certain income tax advantages if it is doing a sufficiently large volume of business.

The fourth type of organization is the co-operative, wherein resources of a number of units are pooled for the sake of gaining capital strength or bargaining power. In our economic system there are relatively few production-type co-operatives. Most of the successful co-operatives are those organized to attain bargaining or marketing advantages.

### The Farm Firm as a Business Unit

In the United States, the farm is one of more than ten million business firms that make up our complex economic system. This system is characterized by private enterprise and sufficient government control to perpetuate competitive conditions. Ownership of land and constant efforts to gain possession of other capital goods provide the motive for our capitalistic system. The distinguishing feature of this system is that each unit makes its own decisions concerning methods of production, inputs, outputs, price and distribution. There is no central committee, of a communistic nature, to make these decisions; nor is there the collectively planned activity characteristic of a socialistic society. The business decisions are made by private owners, whether they be sole proprietors, partners or members of a corporation.

Economic decisions of a business firm are generally made with one goal in mind; that is, to secure the highest profit possible. This is true of the farm firm also, except that our numerous family farms provide a way of life as well as a way to earn a living. The farm operator frequently places more value upon his outdoor freedom and rural environment than upon alternative urban opportunities which would increase his capital returns.

The farmer's way of earning a living and his mode of life rest largely upon the combination of resources at his command. Land, labor, capital and management are the essential resources. Labor, capital and management are variable resources as opposed to the fixed land resource. Therefore, tenure arrangements, or conditions and terms of holding land, determine to a large degree the success and well being of the farmer and his family.

Tenure arrangements extend from full ownership of land by the farm operator to lesser degrees of ownership by the part owner, and no ownership at all by the tenant, sharecropper and laborer. These latter three have decreasing degrees of privileges to use the land.

### Government as a Decision-making Unit

As mentioned previously, business firms and individual households are decision-making units. With the emergence of the Keynesian philosophy in the past quarter of a century, government is also recognized as a decision-making unit.[10] No longer is business allowed to proceed uncontrolled in the hope that natural forces will bring about necessary economic adjustments. The government fosters fiscal policies designed to induce certain conditions in the economy. Income, savings, and investment patterns are scrutinized rather closely when some form of economic adjustment appears necessary. If private investment is not enough to maintain a high level of employment, the government assumes the role of fostering additional investment. If unemployment becomes acute, government steps in to create job opportunities or to provide supplementary income in the form of unemployment payments. Welfare benefits in the form of food, clothing, and shelter may also be provided in emergency situations.

### Economic Classes

Our society is generally considered to include a number of economic classes. There are, for example, laborers, landlords, capitalists, and professional people. The classes are not mutually exclusive. It is possible that an individual could be classified under all four classes. This is surely one of the unique characteristics of our democracy. There are no economic, social, or legal barriers to confine a person to the class level acquired at birth.

Since a farmer usually represents several economic classes (laborer, capitalist, and landlord) he is considered a stabilizing influence upon the economy. It may be observed at this point that, when a sharp cleavage exists among different classes because of conflicting interests, there are tendencies to rebel, riot, or revolt. The goals of the individual classes are somewhat different, and it is only through a fair and equitable economic system that pressures for economic reforms remain dormant.

### Institutional Economics

A branch of economics concerned with the regulation and control of economic institutions has come to be known as institutional economics.[11] In the early, or what is generally termed classical, economic thought, the prevailing philosophy was to allow each person to do what

[10] John Maynard Keynes, *The General Theory of Employment, Interest and Money* (New York: Harcourt, Brace & Co., 1935), 245–54.

[11] John S. Gambs, *Beyond Supply and Demand* (New York: Columbia University Press, 1946), 4–26.

was best for himself, and in doing so all of society would benefit. Our recent economic philosophy, however, appears to recognize that not all activities work toward a common good. Uncontrolled competition can lead to economic piracy.

The institutional economist recognizes that competitors do not start at the same starting point, nor with equal handicaps, and competitive behavior can be greatly influenced by politics, wars, collusion, reorganization, capital accumulation, and contracts. Furthermore, the institutionalist looks at the system in its entirety and maintains that for the benefit of the whole it is necessary to mold and blend its constituent parts rather than have the individual parts prescribing the structure of the whole.

Under the standard or classical theory there is a tendency to oppose violently any government intervention in economic matters, but in true life experience the institutionalist recognizes that economic arrangements are constantly being altered by a world of laws and regulations. Under the institutional banner it is felt that economic disorganization requires the controls and guidance of government, that war and other disturbances occur with sufficient frequency to justify government intervention.

The institutional approach may also be called the new economic approach, wherein demand as well as supply is emphasized. The most significant breakthrough into this new area was engineered by Keynes in his book, *General Theory of Employment, Interest, and Money.* He called attention to the relationship between consumer income, consumer spending, savings, and private investment and to the effect of all of these on demand. A measured increase in national income, he said, hinged upon the marginal propensity to consume—that is, the amount of money people spend out of an additional increment of income. In turn, the amount spent generates additional economic activity and results in what he termed the multiplier effect. The end result is a generated income several times greater than the original injection of private income into the system.

The goals under the standard theory were to provide goods and services, but under the institutional theory the goals are visualized as social goals which, in a sense, may also fall into the category of welfare economics. In any case the accumulation of material goods by individuals and the conservation or wise use of resources for the community are still of paramount importance. In achieving these goals economists invariably re-emphasize the importance of evaluating gains in terms of real income rather than money income.

Our total economic system, therefore, embraces at the one extreme a *laissez-faire* economy with the ultimate in freedom of operation—a situation of perfect competition, perfect knowledge, and free pricing—and at the other extreme, government not only regulating economic activities but actually engaged in producing goods and services.

There is an unmistakable trend toward more institutional control. Free competition is disappearing as economies of scale become better recognized. Furthermore, it is evident that conflicts of interest prevail between the individual and society, that monopolies can result in lower costs and better service if properly regulated, and that exploitation of the disadvantaged can only be alleviated through government inspection and control. All of these developments lend increasing credence to the importance of institutional economics.

## The Relationship of Economics and Sociology

The preceding discussions make clear that the prediction of human behavior is the end-goal of both sociology and economics. Behavior patterns in both disciplines which are sufficiently well defined are called " laws," or principles. Presumably, laws are principles which prescribe an action or process with such a high degree of certainty that there are very few, if any, exceptions. Principles, on the other hand, prescribe actions which are reasonably predictable but because of possible variations or modifications cannot be classified as laws. Laws and principles generally provide the framework for formal sociological and economic studies, but they need not be the focus of attention when describing the social or economic system.

The subject of interest in sociology is human behavior per se. In the study of economics attention is focused on production functions and exchange of goods and services. The basic assumptions of the two disciplines are somewhat different. In sociology, it is assumed the goal of the individual is to be accepted by " his " society. In economics, the individual's goal is understood as the provision for his basic needs and the acquisition of wealth, perhaps not wealth for its own sake, but that one might eventually enjoy luxuries or power. The two disciplines come together here because, as long as wealth is acquired through socially acceptable means, the individual is commended, but if it is attained through piracy or other odious schemes, the winner becomes the target for public criticism and censure.

## Socio-Economic Aspects of Tenure

As indicated in an earlier chapter, a basic concept to land tenure is private property, that is, control over things by virtue of possession.[12] This implies ownership and conveys all the rights of ownership subject to approval by society. It is easy to see that this concept has both social and economic considerations, that the use one makes of a possession relates to societal institutions.

Another socio-economic institution, perhaps more social than economic, is personal liberty. Here again is a right, controlled by laws, customs, and tradition.

A third socio-economic aspect related to time is that of freedom of enterprise. The opportunity to tackle new things, to try new techniques, and to exercise initiative. Of course the enterprising efforts must be acceptable to society, and to meet this requirement certain standards are imposed in the form of special training or licenses, or both.

A fourth arrangement bringing economic and social considerations together is freedom to contract. This freedom permits any responsible individual to negotiate a contract or enter into an agreement to perform some service. In doing so, it is recognized that the personal liberty desired under the second objective is relinquished when a contract is negotiated.

A fifth socio-economic custom or institution is that of inheritance. This conveys the right to inherit wealth. Inasmuch as the right of private property is recognized, so also is the right to hand down or dispose of that property to heirs or other designated individuals. In recent years this right has been somewhat narrowed by the sovereign right of the state to take away a share of this inherited wealth.

Along with the five socio-economic rights mentioned above, a sixth shares major importance. This is the protection granted to certain interests through patents and copyrights. Presumably these are justified by providing profit incentives to those contributing new ideas or new techniques to society.

Other examples of how social and economic considerations come together might be given. However, the foregoing discussion serves to illustrate the interdisciplinary nature of the study of land tenure.

---

[12] G. W. Forster and Marc C. Leager, *Elements of Agricultural Economics* (New York: Prentice-Hall, Inc., 1950), 30–33.

# CHAPTER THREE

# Basic Types
# of Land Tenure Systems

THE PARTICULAR TENURE forms to be found in any country appear to a great extent to be the function of government. They are closely related to the social and economic well-being of the people. The latter fact sets the stage for the discussion in this chapter. Its concern is the major forms or systems of land tenure and the distinct patterns of social and economic relationships characteristic of each.

## The Relation of Land Tenure Systems to Social and Economic Organization

Pitirim Sorokin, Carle Zimmerman, and Charles Galpin developed the idea that forms of land ownership and land possession, as well as forms of social structure and function, should be considered in classifying types of rural population aggregates.[1] In so doing they pointed out that cultivators (farmers) could be divided into two broad groups —owners and nonowners. Farm owners might further be divided into individual owners (including families) and collective owners such as village communities. Nonowners were divided into: (a) tenants of private landlords and tenants of collective landlords (both public and private), and (b) laborers and employees of private and collective landlords. The thesis of these scholars is that social organization in a given rural community would reflect orientation to a particular tenure system. By way of illustration they point out, among other examples, that individualism and individual initiative are usually more developed in a community of individual farm-owners on small holdings than in a community where one or a few men own all the land and

[1] Pitirim A. Sorokin, Carle C. Zimmerman, and Charles J. Galpin, *A Systematic Source Book in Rural Sociology* (2 vols.; Minneapolis: The University of Minnesota Press, 1930), I, 558–645.

the workers are serfs, laborers, or nonmanaging tenants of one kind or another.

Many other scholars have developed the same theme. One of the foremost writers on this subject is T. Lynn Smith. In discussing size of holdings, Smith summarizes the social and economic implications of various tenure forms as follows:

> The extent to which the ownership and control of the land is concentrated in a few hands or widely distributed among those who live from farming is probably the most important single determinant of the welfare of the people on the land. Throughout the world wherever there is a widespread distribution of land ownership and control one also observes (1) the strongest propulsions to steady work and the maximum of thrift: (2) the highest average levels and standards of living; (3) the least development of social stratification, the fewest class distinctions, the relative absence of caste, and very little class conflict and class struggle; (4) a high degree of vertical social mobility so that the individual comes nearest to occupying the social position commensurate with his natural abilities and the amount of effort he personally is willing and able to put forth; (5) general intelligence that is at a high level and a minimum in range; and (6) a rural population possessed of well-rounded and highly developed personalities.[2]

The above discussion emphasizes the social and economic significance of tenure forms. It also indicates why type of ownership may be used as a major criteria for classifying systems of tenure.

## The Major Types of Tenure Systems

There is a voluminous literature on land tenure which dates back to early times. Although these writings represent a multitude of interpretive views, they agree generally on historical fact. It is thus possible to detect and categorize representative types of tenure systems at different points in time. In attempting to select and describe basic tenure systems, the writer is well aware that it is possible to differentiate a great variety of systems on the basis of one or more specific

[2] T. Lynn Smith, *The Sociology of Rural Life* (3d ed.; New York: Harper & Bros., 1953), 297.

criteria. However, if differences in detail are set aside, at least five general types emerge.

### Restriction of Rights to the Use of " Free " Land

The first indication of tenure considerations is found among certain preliterate or primitive societies. Among these groups the appropriation of land has not assumed importance in and of itself and the land is viewed as free in total. Yet, even in societies which have progressed no further than a hunting and fishing economy, exclusive claims sometimes are made on certain parcels of land. Such spots may have religious significance, such as burial sites, or they may represent choice hunting and fishing grounds. Whatever their value, they are jealously protected against trespassers.[3] These types of tenure are termed " emergent " because they usually have led to the concept of property in land.

Interestingly, where the right of property is established by religion, it is much more complete and absolute in its effects than it can be where it is founded on other principles. This is illustrated by the fact that landed property related to domestic religion cannot be renounced without renouncing the religion itself. The history of ancient peoples is full of accounts of beliefs in the sacred nature of land, and this thought persists in many modern societies.[4]

*Social and economic organization:* It should be clear to the reader that these so-called emergent forms of tenure are only found in certain types of societies—those which have not progressed beyond a hunting, fishing, and gathering economy. When people are nomadic and characteristically rove over large areas in search of food and other necessities, individuals have little cause to attach great value to a specific piece of ground.

The social organization of nomadic groups is usually relatively simple —certainly law is for the most part uncodified and familistic in nature. Tribes, clans, etc. are under the leadership of a chief or elder, and every tribesman is linked to every other tribesman by intimate personal bonds. Social differentiation is at a minimum as is social mobility.

---

[3] For a comprehensive coverage of such customs in primitive societies see Robert H. Lowie, *Primitive Society* (New York: Horace Liveright, 1920), 205–56.

[4] For a latter day argument to this effect see James B. Converse, *The Bible and Land* (Morristown, Tenn.; Rev. James B. Converse, publisher, 1889).

Not only is there little differentiation or stratification in preliterate nomadic groups, but economic institutions are simple and traditionalistic in form. Change is usually frowned on, and the old ways are considered best. Apparently change is accepted more readily by sedentary groups, as is witnessed by their development of more involved tenure forms and use of higher technology in areas where nomadic groups and sedentary groups are still present. In the first form of tenure discussed, it can be seen that both economic and social efficiency are at a bare minimum.

*The agregados of Brazil—a unique modern example of an emergent tenure form:* T. Lynn Smith describes a present-day practice in Brazil which may be classified as an emergent form of land tenure. This process is unique because the first tenure relation is one of renter or share-tenant.

Throughout a large part of Brazil land is very cheap, and is held in extremely large holdings by proprietors who are primarily interested in keeping enough people about so that they can secure required help. Always there is the *falta de bracos* in Brazil. It is not easy to retain a labor force because population is sparse, it is easy to secure the means for satisfying basic creature wants, and the lower classes lead a nomadic type of existence. Under these circumstances tenure relationships tend to become very informal indeed. Through long practice the rural people (the *caboclos, matutos, sertanejos*, etc.) feel free to " squat " where they please. They may establish their temporary quarters almost anywhere, erecting rough temporary shelters, making small rocas from which to harvest a little mandioca or maize, collecting and shelling babassu, preparing carnauba wax, searching for diamonds, cutting wood, or fishing. If left to themselves this class of people will continue to live a nomadic life, gaining a precarious livelihood by hunting, fishing, collecting, and destroying the forests in order to get a little corn or mandioca from the rocas they make. Since labor is always the limiting factor in Brazilian production, the landowner may find it to his advantage to allow these rural folk to live on his land; even foreign concerns soon discover that it is a mistake to try to fence them out. Moreover, if the person who owns the land supplies a needed axe, offers a little ammunition now and then, provides necessary medicines, furnishes a few of the minimum essentials for improving the hut, aids them in getting fishing equipment, allows the use of a pack animal, etc., he may in time get them to agree to bring in a pig now and then, or a few chickens, or a portion of the corn crop, a little mandioca, or finally to work a day once in a while. . . . By degrees some of these people may come to be part of the fazenda, the owner's agregados, and the others move on. The nature of their tenure is not very clear-cut, or rather, it does not fall into the categories familiar to students of land tenure in the United States.[5]

## Communal Arrangements for Use and Control of Land

The second form of tenure arrangement to be taken up is what has been called village communities of joint owners. Examples of this type of arrangement were or are found in China, India, Germany, England, and many other places. It should be noted that true communal farms are differentiated from so-called collective farms managed or operated by state governments. The latter are discussed as examples of large farms under public control and management.

*Social and economic organization:* Under communal tenure patterns the inhabitants are almost always grouped into villages. They are bound together by a series of social, economic, and political ties. Since everyone is considered a co-owner of the land, social differentiation and stratification is relatively slight, and members of the community are homogeneous. Little social mobility is evidenced, as each person's place and tenure status is pretty well set at birth.

Communal communities are self-governing, with the usual pattern being that the elders are considered the leaders. Since the norm is collective action in work, recreation, ceremonies, and even religious rites, a strong sense of unity develops along with a firm traditionalism.

It has been observed that communal communities exhibit a greater sense of co-operativeness than found in communities characterized by other forms of tenure. However, from an economic standpoint such communities do not appear as well-off as communities characterized by full owners or operators on small holdings. Seemingly, the incentive to work and save is not as strong. The character of communal villages can best be seen in an illustrative description. The mark, characteristic of early Europe, serves admirably for this purpose.

[5] From T. Lynn Smith, *Brazil: People and Institutions* (Baton Rouge: Louisiana State University Press, 1946), 459–60.

*The mark as an example of a communal community:* The mark
had its most extensive history in early Germany.[6] It consisted of an
area of land owned, occupied, and cultivated by a group of families
in common. Usually, one mark was separated from another by a tract
of waste land. The mark itself, as Enoch Bryan points out, was
composed of:

> (1) the village area, divided into lots of equal size, which were
> assigned to the members of the community; (2) the arable mark
> (Feldmark), or arable land lying about the village in two or three
> fields and apportioned in holdings of equal size among the free-
> men; (3) the common mark, or pasture and waste land surrounding
> the arable, which was the common property of the community.
> Each family of the mark organization or rather each freeman,
> as the head and representative of this social unit, had an equal
> share in the arable land and equal rights in the common mark.
> In the earliest times the allotment of this share was supposed
> to have been made annually by lot or otherwise.[7]

In summarizing the important features of the mark as a communal
society, Bryan points out three interesting essentials of the community.

> First and most important is community of property. The theory
> on this point is not always clearly stated. At one time the land
> is said to be owned by the entire village community; again it is
> alleged that there is no ownership, merely undisputed possession
> is communal, and private property is nonexistent. It must not
> be forgotten this ownership by the mark is distinctly different
> from family ownership. It represents a different state from that
> in which the family is the proprietary unit. It is true that,
> according to the theory, holdings are distributed to the families
> as represented by their heads, the freemen. But the ownership,
> if such it may be called, remains with the community. Nor is it
> the same as joint ownership. The mark was not a company of
> which the individual markmen were the members and of whose
> property they were co-proprietors. The units of which the mark
> was composed became vested with no proprietary rights which

[6] For a detailed description of the mark see Enoch A. Bryan, *The Mark
in Europe and America, A Review of the Discussion on Early Land Tenure*
(New York: Ginn & Co., 1893), 7–19.
[7] *Ibid.*

they might sell, donate, or bequeath. When the holder of a portion of the arable and rights of common died, the holding reverted
to the community and was again allotted.

The second essential feature is that of freedom and self-
government. Slavery may have existed, but the mass of the
people were free.

The third essential feature is the substantial equality of the
markmen. All members had equal political rights and privileges.
And it was the equality of sovereigns. Together they made the
simple laws and administered the simple justice which such a
state of society required. The same equality extended to the
holdings of land and rights of pasturing stock and feeding pigs
and gathering wood in the forest. The manifest and intentional
tendency of this arrangement was toward equality of possessions
and social standing, though some writers have admitted that
there were grades of wealth and rank.[8]

The above correctly implies that true communal systems can only
operate in relatively simple societies, where a subsistence agriculture
suffices. In advanced societies the problems of social control are such
as to make it impossible to maintain impartiality in the distribution
of lands and produce.

### Control of Land by Independent Classes of Small Owners or Tenants

A third basic type of tenure arrangement also has its origin in
antiquity. This is the ownership or control of relatively small holdings
of land by free farmer classes. An outstanding example of this type
of tenure is the family farm in the United States.

*Social and economic organization:* The characteristics of rural populations where holdings are small and individually owned or operated
differ considerably from communal communities. In the first place,
houses tend to be dispersed as each farmer strives to live on his own
land. There are, of course, many examples of village patterns of
settlement, but these are not as characteristic as under communal
arrangements.

A second difference is found in the tendency for more social differentiation and higher social stratification where men are free and control their own holdings. Some farmers may be relatively rich, while others

[8] *Ibid.*

are relatively poor due to differentials in ability, work, or good fortune. Under communal holdings all would remain at approximately the same level. Communal groups are more general practitioners of mutual aid, equality, and cooperativeness.

Another difference between communal rural aggregates and aggregates of individual farm owners or renters is that social mobility is greater. This is true because property is easier to come by and there is incentive to better oneself. The " agricultural ladder " provides the steps whereby one may climb from laborer to owner in the course of a lifetime. (See Chapter 8.) There is no hope of eventual betterment in communal communities or where land is controlled by a few.

When farmers are free, they are more likely to be characterized by contractual types of exchanges. Perhaps in no other tenure form is individualism, initiative, rationalism, and modernism as well developed as it is among independent classes of farmers on small holdings. It is here that opportunity for change is found, because behavior, belief, and the mores in general are more plastic than in all other types of rural tenure arrangements.

*The family farm in the United States:* There never was a peasant agriculture in the United States, although some of the first settlers attempted to establish socage tenure. Rather there developed a class of small freehold farmers characterized by a strong belief in democracy and social equality. Of course, there were other forms of land holding but these were relatively minor, except for the sharecropper system in the southern region of the nation. Also, there developed an ideal that a man should own and operate his own farm, which has persisted until the present time.

In the United States the family-sized farm is generally thought of as the ideal unit, from the social, if not always the economic, point of view. What is meant by " family farm " is generally understood, but the term is nevertheless difficult to define precisely. Joseph Ackerman and Marshall Harris provide one of the clearer definitions when they indicate that the family farm (1) vests entrepreneural functions in the family, (2) requires farm family effort greater than that of outside labor to operate the farm, and (3) is large enough to employ farm family labor resources efficiently.[9] Estimates of the number of

[9] Joseph Ackerman and Marshall Harris, *Family Farm Policy* (Chicago: University of Chicago Press, 1947), 389. A detailed description of the U. S. family farm is not given here because of the numerous discussions of this tenure form throughout the remainder of this volume.

family farms in the United States range from one-half to two-thirds
of all farms. So whatever the definition and despite organizational
trends in nonagricultural business, the family type farm has demonstrated a noticeable persistance.

Family farms in the United States weave a pattern of widely dispersed or scattered homesteads. Each family tends to live on the
farm it operates, and homes are placed to best advantage in relation
to topography, roads, and farm operation rather than in relation to
the neighboring farms. The nearness and symmetry of farm dwellings
is dependent on topographical conditions, type of farming, and straight-
ness of roads. Nevertheless, the general pattern is that of farmsteads
" scattered " over the countryside.

There are many examples of farms held and operated by free classes
of owners or renters in today's world, but these examples seem to be
more numerous in the so-called democratic-capitalistic countries where
fee-simple ownership is permitted.[10]

## Control of Land by Owners of Large Private Estates

The fourth type of tenure arrangement which has long been practiced is characterized by large holdings in the hands of private owners.
Through the years the word *latifundia* (of Latin origin) has been used
to mean large properties managed as single units. In Europe, latifundia appeared on the scene during the medieval and modern ages.
Helen Irvine states that they were not a survival of earlier times
but one of the forms of decadence associated with the decline of the
small owner or tenant type of holding.[11] A latifundium came into
being when a landlord achieved complete victory over his tenants,
reducing them to paid laborers. In other words, all rights of property
and decision-making became concentrated in the landlord. In contrast
to the feudal system, where the landlord was considered only a holder
of the land in return for duties and payments to his overlord, the
latifundium owner's sole function, beyond paying taxes, was that of
using his land for personal pleasure and profit.

Latifundia have originated in widely separated times and places,

[10] For an excellent account of life in such a community see W. M. Williams,
*Gosforth: The Sociology of an English Village* (Glencoe, Ill.: The Free Press,
1956).

[11] Helen Douglas Irvine, *The Making of Rural Europe* (London: George
Allen and Unwin, Ltd., 1923), 49–64.

but certain circumstances have constantly surrounded their birth.[12] First, the principal interest of the landlord is not the land he controls nor the welfare of its cultivators, but rather an income which is as large as possible, easily collected, certain, and portable. Thus, rents in kind or rents varying with the weather or economic fluctuations are of little use to him. Second, latifundia thrive best in places where an unusual demand for agricultural products—wool, meat, etc.—is found. Third, latifundia have frequently followed some event in history which has decimated the population and made it easy to acquire large acreages without the eviction of a large number of tenants. Finally, and this is a recurrent theme among writers, latifundia come into being and persist amid popular discontent. Almost always the peasant or serf has seen the latifundium as an encroachment of his right.

*Social and economic organization:* Typically, the population of latifundia type holdings consists of the owner or his representative and a large number of laborers. The latter, in the present day, are likely to be free, in theory at least. That is, they are at liberty to move from the holding provided all indebtedness and service due the owner have been properly settled. In the past there have been many accounts of the large holdings of private owners being worked by slaves or serfs who did not have the right to leave the land or the service of their landlord.

The ecological and social patterns vary on large private estates, but the most usual arrangement is as follows: The central building is the home, castle, or office of the landowner. Around this edifice, at various distances and locations, is found a cluster of small homes used by the workers. These homes are usually far from pretentious and include only the bare necessities in living accommodations. In some of the more highly developed areas, skilled workers and lesser supervisors may live in a better class of house.

The latifundia population is conspicuously stratified. The landlord and his immediate representative stand at the top of the social pyramid. At the bottom of the social pyramid are the laborers, who may be paid in cash or in kind. Their sole function is to receive and carry out the orders of the owner or his representative. The exact compensation which laborers receive depends on their status as free or bound agents. The former will receive such wages or produce as

[12] *Ibid.*

may be agreed on between him and his landlord and will enjoy the
right of mobility once his part of the bargain is consummated. Slaves
seldom receive more than the necessities of food, shelter, and clothing,
and the quality of these will depend on the good nature of the owner-
master.

Horizontal social mobility is evident in the movement of tenants
from one farm to another and is usually higher in areas of large private
holdings than elsewhere. Laborers are continually seeking better
arrangements, a better landlord, or better land. Only the careful and
wise landlords have a fairly stable labor force. When landlord-laborer
relations are of the familistic-patriarchal type, longer tenure is encouraged. Where landlords are extremely demanding and fail to be
understanding in their relations with their laborers, a definite an-
tagonism develops, and the yearly turnover of laborers is very high.
Where laborers are bound by servitude, there is, of course, little chance
for mobility of any kind.

The pattern of large private holdings, even at its best, does not
encourage strong vigorous institutions and communities. Many of the
usual functions of the worker families, such as education, social control, recreation, etc., are performed inadequately by comparison with
families living on owner-operated family farms. Churches and schools
are either totally lacking or apparent in rudimentary forms only. In
slave or other intolerable situations there is a tendency toward riots
and disorders. All in all, there is little wonder why laborers on large
estates are usually characterized as without ambition, of low moral
standards, and unstable.

*A typical modern-day hacienda:* The description which follows is
of a modern-day latifundian type estate. It is located in the coffee-
growing area of Costa Rica. This particular holding, known as
*aquiares,* was chosen for case presentation because it is somewhat
typical of many large holdings. It spreads out over 1,372 manzanas
(one manzana is 1.72 acres). Loomis and his associates describe the
holding as follows:

> There are approximately 1,200 persons living on the hacienda
> who make up about 200 families. Each year there is a labor
> turnover of about 40 families on the hacienda, but most of the
> families have been long-time residents. Seventy-five families
> live as sharecroppers (*colonos*) and 125 families are employed
> as wage earners.

. . . To facilitate the analysis, the personnel involved in the operation of the hacienda may be divided into three groups: a proprietary class, a skilled-supervisory class, and a labor class. . . . The proprietary class of the hacienda consists of the foreign-born *patron* (owner) and his administrator, who is responsible for the day-to-day operation of the hacienda. The owner has legal title to the land on which the hacienda is located and all equipment belongs to him, including the school and the church.

. . . The supervisory class consists of three men in charge of distinct divisions of the hacienda and their subordinates. The overseer has a group of crew bosses under him and supervises the labor force assigned to cultivate the coffee and cane. Three of the crew bosses supervise the operations of sharecroppers, three are assigned to daily work crews, and the remainder include the boss of the ox-drivers, the foreman of the crews working in cane, stable workers, and the chief mule driver. The foreman of the *beneficio* supervises the receiving, breaking, washing, drying, sorting, packing, and shipping of coffee. The *beneficio* requires the most highly skilled operation on the hacienda and, although the labor force of 20 to 30 people and their crew bosses is small, the importance of this phase of coffee processing gives additional prestige to the status of these people. The chief carpenter supervises four shop carpenters and four carpenters who repair buildings, gates, and fences on the farm.

. . . In the lower part of the social hierarchy are the daily wage earners and *colonos* of the labor class who are at the greatest distance from the control of means of production, and possess least property, money capital, economic skills, and for these reasons are identified with the lowest stratum in Costa Rica society. Authority flows ultimately via the administrator from the *patron*. . . . Such legitimate, explicit, formally sanctioned prerogatives to command others in a system is delegated authority. Delegated authority operates, as it were, to bring the gears of the machine into their proper relationship to each other in order that the machine may function.[13]

The above description makes clear the kind of operation and power-structure characteristic of large private estates. The economic effici-

[13] Taken from Charles P. Loomis and associates, *Turrialba, Social Systems and the Introduction of Change* (Glencoe, Ill.: The Free Press, 1953), 91–118.

ency of such an operation has a high potential, but social efficiency
can be attained only under the most ideal situation.

## Large Estates Owned or Controlled by Church, State, or Other Public Body

Historical evidence indicates that, in one part of the world or
another, large land holdings have been owned or controlled by public
bodies since ancient times. Most frequently these estates have been
run by states, churches, or cities.

*Social and economic organization:* Insofar as the state is concerned,
it is possible to distinguish two types of public control over land:
(1) The state may exercise its rights as sovereign only, with private
ownership permitted within the limits of existing state control. (2)
The state may exercise both the right of sovereign and owner, thus
assuming complete control. Several patterns have emerged under the
latter arrangement. Where the government is monarchial in form, the
monarch may control part of the state lands as sovereign and own
part outright as his private property, or he may be considered sole
owner of the entire state. In republics, the situation is essentially the
same except the role played by the monarch is played by the government. The government, of course, exercises its rights of ownership
and control only on the lands owned by the state. (3) The third
major type of public control over land is seen in the example of the
socialist state, where private property in land is completely abolished.
Here the rights of sovereignty and land ownership belong only to the
state and are to be exercised only by the government.

Whatever the type of control exercised by public bodies, the land
is customarily divided into large latifundian type estates. These
holdings are similar in layout and operation to the large private estates
previously described. The chief difference between the two is that the
estate is managed by an agent of the state or monarch rather than by
an owner or his representative.

Historical accounts show that public lands like private lands have
been tilled by various tenure groups, from free laborers and tenants
to slaves and serfs. Although it is hazardous to generalize, it appears
that laborers and employees on public lands have tended to fare better
than the workers on private estates. However, with respect to community development and social efficiency the two types of rural aggregates are quite similar. Feudal systems, described below, are traditionally associated with large holdings under public ownership.

*Feudal systems:* Perhaps the best early example of a tenure system characterized by public ownership is found in feudal arrangements. F. W. Maitland describes feudalism as "a state of society in which all, or a great part of public rights and duties are inextricably interwoven with the tenure of the land, in which the whole governmental system—financial, military, judicial—is part of the law of private property." [14] A brief description of feudal order as it was practiced in medieval England serves to bring out the high points of this system of tenure. [15]

The starting place for feudalism was simply that all land was held under the sovereignty of the king. All persons who lived on the land and cultivated it were but tenants. However, there could be several intermediate lords who stood above the tenant but below the king. Each tenant owed service or produce to his immediate superior who in turn was owing to his superior up the scale to the king.

In England during the fourteenth century six types of tenure were recognized: (1) Frankalmoign—the holding of lands by religious bodies or religious persons in return for spiritual service rendered the king or lord. (2) Knight service—the requirement that tenants serve in the king's army for a specified period of time in case of war. A knight's fee included the service of a fully armed horseman for a period of forty days. (3) Grand serjeanty—which differed little from knight service. However, instead of being bound to serve as a knight in wars, the tenant was bound to do some other service for the king, such as carrying his banner or sword or acting as his constable or marshal. (4) Petty serjeanty—this form of service was simply an obligation to provide the king or lord with military implements such as a sword or lance. In many ways the laws regarding petty serjeanty were almost the same as those of socage. (5) Free socage—the term free socage was used to mean a tenure held by some service not of a military nature. The general practice was for the socager to pay rent in money or agricultural produce. Quite frequently he was bound to do a certain amount of work for his lord. (6) Villeinage—the holding of land in an unfree state. All the preceding classes of tenure were considered free holdings, and though the tenant was bound to do certain work

[14] F. W. Maitland, *The Constitutional History of England* (Cambridge, England: The University Press, 1920), 23–39.
[15] For an account of the age of feudalism in China see Owen and Eleanor Lattimore, *China, A Short History* (New York: W. W. Norton & Co., 1947), 64–70.

on the lord's land or serve in his army, he was protected by the king's laws and enjoyed freedom of movement. However, under villeinage tenure the tenant was literally a serf and did not have recourse to the king's court (with few exceptions) but was totally subject to his immediate lord's will. Such tenants were unfree to move about.

In theory, the perfect feudal arrangement was one in which all judicial and governmental organization was determined by tenure. The king, as highest landlord, would have a court of his chief lords, and each of these in turn would have his own court of sublords who again would have their own court. Each lesser tenant would have recourse only to the court of his immediate superior and owed no fealty or homage to anyone but him.

Although the feudal system was widespread throughout the world during medieval times, it is noteworthy that it has survived in only a few places. Such a system serves well in a nonmoney economy characterized by constant need of defense against warring neighbors and where individual rights are determined by a system of noble rank decided by birth. However, it is not compatible with a money economy and a democratic form of government. As H. Michel points out, " A feudal aristocracy is an anachronism in an age of advancing wealth and culture and, sooner or later as circumstances dictate, must be supplanted by a more democratic, or perhaps more accurately, a more bourgeois form of economy." [16] Thus, the great feudal systems of Europe, the near East, and the Orient all passed out of the picture in the course of time. It may be noted that a feudal system was attempted by the Dutch and English in early America without success.

*Large public holdings of today:* In the present day world there are some outstanding examples of state-owned and controlled land— namely in China and Russia. Little is known about the former, but much has been written about the so-called " collective farms " of the U.S.S.R. The operation of this system in its earlier years is described as follows:

> With the exception of the Communist managers and super-intendents, the independent peasant who goes to a collective farm is nothing but a subordinated manual laborer who has to do what his new bosses order without protest or objection. He can neither protest nor quit the collective farm, because in that

[16] H. Michel, *The Economics of Ancient Greece* (Cambridge, England: Macmillan Co., 1940) , 40–45.

case he is accused of counterrevolution and is pitilessly punished, often executed. He is paid very poorly and exploited most un-mercifully. Thus his status approaches that of the Roman colonus or the medieval serf, the only difference being that the serfs often belonged to private landlords, while he, like the serfs during Ptolemy's regime in ancient Egypt or those of Rome after Diocletian, is subjugated to the members of the Communist party and the Soviet agents. This difference does not make serfdom any sweeter for the Russian peasant.[17]

Besides the collective farms, which are designated *kolkhoz*, there are the so-called co-operative farms or *artel* in the Soviet system. Both types of farms are required to grow and turn over to the state a certain amount of farm produce. However, *artels* apparently allow for somewhat more private initiative; i. e., some decisions are made by the group, although quotas are set by the government. Both types of farms represent an economic and social unit under the direct control of the government.

Collectivization policies in the Soviet Union reportedly have been relaxed somewhat in later years. Whether or not this type of " public " ownership and control of land will suffer the same rise and decline as did the feudal system remains to be seen.[18]

[17] Sorokin, Zimmerman, and Galpin, *A Systematic Source Book in Rural Sociology*, I, 628.

[18] For recent land tenure developments in the U. S. S. R. see Lazar Volin, " Land Tenure and Land Reform in Modern Russia," *Agricultural History*, Vol. 28 (April, 1953), 48–55; *id.*, " Soviet Collective Farms Become Fewer But Larger," *Foreign Agriculture* (October, 1959), 17–18; Alex Inkeles and Kent Keiger (eds.), *Soviet Society: A Book of Readings* (Boston: Houghton Mifflin Co., 1961), Chap. 3.

# *Part 2:* Tenure Programs, Policies, and Classes in the United States

LAND TENURE INSTITUTIONS in the United States have had a long and dramatic history. In a very real way the progress and development of the nation has been tied to the programs and policies devised to cope with problems related to the land.

Part II presents the more important public actions which have influenced land tenure institutions and reviews the tenure systems and classes which have evolved. Chapters 4, 5, and 6 are devoted primarily to the former assignment, while Chapter 7 addresses itself to the latter tasks. It should be noted that land tenure institutions have not emerged in a vacuum, but rather as part of a complex of national social systems. This will be apparent in the discussions contained in Part II.

# CHAPTER FOUR

# Public Policies and Programs Relating to Land Tenure: Settlement, Education, Credit, and Conservation Programs

LAND TENURE INSTITUTIONS in the United States, as in other societies, are a part of the complex of forces called the social environment. At one and the same time, land tenure institutions have been both subject to the influence of other forces within the social environment and, in turn, themselves have influenced other forces. Chapters 4, 5, and 6 will briefly describe and discuss the more important policies and programs of government that have influenced land tenure institutions in the United States.

Some public policies and programs have been of a general nature, touching both urban and farm life. Others have primarily affected agriculture and farm people. The kinds of public policies and programs considered in this and the following chapter are those that have particularly touched agriculture and the relationship of rural people to the land.

## Colonial Origins of United States Land Policy

The family-sized owner-operated farm, the ideal of American agriculture since colonial days, has deep roots in our past. During the early colonial period the principal basis for granting land in most colonies was the " headright " system, under which, according to Marshall Harris,

> . . . land grants were made to any person who would either pay
> his own way or pay for transporting one or more persons to

America. With land as a reward, people of moderate means were induced to leave overcrowded Europe and come to America. Headright land also interested wealthy persons in providing funds for others to pay their way across the ocean.[1]

The headright system was designed in general to yield financial returns to the settlement agency in each colony. As a consequence of this goal, however,

> . . . the whole spirit of the colonial land policy . . . was to allow the settlers as much land as his financial position or business ability would permit. . . . A definite tendency existed to place land in the hands of occupying farmers of family-sized units. Indeed, most headright holdings were of this size.[2]

After the Revolutionary War and the founding of the republic, our federal land policy consistently sought to aid squatters and home-steaders in establishing family farms from public lands. Up to the year 1891 good farm land was sold by the government for $1.25 an acre or less. Thus the colonial pattern of distributing land resulted for the most part—but with notable regional exceptions—in land-holding settlers who were in sympathy with the family-farm idea. The popular preference for the family farm that derived from the colonial period during the nineteenth century produced land policies which in turn further reinforced the family-farm ideal.

Although this preference for the family-sized owner-operated farm has frequently been more an article of faith than part of a carefully integrated philosophy, some of its most articulate advocates have explicitly emphasized that the family farm should be the means of achieving a better society rather than an end in itself. Jefferson's views on agrarian democracy are perhaps the most representative expression of the agrarian tradition in America.

Although Jefferson did not originate the century-old tradition of reverence for agriculture as the most noble of human occupations, he gave it a uniquely American interpretation. " Agriculture, to him, was not primarily a source of wealth but of human virtues and traits most congenial to popular self-government. It had a sociological rather than

---

[1] Marshall Harris, *Origin of the Land Tenure System of the United States* (Ames: Iowa State College Press, 1953), 194.
[2] *Ibid.*, 197.

an economic value." [3] Jefferson desired a nation of small farmers, because he considered the political freedom of the individual to be the "greatest good." In his view, enlightened self-government depended on the independence and self-reliance of the individual, and these latter rested upon social equality and economic security. Only one who tilled his own lands could feel the independent farmer's pride of possession and his sense of economic security. Hence, agrarianism and private property in farm land were not, for Jefferson, ends in themselves but were the means to democracy and individual freedom.

Through the years, however, some advocates of the agrarian tradition have ignored this emphasis, but others have reaffirmed it. At an international conference on Family Farm Policy held in 1946, the Committee on the Place of the Family Farm in Our Land-Tenure System again felt impelled to deplore " the common mistake of looking upon the family farm as an end of agricultural policy rather than as an instrument through which agriculture and rural life can be made a richer and a more satisfying experience for those who farm, and a stronger institution in the American economy." [4]

## Land Settlement During the Nineteenth Century

### Disposition of the Public Domain

Colonial experiences with the indiscriminate type of settlement, in which there was no preconceived method of allocating land prior to actual settlement, had been unsatisfactory. When the American Revolution ended, it was anticipated that the states with claims to western lands would cede such lands back to the central government. The Congress of the Confederation in 1784, therefore, appointed a committee to prepare an ordinance for the surveying of these western lands, so that in the future the trouble inherent in indiscriminate land settlement would be avoided. With major changes the report of this committee was enacted by the Congress of the Confederation as the Ordinance of 1785. One of its most important provisions prescribed a rectangular system of land division for the public domain, under which surveyors were to divide the new lands into townships six miles square,

[3] A. Whitney Griswold, *Farming and Democracy* (New Haven: Yale University Press, 1948), 19.

[4] Joseph Ackerman and Marshall Harris (eds.), *Family Farm Policy* (Chicago: University of Chicago Press, 1947), 390.

with lines running due north-south and east-west and with a progressive numbering of the two ranges and sections.

This rectangular system of land division, under which most of the remaining territory that eventually comprised the United States was surveyed and settled, had several far-reaching consequences. It was a simple and unambiguous system for identifying and describing a particular parcel of land, preventing both overlapping claims and interspersed gores of no-man's land. In contrast with the European " longlot " system of dividing land and its village-community type of settlement, the rectangular survey produced a scattered type of settlement with isolated farm homes. The rectangular plan of land division is appropriate for level and only slightly rolling land, but it is not well adapted to strongly rolling and hilly land, where cultivated fields should be located in relation to the terrain. Furthermore, providing community services—roads, mail delivery, schools, churches, medical services, and (in recent decades) telephones, electric lights, and power —to isolated farm residences is inevitably more difficult than to inhabitants of a farm community.[5]

Other important provisions of the Ordinance of 1785 were as follows: In every township of thirty-six sections, four particular sections were to be reserved for future sales; one-third of the gold, silver, lead, and copper mines were to be similarly reserved; section sixteen in every township was retained for the maintenance of local public schools; half of the townships were to be sold entire, the other half in single sections of 640 acres each; sales of land were to be by public auction for cash; and the minimum price was one dollar per acre in specie or its equivalent, but with competitive bidding the actual price was expected to average much more. The latter provisions of the Ordinance of 1785, conservatively designed for prudent use of public lands as a source of revenue, were resented by those who advocated a generous land policy. With the smallest size tract selling for a minimum of $640 in cash, a sizable amount in those days, people of ordinary means were excluded as purchasers.[6]

The Ordinance of 1787 was the second major action relating to

[5] F. J. Marschner, *Land Use and Its Patterns in the United States* (Agr. Handbook No. 153 [Wshington: USDA, 1959]), 15–31.

[6] Murray R. Benedict, *Farm Policies of the United States* (New York: Twentieth Century Fund, 1953), 11–12. See also Homer C. Hockett, *Political and Social Growth of the United States* (Rev. ed.; New York: Macmillan Co., 1936), 267–76.

public lands. It applied to the Northwest and provided for (1) territorial status with limited self-government for any area with five thousand or more inhabitants, and (2) eligibility for statehood and full self-government within the federal system as soon as an area came to have sixty thousand or more inhabitants. Slavery was prohibited in the then-existing public domain—what is now Ohio, Illinois, Indiana, Wisconsin, and Michigan. The Ordinance also directed that schools and religious training be encouraged and contained provisions safeguarding freedom of worship, property rights, and trial by jury. It also included detailed provisions concerning the division of estates of persons dying intestate (prohibiting primogeniture) and other related matters.

The federal land policies which evolved from the Ordinances of 1785 and 1787 were the result of struggles between different schools of political thought, different sections, and different economic groups. Landowners and manufacturers of the eastern seaboard tended to advocate the conservative view, which urged that the government dispose of its land with prudence. This view prevailed at first. Frontier farmers, speculators, and most western residents demanded a generous land policy. The clash of these two views constituted the central theme of American land policies during the period from the American Revolution to the enactment of the Homestead Act of 1862.

The conflict of interest concentrated on three specific details: the minimum amount of land offered for sale, the price per acre, and the terms of payment. Whereas the smallest amount purchaseable in 1796 was 640 acres, by 1820 the minimum unit was 80 acres, and in 1832 this was reduced to 40 acres. The minimum price, established at $2.00 an acre in 1796, was reduced to $1.25 an acre in 1820. Furthermore, in practice the minimum price tended to become the maximum. Although credit terms for a time became more liberal, after 1820 immediate cash payment was required because speculators and actual settlers had become badly in arrears.[7]

Land legislation also tended to center about three political and economic issues—graduation, pre-emption, and homesteads. Farmers and speculators selected only the better lands as they pushed westward. The remaining islands of poorer land resulted in demands to

[7] Everett E. Edwards, "American Agriculture—The First 300 Years," *Farmers in a Changing World, 1940 Yearbook of Agriculture* (Washington: Government Printing Office, 1940), 194–98.

lower the price of such lands. In 1854 a graduation act reduced the minimum price to a dollar an acre on land that had been open to sale for ten years and to 12½ cents on land that had been listed for thirty years. The pre-emption issue came to the fore because some frontiersmen had become "squatters," settling on choice locations without waiting for or without reference to official land surveys. After sanctioning the action of particular squatter groups from time to time, Congress in 1841 enacted the pre-emption law by which heads of families, men over 21, and widows were allowed to settle on 160 acres of unsurveyed public land, with the right to purchase their holdings at the minimum price when the land was actually placed on sale. The triumph of the advocates of liberal land policy was complete with the enactment of the homestead principle into law in 1862.

The Homestead Act provided for the grant of full title for 160 acres to the actual settler after five years of residence. Because the first and later homestead acts were loosely drawn and badly administered, not all the consequences were good. Immense acreages of the best timber and mining lands passed into the hands of large corporations through one ruse or another. Some individuals found their land unsuited for crop farming and others found the homestead unit too small for the types of agriculture feasible in the semiarid areas in which they had settled. But the homestead procedure was an unplanned development altogether in keeping with the spirit of a period in which natural resources seemed inexhaustible and a conservation tradition was yet to be developed.[8]

## A Favorable Ratio of Population to Farm Land

During the colonial period and for some time afterward the amount of agricultural land available to the American people was abundant, relative to their numbers, because unused but potentially productive agricultural land was available beyond the frontier of settlement. Down to the present day the United States continues to have a relative abundance of land. In the United States in 1960 the 3.1 acres of arable land per capita of total population contrasted with approximately comparable figures of 1.28 for the world as a whole and figures as low as 0.89, 0.29, and 0.20 for India, China, and Japan, respectively.[9]

There can be no doubt that this relative abundance of agricultural

[8] Benedict, *Farm Policies of the United States*, 18–20.

[9] W. S. Woytinsky, *World Population and Production, Trends and Outlook* (New York: Twentieth Century Fund, 1953), 476.

land in the United States from colonization down to the present time
has tended to make land-tenure "problems" less acute than they
would have otherwise been. During most of the time, and outside of
the deep South, there have not been, for the most part, permanent
"tenant" and "hired laborer" classes into which persons are born
and above which they cannot hope to rise.

### The Family-Farm Ideal as a Stimulant to Capital Formulation in Agriculture

The ideal of farm-owner-operatorship was a powerful motive for
the hard work, self-denial, and thrift which farm people practiced
while settling this continent and developing its agricultural resources
during the nineteenth and the first part of the twentieth centuries.
It is doubtful if, during this era, such rapid economic development of
agriculture would have been possible under any other system of values
and with any other institutions. In developing American agriculture
out of the uninhabited wilderness of the frontier, the vitality and
pervasiveness of the Jeffersonian ideal of farm-owner-operatorship,
together with the Protestant ethic of work (and the institutions such
values generated), are out of all proportion to the short space required
to mention these considerations.

### Significance of the "Frontier"

It is tempting to attribute the worsening of the farm-tenure situation after 1880 to the so-called "closing of the frontier." When the
frontier had disappeared and most agricultural land had been taken
up, good land to some extent was less readily available, and it became
somewhat more difficult for a young farmer to own the land he tilled.
Thus, one might expect that in 1880 or 1890 the western states would
have had a relatively high percentage of owner-operators among their
adult male agricultural workforce, because at that time these states
still had unsettled areas or had only very recently passed out of the
frontier period. Also, as these original settlers died off or retired during
the next few decades, one would expect these states to have experienced a decrease in the percentage of owner-operatorship. In a general
way the state data reveal evidence of this tendency. The idea that
the disappearance of the "frontier" influenced the subsequent tenure
composition of the male agricultural workforce of the nation or of
particular areas should not, however, be applied too literally or over-
emphasized. To understand the influence of the frontier, one must

consider the sequence of events in settlement, the pattern of population movement, and the economic costs and physical difficulties of making forest or prairie land into a farm.

First, the so-called " frontier of settlement," defined by the census as the population-density limit of two settlers per square mile, was only a conceptual line. Substantial areas behind the frontier, although averaging more than two persons per square mile, were still largely unsettled. As much as three-fourths of an area behind the frontier might be unclaimed, since most households probably contained at least two persons and the pre-emption limit was commonly 160 acres— one-fourth of a square mile. Land settlement and development activities behind the frontier were for some time probably more active than beyond it. For example, between 1890 and 1930, four times as much land was homesteaded as in the three preceding decades.

Second, the frontier was in no sense a straight line that moved steadily from the East to the West. Actually, the frontier was a ragged fringe of settlement and only the general direction of its expansion was westward. In 1880, for example, small parts of such " old " states as Maine, New Hampshire, New York, Michigan, Wisconsin, and Minnesota were still " beyond " the frontier, along with large parts of all the states on or beyond the one hundredth meridian.[10]

Third, farm-making on or near the frontier was not as easy nor as inexpensive as one might suppose. Much of the potentially more desirable farm land was quickly taken up by neighboring farmers and by speculators who, anticipating a future rise in land value as settlement became more dense, sold it to latecomers for as much as they could get.

Cost of improving raw farm land—including out-of-pocket expenses for both farm development and family subsistence—was considerable, when related to comparable wage rates on farms or in towns. The pioneer had to procure transportation to the West for himself and family and provide subsistence during the period until the first crops were in. His land, if forested, had to be cleared of trees; or if prairie, the sod had to be broken and rotted. If the pioneer did all this work himself, the period of waiting for his first harvest was greatly increased, and during this period the family had to purchase its subsistence. If he had this work done on contract by others, the cash

[10] R. H. Gabriel, *The Lure of the Frontier, A Story of Race Conflict* (" Pageant of America," Vol. 2 [New Haven: Yale University Press, 1929]), 275, 289.

cost was substantial. A shelter also had to be built and fences had to be raised—both especially difficult and expensive in prairie country. As in older agricultural regions, a pioneer farmer also needed capital for implements, seed, draft animals, and other livestock. Frontier farm-making was thus not an easy process available to all. In the 1850's, for example, the minimum capital required for farm-making was in the neighborhood of $1,000, and during this period one would have done well to save $50 per year, working for the prevailing wages in town or on a farm.[11]

Finally, even before the so-called disappearance of the frontier, the new lands were not all available to native-born American farmers. News of free or cheap land in America induced substantial numbers of European immigrants to settle in rural America. Both before and after 1890 their coming tended to increase the difficulty of access to farm land for both native- and foreign-born farm people.[12]

In summary, it can be said that the disappearance of the so-called " frontier " after 1890 was doubtless one—but probably not the most important—of the reasons for the deterioration in the farm-tenure situation toward the end of the nineteenth century. Other nationwide and local developments tending to reduce the relative frequency of owner-operators among the agricultural workforce were probably more important.[13]

## Public Sponsorship of Agricultural Research and Education

An important but little noted influence on American agriculture in general and its farm-tenure institutions in particular has been the policy of federal-state cooperative sponsorship of agricultural research and agricultural education. This policy was in the tradition established in the Ordinance of 1785, which reserved one section in every sixteen for the maintenance of local public schools. The land-grant college system was established under the Morrill Act of 1862, under

[11] Clarence Danhoff, " Farm-Making Costs and ' Safety Valve,' 1850–1860," *Journal of Political Economy*, Vol. 49 (June, 1941), 317–59; Fred A. Shannon, " The Homestead Act and the Labor Surplus," *American Historical Review*, Vol. 41 (July, 1936), 637–51.

[12] Fred A. Shannon, " A Post-Mortem on the Labor Safety-Valve Theory," *Agricultural History*, Vol. 19 (January, 1945), 31–37.

[13] Frank H. Maier, Sheridan T. Maitland, and Gladys K. Bowles, *The Tenure Status of Farm Workers in the United States* (Technical Bulletin No. 1217 [Washington: USDA, 1960]).

which each state received a grant of land in proportion to its population, the proceeds to be used for the endowment, support, and maintenance of at least one college in each state. Although the land-grant college system at first lacked central direction, it potentially provided a comprehensive framework for agricultural research and experimentation. Under the Hatch Act (1887), the state experiment stations received financial support from the federal government and coordination through its Office of Experiment Stations (now called the State Experiment Stations Division of the Agricultural Research Service). The Smith-Lever Act (1914) established the co-operative federal-state system of agricultural extension to disseminate the improved agricultural knowledge resulting from research. Under this act the states receive federal matching grants for extension work. The Smith-Hughes Vocational Education Act (1917) encouraged the teaching of agriculture in elementary and secondary schools through federal grants to states willing to expand their secondary school systems to include vocational education in agriculture, the trades, industrial skills, and home economics.[14]

As agriculture is an industry characterized by small family-sized units, individual farmers could not themselves carry on technical agricultural research. A limited amount of research might have been done by business firms selling to farmers. But such firms can only be expected to carry on research and to disseminate its results to the extent and in the ways that are profitable to them individually. Co-operative federal-state sponsorship of agricultural research, teaching, and extension, however, led to technological advances in production and marketing that have made the American farmworker the most productive in the world. These advances have changed the character of American agriculture to production for sale, using many purchased inputs, rather than production for home use, using almost no purchased inputs. They have also contributed to the trend toward increasing size and decreasing number of farms.

Although the productivity of American agriculture has been increasing for over a century, the pace thereof has accelerated in recent decades. This improvement in the efficiency of farm production has many facets. Machine power has largely replaced animal power. The acreage formerly required to produce the feed for those animals has been released for the production of output for human use—almost a

[14] Edwards, " American Agriculture—The First 300 Years," *loc. cit.,* 250–56.

quarter of our harvested acreage having been released in this manner between 1915 and 1955. The increased use of mechanical power also made possible an increased use of labor-saving machines. Fertilizer use increased fivefold since 1920 and will probably continue to increase for some years to come. Other improved production practices increased output with little or no increase in inputs—improvements in breeds and varieties of plants and animals, improved rations, new and better control of insects and diseases, and improved tillage practices. Better management of farms came about as a consequence of technical research by public and private agencies, improved general and technical education, and better public and private channels of communication.

Although rural as well as urban living has been enriched generously by the technological advances, in large measure made possible by publicly sponsored agricultural research, teaching, and extension, farm people, as a consequence, have been required and will continue to be required to make difficult economic and personal adjustments. Because of the continuous increase in the efficiency of agricultural production, year after year fewer people are needed in the agricultural labor force. At the same time, however, birth rates among farm people have continued to be such that the children of farm families more than replace their parents. Thus, a substantial movement of farm people into other pursuits has been necessary and will continue to be necessary. But the *necessity* to maintain a net movement of farm people into other pursuits means that the prices of farm products and the incomes of farm people are lower than would be the case in the absence of the need for such a reallocation of human resources out of agriculture. Lower incomes of farm people not only mean that the material levels of living of farm people are lower. Such lower incomes of farm people also mean that it is more difficult for the young farm people who do not inherit a farm but choose to remain in agriculture to get started in farming and eventually become owner-operators. Off-farm migration also drains capital from agriculture. The necessity to maintain a net vocational movement out of agriculture thus in several ways tends to make the farm-tenure situation diverge more widely from the ideal than would otherwise be the case.[15]

At first glance, it might appear that farm people could escape from the cost-price squeeze and its associated farm-tenure difficulties by retarding or terminating agricultural research and education. Such

[15] Maier, Maitland, and Bowles, *The Tenure Status of Farm Workers*, 39–52.

an approach, however, would in the long run be disastrous for both farm and city people alike. Research and education in agriculture are the difference between scarcity and abundance in the whole economy.[16]

The social effects of the widespread program of rural education were no less significant. It helped to break down the farmers' isolation, stirring up fresh currents of thought and bringing more mobility to rural life. Having stamped agriculture with academic approval by introducing agricultural courses into high schools and colleges, rural education made agriculture seem more attractive to farm youths and helped to restore the farmers' self-confidence and pride.

## Public Encouragement of Farm Credit

With the rapid rise in farm land values and the scarcity of good land for homesteading toward the end of the last century, farmers became increasingly concerned about the availability and cost of credit, especially mortgage credit. The fast growing western farm areas had been short of loan funds from the beginning. Interest rates were high and loans were limited to short periods. Abusive lending practices were common—excessive charges for renewals of loans, repetitious title searches, and perfunctory foreclosures in times of scarce credit. The privately owned farm-mortgage corporations which came into being to buy and sell mortgages were often inadequately capitalized, loosely supervised, and irresponsible in their ways of doing business.[17]

### The Co-operative Farm Credit System

The first federal intervention in the farm credit situation was the Federal Farm Loan Act of 1916. This act authorized both a co-operative system of federal land banks and national farm loan associations (now called Federal Land Bank Associations), which became widely used and accepted, and a system of private joint-stock banks, which was eventually abandoned in 1933. Both systems were to serve directly the long-term credit needs of farmers, were required to adopt the amortization plan of retirement, and were to be supervised by the newly created Federal Farm Loan Board. In the long view the signifi-

---

[16] W. L. Gibson, *Research and Extension in Agriculture* (Va. Agr. Ext. Tech. Bul. No. 260 [Blackburg: Virginia Polytechnic Institute, March, 1959]).

[17] Benedict, *Farm Policies of the United States*, 145–46. See also James A. Munger, " Borrowing Money to Purchase Land," *Land—Yearbook of Agriculture, 1958* (Washington: USDA, 1958).

cance of the Federal Farm Loan Act of 1916 was its establishment of the co-operative system of regional federal land banks and local farm associations.[18]

The second major federal legislation on farm credit was the Agricultural Credits Act of 1923. It set up a system of twelve Federal intermediate credit banks, associated with the twelve federal land banks and supervised by the Federal Farm Loan Board. These intermediate credit banks could not, however, loan directly to farmers, because they were empowered only to make loans to co-operative associations and to discount commercial paper submitted by agricultural finance corporations, livestock loan companies, and local banks. When it developed that co-operative associations and local banks made little use of the facilities of the federal intermediate credit banks, the performance of the new system for a time proved to be less helpful to farmers than had been anticipated.

The final step in the establishment of a balanced and integrated federal farm credit system for commercial farmers was taken during the acute financial distress experienced by farmers in the early 1930's. Two new groups of credit agencies were set up by the Farm Credit Act of 1933: (1) a central bank and twelve regional banks for loans to farmer co-operatives and (2) a system of twelve production credit corporations to organize, supervise, and finance local production credit associations. The latter system enabled farmers to borrow from the intermediate credit bank. The Farm Credit Administration was created in 1933 by executive order, bringing the previously piecemeal federally sponsored, farm-credit agencies into one well-coordinated system.

Since 1933 the co-operative Farm Credit System, supervised by the Farm Credit Administration, has functioned effectively as a source of credit for farmers in both emergency periods and normal times. Furthermore, the desirable lending procedures and standards that it introduced were later adopted by other lenders.

For the most part the agencies of the Farm Credit System have been used by commercial family farmers rather than by operators, who could be classed as "low income" farmers. Loan policies of FCA agencies have been conservative, both because of legal restrictions on their lending practices and because of necessity of keeping loan losses within the capacity of the system's earnings. The policy of having

[18] Marie Puhr (comp.), *Years of Progress with the Cooperative Land Bank System* (U. S. Farm Credit Admin. Cir. E. 43 [Washington: Government Printing Office, 1957]).

FCA agencies serve mostly commercial farmers appears to be desirable public administration, since it makes possible unambiguous identification of the program's objectives, accurate assessment of the efficiency of its administration, and clear evaluation of how well its objectives are achieved. The credit problems and needs of underemployed low-income farmers require a different program from that serving commercial family farmers.

Without doubt, the comprehensive publicly sponsored farm credit programs supervised by the Farm Credit Administration have had an important and beneficial influence on the farm tenure situation. This influence has been exerted in two ways: (1) the direct impact of the policies of the co-operative Farm Credit System and (2) their indirect impact on private lenders who have adopted many of the lending innovations first pioneered by FCA agencies. The effect of the programs of the co-operative Farm Credit System has been both to facilitate more efficient farming with better capital and financing and also to encourage more widespread farm-owner-operatorship.

### The Farmers Home Administration

The idea of a federally sponsored farm-credit system specially designed to serve the disadvantaged within agriculture first gained prominence during the 1930's. This approach has had two distinguishing characteristics: (1) it serves those farmers unable to obtain credit from other public and private agencies, and (2) its borrowers also receive educational and technical assistance. The principle of supervised public credit for farmers otherwise unable to obtain credit was first put into effect on a small scale under the Resettlement Administration. It was enacted into law on a larger scale under the Bankhead-Jones Farm Tenant Act of 1937, shortly after which the name of the organization was changed to the Farm Security Administration. Since 1946 the program has been administered by the Farmers Home Administration, following passage of the act from which its name was taken.

The original provisions of the Bankhead-Jones Farm Tenant Act of 1937 that are of long-range importance include the two direct loan programs for farm ownership and operating credit. In 1946 the Farmers Home Administration was authorized to insure certain farm-ownership loans made by private lenders. The interest rates for direct and insured farm-ownership loans are low (not more than 5 per cent per year), and the amortization periods are long (up to forty years).

Also important is the provision that direct farm-ownership loans (and, after 1961, insured loans also) may be, and in fact generally have been, 100 per cent loans; that is, the loan may be for the full " normal value " of the farm, which may be less than the current market value.[19] These farm-ownership and operating credit loan programs are distinctive among the activities of private and public lenders that serve farmers, because several of their objectives and criteria are explicitly stated in terms of land tenure.

Direct and insured farm-ownership loans are made to farmers and ranchers who " are or will become owner-operators of not larger than family farms " for " acquiring, enlarging or improving farms, including farm buildings, land and water development, use and conservation, refinancing existing indebtednesses, and for loan closing costs." Preference shall be given " to persons who are married or have dependent families and, whenever practicable, to persons who are able to make initial downpayments, or who are owners of livestock and farm implements necessary successfully to carry on farming operations." [20] The basic objective of the Farmers Home Administration in making farm ownership loans is " to assist eligible farmers and ranchers to become owner-operators of not larger than family farms, to make efficient use of their land, labor, and other resources, and to carry on sound and successful farming operations." [21]

The Consolidated Farmers Home Administration Act of 1961 served to broaden the agency's authority in the matter of the kinds of farm families to whom real estate credit and supervisory assistance may be extended. Formerly, except for two special categories of lenders, real estate loans were restricted to farm operators whose income *from farming alone*, disregarding other sources of income, was adequate to meet living and operating expenses and amounts due on their loans and whose off-farm employment did not take up a substantial portion of their time. Under the 1961 act, farm ownership loans may be made to families if their farm income will be at least a *substantial* portion of their total income. Thus, larger numbers of part-time farmers with

---

[19] *Bankhead-Jones Farm Tenant Act*, Title I, Sections 3 and 12 (16 U. S. C., 1001) July 22, 1937; and Section 305 of the *Consolidated Farmers Home Administration Act of 1961*, P. L. 128, 87th Congress (7 U. S. C., 1925).

[20] *Consolidated Farmers Home Administration Act of 1961*, Sections 302 and 303 (7 U. S. C., 1922–23).

[21] *Farm Ownership Loan Policies, Procedures, and Authorities* (FHA Instructions 443.1 [Washington: Government Printing Office, 1961]).

low incomes are now eligible for FHA farm-ownership loans than was formerly the case.

To be eligible for an FHA farm-ownership loan, an individual must meet each of several requirements: (1) be a citizen of the United States; (2) possess legal capacity to incur the obligation of the loan; (3) have had a farm background and either training or farm experience sufficient to assure reasonable prospects of success in the proposed farming operations; (4) possess the character, industry, and ability necessary to carry out the proposed farming operation and honestly endeavor to carry out the undertakings and obligations required of him in connection with the loan; (5) be unable with his own resources to obtain sufficient credit elsewhere to finance his actual needs at reasonable rates and terms; (6) be able, when the loan is made, to become the owner-operator of a farm which will provide a substantial portion of his total income; and (7) be (or intend to be) the operator of a farm not larger than a family farm.

Limitations on the maximum amounts of farm real estate loans to any one borrower were raised somewhat by the 1961 act. Under this act, the total unpaid indebtedness against the farm or other security at the time of the loan may not exceed $60,000 or the normal value of the farm or other security. The amount of the loan cannot exceed the amount certified by the county FHA committee.[22]

The second important category of Farmers Home Administration credit is operating loans, which are made " for (1) paying costs incident to reorganizing the farming system for more profitable operation, (2) purchasing livestock, poulty, and farm equipment, (3) purchasing feed, seed fertilizer, insecticides, and farm supplies and to meet other essential farm operating expenses including cash rent, (4) financing land and water development, use and conservation, (5) refinancing existing indebtedness, (6) other farm and home needs including but not limited to family subsistence, and (7) for loan closing costs." [23] The basic objective of the Farmers Home Administration in making operating loans is to assist eligible family-farm operators " to carry on a successful system of farming, to make efficient use of their land, labor, and other resources, to make needed improvements in their living conditions and economic situation, and to qualify

[22] *Consolidated Farmers Home Administration Act of 1961*, Section 305 (7 U. S. C., 1925).

[23] *Ibid.*, Section 312.

for credit from private or cooperative sources within a reasonable time."

Eligibility requirements of farm owners and tenants for receiving operating loans are similar to those for receiving real estate loans. The maximum total amount of operating credit that may be extended to any eligible farm operator was increased by the 1961 act. The total outstanding indebtedness of any farm operator for FHA operating loans may not exceed $35,000 nor the amount certified by the county FHA committee. A further overall limitation is that not more than one-fourth of the total available for FHA operating loans may be used for loans that cause FHA operating credit to any borrower to exceed $15,000. The interest rate may not exceed 5 per cent per year, and the loans may not be for longer repayment periods than seven years but may be renewed for not more than five additional years.

In addition to extending operating and real estate credit, the Farmers Home Administration is also empowered to make various kinds of emergency loans, rural housing loans, water development and soil conservation loans, and watershed loans. Of loans in these four categories, emergency loans have drawn the largest numbers of borrowers and involved the largest total outstanding indebtedness.[24]

Emergency loans are made to eligible farmers in designated areas where natural disasters such as floods and droughts have brought about a temporary need for credit not available from other sources. Rural housing loans are made to eligible farm owners and owners of nonfarm tracts in rural areas and small rural communities with populations of not more than 2,500 for the construction and repair of needed homes and essential farm buildings. The initial response to the 1961 broadening of FHA authority to make loans for rural housing suggests that this phase of FHA activity may greatly increase in volume and importance. Loans for water and land development, use, and conservation are made to eligible individuals and groups of farmers and rural residents to finance development of water systems for irrigation, household use, and livestock; draining of farmland; and carrying out of soil conservation measures. Watershed loans are made to local organizations to help finance projects that protect and develop land and water resources in small watersheds under plans approved by the Soil Conservation Service and, under certain conditions, by the Congress.

[24] *Agricultural Statistics* (1960), Tables 732 and 733 (Washington: Government Printing Office, 1961).

The Farmers Home Administration ordinarily gives supervisory assistance only to families who take out FHA farm-ownership loans, operating-credit loans, and some types of soil- and water-conservation loans. These borrowers receive assistance in preparing farm and home plans, keeping farm records, obtaining advice on farm and home problems, and analyzing their operations. As already mentioned, such FHA educational and technical assistance is unique in the extension of loans for farm ownership and operating credit.

The FHA loan programs of greatest importance for the tenure status of farm people are the program of operating credit and the programs of direct and insured farm-ownership loans. As discussed below, these programs have not, however, directly benefited relatively large numbers of farm families. From 1936 through 1960 the operating-credit loans made totaled approximately $2.9 billion. During the same period direct farm-ownership loans totaling approximately $636 million were made to 80,800 new borrowers, and from late 1947 through 1960 FHA insured farm-ownership loans totaling approximately $260 million were made to about 22,875 new borrowers.[25] However, larger numbers of farm families were also benefited indirectly.

The relatively small scale of operations of the FHA farm-ownership loan program has resulted from several factors. The statutory limitation on the maximum amount that may be appropriated annually for direct farm-ownership loans was $50 million until 1961, when the Consolidated Farmers Home Administration Act was passed without any limitation on appropriations. The statutory limitation on the maximum amount of insured farm-ownership loans that may be made during any one year was limited to $125 million until 1961, when it was increased to $150 million.[26] In many years, however, the amounts actually appropriated for direct FHA farm-ownership loans were less than half the maximum authorized, and the private credit available for FHA insured farm-ownership loans was well under the maximum that may be insured annually. During the fiscal year 1961–1962, however, an increase in the interest paid investors increased the attractiveness of insured loans, and the ceiling was reached before the year ended.

The Bankhead-Jones Farm Tenant Act, as amended, placed no

[25] *Agricultural Statistics* (1957), 623–24, and *Agricultural Statistics* (1960), 524–25.

[26] *Bankhead-Jones Farm Tenant Act*, Title I, Sections 5, 12 b, and Section 308 of the *Consolidated Farmers Home Administration Act*.

statutory limitation on the maximum amount that may be appropriated annually for operating loans, authorizing the appropriation of "such sums as the Congress may from time to time determine to be necessary to enable the Secretary (of Agriculture) to carry out the purposes of this title." The Consolidated Farmers Home Administration Act of 1961 likewise contained no statutory limitation on the maximum amount that Congress may appropriate for operating loans.

To understand what effect the FHA farm-ownership and operating-credit loan programs have had on the tenure status of disadvantaged farm people, one must distinguish between the direct and the indirect influences of the program. Considering first the indirect influences, we see that FHA lending activities have indirectly benefited many people who were not directly served by its programs. Not only does FHA credit tend to ease the overall credit situation in rural areas where it operates, but FHA lending policies have doubtless also had a favorable influence on the lending policies of private financial institutions serving rural areas.

Considering next the direct effects of FHA farm-ownership and operating-credit loan programs, two considerations must be examined —the volume of such loans and the income levels of farm families who are assisted by these programs. As to the first, it has already been noted that the number of farm families who have directly benefited from farm-ownership and operating-credit loans of the Farmers Home Administration has not been relatively large. As to the second consideration apparently for the most part the farm-ownership and operating-credit loan programs of the Farmers Home Administration have not reached the farm people who constitute the low-income problem in its most difficult form. Had more funds been available for farm-ownership and operating-credit loans, it is possible that a larger number of the most disadvantaged farm families might have been assisted by these FHA programs.

FHA farm-ownership loans have been administered mainly to help qualified farm families become established as owners of family-type farms. Under FHA regulations, in effect until 1961, a family-type farm was defined as "a farm (1) that is of sufficient size and productivity to furnish income that will enable a farm family to have a reasonable standard of living, pay operating expenses . . . , pay their debts and have a reasonable reserve to meet unforeseen emergencies; (2) for which the management is furnished by the operator and his immdiate family, and (3) for which the labor is furnished primarily by such operator and family except during seasonal peak-load periods." [27]

Similarly, before 1961 FHA operating loans were made only to "full-time operators of family-type farms," except for the moderate program of operating loans to part-time farmers authorized as a part of the Rural Development Program.[28] During the mid-fifties the number of all FHA operating loans (including new loans and loans to borrowers already indebted to FHA) made each year to family-type farmers was around 80,000. But probably less than half of these were to families who could be called low-income farmers having gross farm sales of $2,500 per year or less. This is shown by the fact that, in a sample of all FHA operating-loan borrowers who repaid their loans from July, 1954, through June, 1955, and continued to farm, the average gross farm income was about $3,300 during the year before receipt of the FHA loan.[29] In contrast, the number of full-time farmers in 1954 selling farm products with a gross value of less than $2,500 was about 1,225,000.[30] Therefore, the number of low-income farm families who received FHA operating credit during the mid-fifties was not large compared with the number of full-time farmers with low incomes.

Certain changes in FHA lending authority that were made in the Consolidated Farmers Home Administration Act of 1961 will permit the lending activities of the Farmers Home Administration to reach somewhat larger numbers of the most disadvantaged farm families than were served prior to 1961. As discussed above, the 1961 act (1) removed the limitation that FHA farm-ownership loans be restricted to full-time farm families whose farm income (disregarding other sources of income) was adequate to meet living and operating expenses and amounts due on their loans and (2) increased the maximum total amount of operating credit that may be extended to any one family. At about the same time, in administrative action greater

[27] U. S. Farmers Home Administration, *Insured and Direct Farm Ownership Policies and Authorities* (FHA Instructions 443.1 [Washington: Government Printing Office, 1956]).

[28] U. S. Farmers Home Administration, *Operating Loans to Part-time Farmers, Policies and Authorities* (FHA Instructions 441.2 [Washington: Government Printing Office, 1956]).

[29] U. S. Farmers Home Administration, *The 1955 Operating Loan Family Progress Report for Borrowers Paying Their Loans in Full and Continuing to Farm* (Washington: Government Printing Office, 1955).

[30] *U. S. Census of Agriculture, 1954*, Vol. 2, p. 144.

emphasis was placed on serving the most disadvantaged farm families, and local offices were urged to be more lenient in serving low-income farm families.

The publicly sponsored programs of supervised credit now under the Farmers Home Administration appear to have helped the farm-tenure situation both indirectly through popularizing new credit practices and directly by assisting the class of low-income family farms served by these programs so far as the available resources of the programs permitted.[31] We have seen that the financial resources of these programs and the numbers of people directly served by them have been relatively moderate and that most of the persons served have not been from the most disadvantaged farm-tenure groups. However, this does not imply that it would necessarily be desirable to expand FHA programs to serve *all* disadvantaged farm families, even those with the very lowest farm incomes and the least prospects for reasonable success in farming.

Several other important questions are relevant to this major policy decision and need to be recognized: At the present time is any publicly sponsored farm-credit program assisting a substantial number of the most disadvantaged farm families? Is credit the critical need of these low-income farmers? Or is a different and even more comprehensive approach than supervised credit required, one that is more appropriate to the complexities of their problem? Though the question sounds harsh and drastic, would the occupational opportunities of some of the most disadvantaged farm people and of their children be better outside of rather than within agriculture and should public policy further such a voluntary vocational transfer? On the other hand, are certain dangers implicit in recognition of the need for the continuous net movement of people out of farming that is necessary because of high rural birth rates and reduction of employment opportunities in agriculture? Is there danger that this knowledge and emphasis may cause the public, legislators, and administrative officials to be less resourceful and less aggressive than they could be in using public policy (1) to encourage the development of nonfarm employment opportunities in depressed rural areas and (2) to assist those remaining in agriculture to become more efficient and successful family farmers? Also can very many low-income farm couples who are middle aged or older and have had only modest educational attainment and little

[31] William E. Hendrix, *Approaches to Income Improvement in Agriculture* (Production Report No. 33 [Washington: USDA, 1959]).

nonfarm vocational experience be expected to make working and living adjustments either in farming or in nonfarm employment that change drastically their way of life? If these families are to be assisted, will most of them have to be helped in farming, which is where most will in any case probably spend the remainder of their lives? And can enough new nonfarm jobs be found for all the children of disadvantaged farm families who will seek a better material living from nonfarm employment? These questions are at the core of the problem of low incomes among farm people in " depressed " agricultural areas. Some of these questions will be considered separately in a later chapter.

## Public Programs for Resource Development and Conservation

The American people have a long history of governmental encouragement of the development of the nation's physical resources. This has taken many forms, both indirect and direct, and has involved all levels of government. At various times probably all sectors of the nation's economy have benefited.

One of the most conspicuous cases of public encouragement to resource development was the grants of credit and land by the federal and state governments to private business companies for the construction of canals and railroads. The great period of canal building between the War of 1812 and the financial panic of 1837 was possible only because of various kinds of substantial financial assistance and encouragement.

The unprecedented period of railroad construction during the 1850's and 1860's that opened up the sparsely settled West occurred earlier than would otherwise have been possible as a result of lavish federal and state grants of credit and public lands. Many counties, cities, and towns were also so anxious to secure a railroad that they bonded themselves and turned the proceeds over to the railroads as outright gifts or in exchange for their securities.[32]

Although individual investors, some of whom were farmers, often lost all they invested in railroads, agriculture in general greatly benefited from the coming of the " iron horse." Railroads expanded the market for the farmers' produce and induced a rapid increase in the value of his land. Thus, besides being an example of governmental

[32] Chester W. Wright, *Economic History of the United States* (New York: McGraw-Hill Book Co., Inc., 1941), 336–58, 569, 583–88.

fostering of resource development, governmental encouragement of railroad construction also had an important secondary effect which, in some respects at least, benefited farm people.

In the present century several public programs have provided directly for the development and conservation of farmers' landed resources. These will now be considered briefly.

## The Federal Reclamation Program

The oldest of these is the program for the development of arid and semiarid lands in the seventeen western states. This is accomplished through the construction, operation, and maintenance of works for the storage, diversion, and distribution of water for irrigation.

The first irrigation developments in the semiarid West were on private account and depended entirely on the simple diversion of natural stream flow. As development proceeded, it became evident that further expansion depended on the provision of additional sources of water or on more elaborate means of transporting existing river flows to irrigable land. The construction of storage and/or gravity conveyance systems was relatively expensive and beyond the means of most groups of water users. In response to this need, the federal government entered the irrigation field and has been responsible for the construction of substantial storage and conveyance installations and, in recent years, large scale pumping facilities. These installations have, in turn, provided the basis for the continued expansion of irrigation.

Federal assistance in irrigation took several forms, beginning with Desert Land Acts of 1877 and 1891. The first act of major significance was the Carney Act of 1894, which was designed to encourage irrigation development on public land and provided for land grants to the states for resale to individuals. The states were to provide for the necessary reclamation, each state determining the procedure it would follow. The usual plan was for a state to contract with a construction company to reclaim specified areas, giving the company authority to sell " water rights " as a means of recovering its investment. The land was sold by the states at nominal prices to those who had contracted for the purchase of water rights. Under this act more than a million acres of land were reclaimed. Difficulties arose, however, from the limited financial resources of states and individual promoters and from the absence of sufficient safeguards against inadequate engineering and hydrological studies.[33]

The Reclamation Act of 1902 established the Reclamation Service (in 1923 renamed the Bureau of Reclamation) and overcame many of the above shortcomings. The Reclamation Act not only provided many facilities by federal financing and construction on a reimbursable basis but also established the technical pattern and know-how that has permitted expansion of private development. The act also established the important policy of limiting the Reclamation Bureau to furnishing irrigation water to *not more than* 160 acres in one ownership. This restriction has tended to limit sizes of farms in these areas. Today, about one-fifth of all irrigated lands in the West receive a full or partial water supply from facilities constructed by the Bureau of Reclamation.

The objectives of the Bureau of Reclamation (pursued in co-operation with other federal agencies, states, and local groups) of importance for agriculture include the following:

> The transformation through irrigation of arid and semiarid lands into productive farms; the maintenance of production on lands threatened with retrogression to desert, through the provision of supplemental water for irrigation; the development and administration of sound financial arrangements for the reimbursement by water users of expenses incurred by the government which are allocable to irrigation and subject to repayment; and the transmission and sale or exchange of electric power and energy generated at Bureau projects and at certain reservoir projects under the control of other national and international agencies.[34]

The reclamation program is not, of course, designed exclusively for the benefit of farmers. Among its general objectives are the following: acceleration of economic activity in nearby communities and in the region at large, improvement in the efficiency of resource use, promotion of the economic growth of specific areas and prevention of economic decline in other specified areas, stimulation of diversified production and economic development, and improvement in the general level of living of the region and of the nation as a whole.

[33] Benedict, *Farm Policies of the United States*, 125–26.
[34] *United States Government Organization Manual, 1956–57* (Washington: Federal Register Division, General Services Administration, 1956), 222.

In recent years the activities of the bureau have been concerned with comprehensive river basin developments through construction and operation of multiple-purpose projects. Many of these are in conjunction with other federal agencies, especially the Army Corps of Engineers through its civil functions. In addition to water for irrigation, these multiple-purpose projects also provide hydroelectric energy, flood damage prevention, aids to navigation, and water for domestic and industrial uses.

Reclamation activities are financed principally from congressional appropriations from the revolving reclamation fund and the general fund of the federal treasury. The reclamation fund receives receipts from the sale of public lands, proceeds from the Oil Leasing Act, and receipts from Reclamation Bureau irrigation projects, including revenues from power sales.[35]

A large part of the original cost of multipurpose reclamation projects is charged to irrigation, hydroelectric power, and the municipal and industrial uses of water. A small part is borne by taxpayers in general —the portion chargeable to flood control, pollution control, fishing, wildlife, and other recreational activities. Division of the costs of a large project among its several joint purposes is, of course, very complex.

In the repayment of reclamation costs charged against it, however, irrigation receives preferential treatment. Costs charged to the generation of hydroelectric power and the provision of water for municipal and industrial uses are repaid with interest. But costs charged to irrigation are repaid without interest. As the repayment period in recent years is commonly fifty years for irrigation costs, the interest-free feature is an important encouragement for irrigation. It cuts the amount of a farmer's annual installment to half of what such payments would be if interest were charged at 3 per cent. In addition, some of the original costs charged to irrigation are being repaid out of the proceeds from hydroelectric power.[36]

[35] U. S. Senate, *Report of the Senate Committee on Governmental Operations*, 84th Congress, 2d Sess. (Senate Report No. 1572), 110.

[36] " Our National Reclamation Program," remarks by United States Commissioner of Reclamation, W. A. Dexheimer, before the 43rd Annual Convention of the National Rivers and Harbors Congress at the Mayflower Hotel, Washington, Friday, May 11, 1956.

*The Programs of Agricultural and Soil Conservation*
*(ACP and SCS)*

Two distinct but closely related activities that encourage the de-velopment of agricultural resources are those of the Soil Conservation Service (SCS) and the Agricultural Conservation Program (ACP), both in the United States Department of Agriculture.

The federal government through the Agricultural Conservation Pro-gram (ACP) shares with farmers and ranchers the cost of " on farm " soil- and water-conserving practices that are considered in the public's interest. Public funds are authorized by Congress as an investment to encourage farmers to invest also in doing the conservation work that is in the public interest. ACP cost-sharing is available for those con-servation measures that protect and conserve cropland, pasture and range, forests, and agricultural water. Its cost-sharing is not, however, offered to bring additional land into production. Special attention is given to land diverted from normal crop use.[37]

The Soil Conservation Service (SCS) assists farmers and ranchers, who are organized in local farm-directed soil conservation districts, by making available to them the services of its planning technicians and other soil and water conservation specialists who work in the districts. Among the farmers served by SCS personnel are those who receive ACP cost-sharing payments for approved conservation practices.[38]

The Agricultural Conservation Program has been in continuous oper-ation since 1936. Local administration is by farmer-elected county committees, which have had several different names—AAA, PMA, ASC.[39] Operations are carried out at the state and county level through the facilities of the Agricultural Stabilization and Conserva-tion state and county committees, whose activities are supervised by

[37] *U. S. Government Organization Manual, 1956–57*, p. 236.

[38] *Ibid.*, 248.

[39] The local committees now known as the Agricultural Stabilization and Conservation (ASC) committees were created by Congress in Section S(b) of the Soil Conservation and Domestic Allotment Act of 1936, as amended. Former names of these committees were: Agricultural Adjustment Admin-istration (AAA) committees, 1936 to 1946; and Production and Marketing Administrative (PMA) committees, 1946 to 1953. The ASC committees, so designed since 1953, are directed by the Agricultural Stabilization and Con-servation Service (formerly called the Commodity Stabilization Service) of the U. S. Department of Agriculture.

the Agricultural Stabilization and Conservation Service (formerly called the Commodity Stabilization Service).[40]

The Soil Conservation Service was established in the Department of Agriculture in 1935 under the authority of the Soil Conservation Act of that year (16 U.S.C. 590 a–f.). It brought together in one agency the limited soil-erosion investigations that had been carried on in the Department of Agriculture since 1929 and in the Department of Interior under the Soil Erosion Service since 1933.

The Agricultural Conservation Program and the activities of the Soil Conservation Service are both close to the grass roots, being carried on in close co-operation with local people and in reference to their situations and needs for conservation.

Each year the Agricultural Conservation Program and its accomplishments are reviewed in the light of changing conditions. Recommendations to improve ACP are made annually, county by county, state by state, and nationally. County and state ACP groups have responsibility for this annual review and planning, with many other agencies and organizations taking part.

Each county ACP group, within the limits of funds, chooses conservation practices and sets the cost-sharing rates for soil- and water-conserving practices on the basis of its understanding of local conditions and conservation problems.

The Soil Conservation Service assists the approximately 2,900 local soil conservation districts and their co-operating farmers and ranchers to plan and apply locally adopted conservation programs. The affairs of each district are directed by a group of farmers and ranchers comprising a local board chosen by the landholders in the district. In each state the activities of the several districts are co-ordinated by a board or committee at the state level. The board of each district prepares a written program of work which serves as a basis for the Department of Agriculture and the Soil Conservation Service to enter into formal agreements to furnish technical assistance. SCS technicians resident in the area assist individual farmers and ranchers to do conservation work on their land in accordance with the district program.

Besides its national soil and water conservation program through local conservation districts, the Soil Conservation Service gives tech-

[40] U. S. Senate, *Report of the Senate Committee on Government Operations*, 34–35.

nical assistance to individual participants in the Agricultural Conservation Program, the Rural Areas Development Program, and the conservation-credit program of the Farmers Home Administration. In addition, the Soil Conservation Service has several other assignments. It carries out the responsibilities of the USDA in watershed-protection and flood-prevention projects. These projects, usually sponsored by soil conservation districts, involve acceleration of land treatment for soil and water conservation plus construction of needed floodwater-retarding dams in small watersheds. Both technical and financial assistance are provided by USDA for this program, which got underway in 1954. SCS also has leadership for USDA for this program which got underway in 1954. SCS also has leadership for USDA in river-basin investigations and administers the federal part of the National Cooperative Soil Survey. SCS administers the Great Plains Conservation Program, a program of specially designed technical and cost-sharing aid in the ten Great Plains states. It also plans and applies measures and practices that reduce flood damage in eleven major watersheds, heads the USDA National Soil and Water Conservation Needs Inventory, and makes and coordinates snow surveys for water supply forecasting in the western states.[41]

### The Incidence of Program Benefits

An interesting aspect of public program for resource development and conservation (and of other public programs that benefit persons of particular tenure status) is the land tenure question of how the benefits of such programs are distributed among the several factors of production. No doubt a quantitative answer to this question would only be possible after careful and exhaustive study beyond the scope of this chapter. Such an answer would consider the details of each program, would treat each resource program separately, and would take account of how socio-economic differences among geographic regions might cause the same program to work out differently in different regions. In the present discussion several possibilities may at least be recognized: (1) whether an important part of the current benefits of such programs may go to the owners of the land factor rather than to the labor factor, (2) whether to some extent the value of the future benefits of such programs may in particular situations

[41] *What the Soil Conservation Service Does* (SCS–Cl–3 [Rev. ed.; Washington: USDA, October, 1960]).

be capitalized into the selling prices of tracts of land, ownership of which entitles one to participate in the benefits of the program, and (3) whether such a program makes it easier or more difficult for young people who do not receive a substantial inheritance to get started in farming and become owner-operators. To the extent that future program benefits are capitalized into land values, when such land is sold, the purchaser will usually pay in advance for a part of the future benefits of the resource development program, while a seller who owned the land while the capitalization of future program benefits occurred will usually receive a substantial capital gain.[42]

Although it is desirable to recognize the existence of such possibilities as these, they may or may not actually apply to any particular public resource program; and, in any case, the importance of these possibilities should not be exaggerated. Several general comments are relevant. First, it is often not easy to define the intent of particular public programs. If some part of the benefits of a particular program go to the land factor, this may well be what was intended by the congressmen voting for the legislation that set up the program. Second, as a practical matter it may be quite difficult, if not impossible, to set up a resource development program under which the expectation of future program benefits does not exert some upward pressure on the sale of the land or other resource that qualifies one for participation in the program. Third, some resource development programs require participants to pay a part, even a substantial part, of the costs of the program. To the extent that participants pay for their program, the public program involves no income transfer but only facilitates participants co-operatively doing at their own expense what they could not have done without the co-ordinating assistance of government.

Finally, the question of access to farming opportunities involves two aspects: (1) accumulating the down payment for purchase of an efficient farm unit and (2) meeting the interest charges and reducing the principal indebtedness. As to the first aspect, the down payment for the purchase of a farm will tend to be larger because of a program that benefits the farm, if the program enhances the total purchase price of the farm and if the same percentage of the purchase price

---

[42] Cf. Frank H. Maier, "Land and One of the Farm Programs," *Land, the Yearbook of Agriculture, 1958* (Washington: USDA, 1958), 310–14; Frank H. Maier, James L. Hedrick, and W. L. Gibson, Jr., *The Sale Value of Flue-Cured Tobacco Allotments* (Va. Agr. Expt. Sta. Tech. Bul. No. 148 [Blacksburg: Virginia Polytechnic Institute, April, 1960]).

is required as a down payment. Should the program, however, also reduce yield uncertainty (or other), it is at least possible that lenders will accept down payments of a smaller percentage of the purchase price. With reference to the second aspect, if future program benefits are capitalized into sale prices of farms participating in a program, it is likely that *only a part* of these future benefits will be so capitalized. This is because purchasers of such lands will always be aware of the possibility that at some time in the future the terms for participation in the program may be changed or that the program or parts of it may be terminated. Thus, later purchasers of land or other resources that entitle one to participate in a program may be expected each year to receive benefits for which in part they paid in advance but in part they paid nothing. The former portion of the program benefits tends each year to cover approximately the interest charge on the amount of its capitalization. The latter portion of the benefits represents additional income available annually for consumption, new capital expenditures, or the repayment of old indebtedness. Hence it is possible, perhaps even likely, that such a resource program tends to make it easier for later participants to become owner-operator farmers, even though they inherited no farm and, as late-comers, found it necessary " to buy into " the program.[43]

[43] *Ibid.*, 42–45.

# CHAPTER FIVE

# Public Policies and Programs Relating to Land Tenure: Production Control and Rural Development Programs

THIS CHAPTER, A continuation of the discussion begun in Chapter 4, is concerned with production control programs in agriculture and with programs for depressed rural areas, as these relate to land tenure.

## Production Control Programs for Agriculture

Since the early 1930's the federal government has assisted farmers directly through various programs that influenced the demand for and supply of farm products. The first several such programs were emergency attempts to alleviate farm distress during the Great Depression that began in 1929.

During the period 1929 to 1932 the Federal Farm Board attempted unsuccessfully to halt the drop in wheat and cotton prices by making loans to national co-operatives marketing these commodities. It slowed somewhat the drop in these prices, until it ceased price-support operations and began to liquidate its holdings; then prices again dropped drastically.

### The First Agricultural Adjustment Act

The Agricultural Adjustment Act of 1933 authorized a wide variety of governmental activities to raise the level of farm prices. The act was to operate as follows: (1) relief was to be brought to the farming population by improving farm incomes through increasing the prices of farm products and through benefit payments; (2) the latter were to be financed largely out of special excise taxes on the commodity, so that consumers and processors would pay a fair exchange value for what was consumed; (3) such supplementary income was to go only to farmers who agreed to participate in the program of controlled production; and (4) the control program was to produce a supply-demand situation that would yield a level of prices fair and remunerative to farmers.[1] The commodities influenced to an important extent were wheat, cotton, tobacco, corn, hogs, sugar beets, and sugarcane. The programs probably had more appeal for the large producers than the small growers, because the latter used mainly the labor of the family and could not cut their costs by discharging hired labor as the large operators could do. It was difficult to know how successful the program was in reducing farm production, because the severe drought of 1934 also had the same effect. When the Supreme Court declared the Agricultural Adjustment Act of 1933 unconstitutional on January 6, 1936, the program as a whole was abruptly terminated.

## The Soil Conservation and Domestic Allotment Act of 1936

This legislation was hurriedly enacted so that some form of aid to agriculture would continue. One aspect of the new legislation provided that farmers be paid for carrying out adjustment plans that diverted acreage from " soil-depleting " to " soil-conserving " crops. In general, the soil-depleting crops were cash crops, the production of which it was considered desirable to reduce. The soil-conserving crops that would protect and rebuild soils did not, for the most part, contribute directly to the burdensome farm surpluses. The payments to farmers who shifted specified percentages of their acreages to soil-conserving crops averaged about ten dollars per acre. Another aspect of the act provided that payments of not more than one dollar per acre might be made for certain approved soil-building practices. Funds for the execution of the program were to be appropriated by Congress from the Treasury, rather than be obtained from processing taxes. Although the 1936 act was acceptable as a stop-gap, it did not satisfy the aspirations of either the farm groups or the administration leaders. Shortly after its enactment Congress began work on more carefully considered long-term agricultural legislation.

---

[1] Edwin G. Nourse, Joseph S. Davis, and John D. Black, *Three Years of the Agricultural Adjustment Administration* (Washington: The Brookings Institution, 1937), 23.

## The Second Agricultural Adjustment Act and Subsequent Amendments

With the passage of the Agricultural Adjustment Act of 1938, government price supports and production controls became important for much of American agriculture. This act with its subsequent amendments provides price supports for various farm commodities, some under production controls and others without controls. As stated in the act, the purpose of the program is " to provide an orderly, adequate, and balanced flow of such commodities in interstate and foreign commerce."

By the time the United States entered World War II surpluses of some of the program commodities were beginning to threaten, despite the controls some of the programs exercised over production. During the war and the Korean conflict the programs were " turned around " and effectively used to increase agricultural production by guaranteeing farmers higher prices. But after the Korean War heavy production of many supported crops caused stocks of these crops to increase and made production controls and greatly expanded price-support activity again necessary.

The Agricultural Adjustment Act of 1938 with its subsequent amendments required the Secretary of Agriculture, under certain conditions, to support the prices of the so-called " mandatory basic " commodities and " mandatory nonbasic " commodities and, at his discretion, was permitted under certain circumstances to support the prices of the so-called " permissive nonbasic " commodities.[6] The level of a commodity's price support is usually specified in legislation as a certain percentage (or a range of percentages) of the commodity's parity price, in some cases depending on the extent to which the commodity is in surplus. The idea of parity price, as expressed in the Agricultural Adjustment Act of 1938, is that " price for the commodity which will give the commodity a purchasing power, with respect to articles that

[2] The six " basic " commodities, as defined by the Agricultural Act of 1949, are wheat, rice, corn, cotton, peanuts, and tobacco. The " nonbasic " commodities whose prices must be supported are the following: tung nuts, honey, milk, butterfat, wool, and mohair (under the National Wool Act of 1954), and in effect the other feed grains—oats, barley, rye, and grain sorghum—whose prices, under the Agricultural Act of 1958, were required to be supported at levels fair and reasonable in relation to the support level for corn. Any other " nonbasic " commodities may be supported at the discretion of the Secretary of Agriculture (the Agricultural Act of 1949, Title III). In

farmers buy, equivalent to the purchasing power of such commodity in the base period." [3]

How do " strong " production controls come into effect? " When stocks of wheat, rice, cotton, peanuts, and tobacco reach a specified level relative to normal domestic consumption and exports, the Secretary of Agriculture must proclaim marketing quotas for the commodity and announce a reduced national rate of production as a goal for the country. The national acreage from which such a reduced national production is expected is then apportioned among the various growers of this crop. In a special referendum, if at least two-thirds of the growers with allotments approve the " strong " type of limitation on production, during that crop year (or for certain commodities, during the next three crop years) individual farmers are subject to both " acreage allotments " and " marketing quotas." Farmers who plant only their allotted acreage—called " co-operators "—are eligible for a high level of price support on the entire crop. But farmers who plant more than their allotted acreage are not eligible for price support on any of their crop and must also pay a substantial penalty on production from the acreage in excess of their allotment.

In the special referendum, if more than one-third of the growers with allotments to produce the crops of wheat, rice, cotton, and peanuts vote their disapproval of marketing quotas, then the only benefits available to those who comply with their acreage allotments are price supports at a low level—50 per cent of " parity." In this case no penalties are imposed on marketings from acreage in excess of a farmer's allotment.

Production of corn, which could not be put under marketing quotas, did not decrease while acreage allotments were in effect, although harvested acreage declined. When corn allotments were removed

---

1958, for example, the prices of the following nonbasic commodities were supported: cottonseed, flaxseed, soybeans, dry edible beans, and unprocessed pine gum.

[3] Under the 1938 act the parity price of a commodity was computed simply by multiplying the average price received for the commodity in a fixed base period by an index of prices paid. The Agricultural Act of 1948 modernized parity by providing for an adjusted base price of a commodity that would reflect trends in the most recent ten-calendar-year period. The " modernized " parity price of a farm commodity may be defined as (1) the average price received for the commodity during the last ten years multiplied by (2) the index of all prices paid by farmers in the current year and divided by (3) the index of all prices received by farmers in the last ten years.

after 1958, larger acreages and higher yields raised corn production 30 per cent above its 1952–1953 level. Production of other feed grains also increased partly as a result of diversion of land from wheat and cotton.[4]

### Other Programs

Several other programs have also had an important influence on the prices and marketings of other agricultural products. Among these programs are the following: various marketing orders (under the Agricultural Marketing Agreement Act of 1937 as amended); the so-

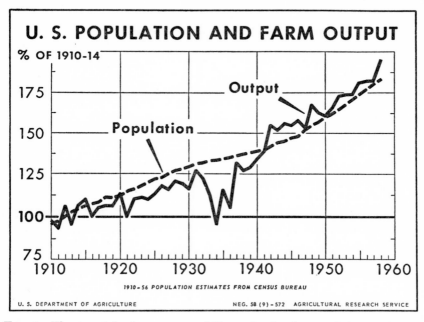

## U. S. POPULATION AND FARM OUTPUT

*1910-56 POPULATION ESTIMATES FROM CENSUS BUREAU*

U. S. DEPARTMENT OF AGRICULTURE  NEG. 58 (9) - 572  AGRICULTURAL RESEARCH SERVICE

Fig. 1. The trend in farm output follows closely the trend in population growth in the United States. Note the stabilizing influence of production controls after 1940.

called "480 program" (Public Law 480, 83rd Congress) and the Section 32 programs (Section 32 of Public Law 320, 74th Congress), both to dispose of surpluses in domestic and foreign markets; the

[4] *Farm Production—Trends, Prospects, and Programs* (Agriculture Information Bulletin No. 239 [Washington: Agricultural Research Service, USDA, 1961]), 29–30.

Sugar Program (the Sugar Act of 1948, as amended); the National Wool Act of 1954; and the Soil Bank Act, enacted in 1956.

*Marketing agreement and order programs:* These programs are authorized by the Agricultural Marketing Agreement Act of 1937, as amended. They seek to establish and maintain orderly marketing conditions for agricultural commodities moving in interstate and foreign commerce. In 1957, for example, programs were in effect for milk; certain fruits, vegetables, tobacco, and tree nuts; for antihog-cholera serum and hog-cholera virus.[5]

*The Soil Bank:* The Soil Bank Act, enacted as part of the Agricultural Act of 1956, authorized assistance to farmers to divert a portion of their cropland from the production of excessive supplies of agricultural commodities and to carry out a program of soil, water, forest, and wildlife conservation. The two parts of the Soil Bank were (1) the Acreage Reserve and (2) the Conservation Reserve. The objective of the Acreage Reserve, which operated only for the crop years 1956 through 1958, was to reduce the production of basic crops by having the government enter into agreements with individual farmers to cut their acreages below allotments. In return, these farmers received payments to compensate for loss of income from land put in the Acreage Reserve, which land ordinarily could not be cropped or grazed. The objective of the Conservation Reserve was to take general cropland out of production and put it to conservation use. Participating farmers receive two types of payments: (1) a payment in cash or in conservation materials and services for carrying out a conservation practice on set-aside acreage and (2) an annual cash payment for the period of the reserve, which is three, five, or ten years. Legislative authority for making new commitments under the Conservation Reserve expired in 1960, but contracts will remain in force until their respective terms expire or they are canceled.[6]

### Lessons Learned from Recent Production Control Programs

Several major conclusions may be drawn concerning acreage-control programs of the 1950's as a means of limiting farm output, preventing the accumulation of stocks of farm commodities, and improving farm-product prices and farmers' incomes. The basis for these conclusions

[5] *Price Programs* (Agriculture Information Bulletin No. 135, [Washington: USDA, 1957]) , 36.
[6] *Ibid.,* 30–31.

are discussed at length in an excellent USDA study entitled " Farm Production—Trends, Prospects, and Programs." [7]

First, for several decades we may expect a large excess of farm production and price-depressing surpluses, even with high levels of employment and rapid growth of the national economy. Technological advances in farm production are outrunning growth in the total United States population and putting agriculture in a long-run squeeze that prevents farm people from sharing equitably in the benefits of their increasing productive labor. Farmers face a dilemma. They desire a program that will balance farm production with demand at fair prices, but the prerequisites of such a program seem to include collective restraints on farmers and their businesses.

Second, acreage-allotment and marketing-quota programs have reduced the output of crops to which they were applied, but not in proportion to the change in acreage. This result was brought about because: the poorer land was taken out of production of marketing-quota crops, while the better land remained in production; there was some diversion of labor, machinery, and other resources from cropland retired from marketing-quota crops to cropland remaining in use; and management practices were improved.

Third, such programs have caused land to be diverted from allotment crops to other crops and probably influenced the total volume of production very little. Diversion of land from wheat and cotton to feed grains only added to the increasingly serious problem of excess production of feed grains.

Fourth, the Soil Bank programs have kept production below what it would have been without them. But reduction of acreage of harvested crops has been only about half that of cropland acreage placed in the Soil Bank, because some cropland that had previously been idle was brought back into use on nonparticipating farms.

Fifth, such long-term rental programs as the Conservation Reserve program of the Soil Bank can assist farm people to make adjustments by providing an important income alternative for older farm people who retire and for others who shift to nonfarm employment but continue to live on their farms.[8]

[7] *Farm Production—Trends, Prospects, and Programs.*
[8] *Ibid.*, 25–26, 36.

*Implications of Production-Control Programs for Land Tenure*

There is wide agreement that recent production-control programs have failed to afford agriculture anything like a complete escape from the cost-price squeeze and the depressed farm incomes that result from technologic advances in farm production. The implication for farm tenure is that production-control programs have only to a very limited extent shielded agriculture from the land-tenure consequences of its tendency toward overproduction. Lowered farm-product prices and lowered incomes of farm people make it more difficult for families to accumulate the net worth for ownership and operation of a well-equipped and productive commercial family farm, if they have not inherited such a farm.

It is now also generally recognized that a system of price supports through production restriction mostly helps only the commercial farmer, most of whose production is for market, and that such a program offers small help to the low-income farmer with little output above what the family consumes. This fact implies that, where farm-tenure problems are largely those of small-size farms with under-employment of family labor, the price-support program does not substantially improve the farm-tenure situation.

Production-control programs also raise the same land-tenure questions that were mentioned in the brief discussion of the incidence of the benefits of public resource-development programs: (1) How are the benefits of a production-control program distributed among the several factors of production? (2) When ownership of allotment land entitles one to participate in a program, to what extent are future benefits of the program capitalized into the selling price of land? (3) What does the capitalization of program benefits into land values imply as to the difficulty young people without an inheritance experience in getting started in farming?

## Programs for Depressed Rural Areas

Widespread poverty has long been a problem in many rural areas of the United States. This kind of poverty is not made up of infrequent isolated cases of individual poverty within a generally prosperous community. Rather it consists of a higher proportion of economically disadvantaged rural families who earn low incomes because their resources—skills, health, land, and capital equipment—are inadequate, compared with the average for the nation. As farmers, these families have too little good land, insufficient livestock and equipment, and lack an understanding of the technology and management necessary for efficient and remunerative farming. As for nonfarm opportunities, such people are likewise handicapped by lack of skills for and/or knowledge of nonfarm employment locally or outside the area.

## Programs of the 1930's

Such chronic concentrations of individual poverty in rural areas were first identified and given widespread attention in the 1930's, after the Great Depression had dramatized the fact that many individual problems are actually social problems, in the sense that the causes of many personal problems are outside of and beyond the individuals in whose lives the problems are manifest. The report of President Franklin Roosevelt's Special Committee on Farm Tenancy in 1937 numbered, among the insecure, farm groups and suggested remedial action for not only " tenants," " croppers," and " owners hopelessly in debt " but also " farm laborers," " families on submarginal land," " families on holdings of inadequate size," and " farm people unable to obtain farms."

Several rehabilitation and resettlement programs were developed and carried on during the 1930's, beginning under the Federal Emergency Relief Administration and continuing under the Resettlement Administration and the Farm Security Administration. Such programs provided for rehabilitation " in place " and by " resettlement." Features of the programs were loans, supervision, debt adjustment, the transferring of selected urban families to subsistence part-time farms, retirement of submarginal land and resettlement elsewhere, camps and camp facilities for migrant workers, and the establishment of farmsteads on a co-operative community basis.[9] The urgencies of World War II and the prosperity it engendered diverted public attention from the problem of chronic widespread poverty in certain rural areas.

## The Rural Development Program (1955–1960)

In the years immediately following World War II, public discussion of farm problems increasingly made the distinction between (1) the

[9] Olaf F. Larson et al., Ten Years of Rural Rehabilitation in the United States (Washington: Bureau of Agricultural Economics, USDA, July, 1947). Also Murray R. Benedict, Farm Policies of the United States (New York: Twentieth Century Fund, 1953), 324–27, 357–58, 362, 491–93.

price and income problems of commercial farmers that resulted from their increasing efficiency and (2) the income problems of disadvantaged rural people, many of whom were small noncommercial subsistence farmers.

On January 11, 1954, President Eisenhower requested in his Special Message on Agriculture that attention be given to the problems peculiar to farmers with low incomes. As a result of this request, the report *Development of Agriculture's Human Resources* was prepared in the United States Department of Agriculture.[10] This report painted a picture of hardship and privation for about 1.5 million farm families. The report stated that such low-income farms " are most numerous in areas of dense rural settlement with high birth rates, where there are few outside jobs, and where topography or other obstacles hinder the use of modern machinery." The following generalized problem areas were identified: (1) the Appalachian mountains, valleys, and plateaus, (2) the Southern Piedmont and Coastal Plains, (3) the southeastern hilly area (the coastal plain west of the Appalachians and east of the Mississippi River), (4) the Mississippi Delta, (5) the southwestern Sandy Coastal Plain, (6) the Ozark-Ouachita Mountains and Border, (7) the northern Lake States, (8) northwestern New Mexico, and (9) the Cascade and northern Rocky Mountains.

The report and its accompanying recommendations called for increased credit, extension service, and technical aid for low-income farmers; special research; better educational and vocational training facilities; improved state employment services in low-income rural areas; possible use of the program of dispersing defense industries to assist areas of underemployed rural labor; more industrial development in the low-income areas; a maximum of local initiative and control; and the development of programs in pilot counties.

The major objectives of the Rural Development Program as stated in the Rural Development Program Handbook, issued by the Committee for Rural Development, were:

—To expand industry in these [underdeveloped rural] areas and widen the range of off-farm job opportunities.
—To help families that have the desire and ability to stay in farming gain the necessary tools, land, and skills.

[10] *Development of Agriculture's Human Resources—A Report on Problems of Low-Income Farmers* (Washington: USDA, April, 1955).

—To help people in these areas enjoy better opportunities for adequate education, vocational training, and improved health.[11]

By July, 1959, work under the Rural Development Program was being conducted in thirty states and Puerto Rico. Research on the extent and nature of the low-income problem in rural areas was greatly intensified during the late 1950's in private colleges and universities, the state agricultural experiment stations, and the United States Department of Agriculture.[12]

There has been widespread popular approval of the new concern with the problem of low farm incomes, as this interest was embodied in the Rural Development Program beginning in 1955. By the end of the decade, however, some serious students of the problem had begun to fear that the low-income rural problem was far too vast and deep-seated to be solved by any program that placed almost exclusive emphasis on local initiative and enterprise. In this view, the other essential ingredients—increased out-migration of population and greater outside financial and technical assistance, both public and private—were being largely ignored and neglected during the mid- and late 1950's. Rather what are particularly needed, say those who stress the deep-seated character of the low-income rural problem, are large increases in federal appropriations and grants-in-aid for such activities in rural areas as the following: improved general and vocational education, a much greater amount of supervised farm credit, more special agricultural research and extension services, more adequate employment services disseminating better labor-market information, and better health facilities.[13]

[11] *Rural Development Program Handbook* (Committee for Rural Development Program [Washington: USDA, September, 1959]), 1.

[12] Results of several such USDA studies are summarized in the following publications: Buis T. Inman and John H. Southern, *Opportunities for Economic Development in Low-Production Farm Areas* (Agriculture Information Bulletin No. 234 [Washington: USDA, November, 1960]); Nelson L. LeRay, *Employment and Underemployment of Rural People* (Agricultural Research Service 43–109 [Washington: USDA, December, 1959]).

[13] "Rural Low-Income and Rural Development Programs in the South," statement by the Agriculture Committee of the National Planning Association, released on February 22, 1959, Washington, D. C.; "Rural Low-Income and Rural Development Programs in the South," address by William H. Nicholls to the Mid-American Conference on Migratory Labor, St. Louis, Missouri, April 7, 1959, co-sponsored by the Council of State Governments and President's Committee on Migratory Labor.

### The Rural Areas Development Program

The Kennedy Administration continued the federal government's concern over the problems of low-income rural areas, changing slightly the name of its rural-development activities to that of the Rural Areas Development Program. Secretary of Agriculture Orville Freeman on March 21, 1961, announced that the United States Department of Agriculture was mobilizing for maximum assistance to state and local groups in a broad program of rural area development and established a technical Rural Areas Development staff and an advisory Rural Areas Development Board.

On May 1, 1961, President Kennedy signed into law the Area Redevelopment Act (Public Law 87–27) to promote new opportunities in urban and rural areas suffering from a chronic lack of full-time jobs. The act, which will greatly supplement the Rural Areas Development Program, authorized $394 million in loans, grants, technical aid, and other benefits over a four-year period. One hundred million dollars in loans are specifically earmarked for use in low-income rural areas. Five broad types of federal aid are authorized by the Area Redevelopment Act:

(1) Loans to help finance industrial buildings and commercial projects, including tourist facilities ($200 million in total, divided equally between urban and rural areas);

(2) Loans ($100 million) and grants ($75 million) for public facilities, such as water and sewage systems and power lines;

(3) Technical aid, through federal, state, and private agencies, to communities for surveys of resources and program planning ($4.5 million);

(4) Retraining grants to enable workers out of jobs and small farmers to up-grade their skills or gain new skills ($10 million for subsistence grants to individuals and $4.5 million to finance retraining programs);

(5) More flexible federal urban renewal aid in redevelopment areas.

A new Area Redevelopment Administration in the United States Department of Commerce was given responsibility for general administration of the program, with the expectation that the Department of Agriculture would be assigned major responsibility for aid in rural redevelopment areas.[14]

[14] *Rural Areas Development Newsletter* No. 34 (Washington: Office of In-

## *Tenure Significance of Programs for Depressed Rural Areas*

The significance for farm tenure of recent public programs for depressed rural areas is that the root causes of tenure and other problems in depressed rural areas are properly identified as people's limited economic opportunities because of their inferior educational opportunities, their lack of vocational skills, and an unfortunate ratio of population to the nonhuman resources of land and capital. Farm land tenure is thus not charged with principal responsibility for all the ills of rural society.

The implication of the foregoing is that intense pressure of farm population on agricultural land inevitably results in a farm-tenure situation that is unsatisfactory from the point of view of working farm people. This is so because pressure of population on land drives down the marginal productivity of labor and the real return to labor as a factor of production. If farm land-tenure reforms are not accompanied by policies to reduce excessive pressure of farm population on agricultural land, such reforms are likely to be of little or no avail. Fortunately, the two recent programs to assist depressed rural areas to some degree reflect an awareness of this principle.

One misgiving, however, does not so much concern the methods employed in recent rural development programs as it concerns the difficulties to be surmounted. This misgiving is the possibility that— especially in southern low-income rural areas—local values, attitudes, and customs may retard or even negate the natural tendencies and the policy actions that are working to raise the depressed levels of productivity and living.[15] Such a possibility readily comes to mind in the context of a farm-tenure discussion, because tenure arrangements both reinforce and are reinforced by other local traditions, values, customs, and attitudes. Of course, it may well be that the other elements of local traditions and attitudes are in this matter even more important than tenure patterns.

---

formation, USDA, May, 1961) ; *Your Community and the Area Redevelopment Act* (Washington: Area Redevelopment Administration, USDA, May 9, 1961 [Preliminary]) .

[15] William H. Nicholls, " Southern Traditions and Regional Economic Progress," *Southern Economic Journal*, Vol. 26 (January, 1960) , 187–98; *id., Southern Traditions and Regional Economic Progress* (Chapel Hill, N. C.: University of North Carolina Press, 1960) .

# CHAPTER SIX

# Public Policies and Programs Relating to Land Tenure: Labor Policies and Programs

FEW PUBLIC POLICIES have explicitly related to farm labor, either as a production input or in the sense of its tenure categories. The one important exception is the institution of slavery. However, various other governmental policies, while not concerned with farm labor as such, have exerted important influences on farm labor, both as a production input and as a tenure consideration. The labor policies of the United States which have related in some determinable way to land tenure are reviewed in this chapter.

## Slavery as an Institution

With the concern here being the farm-tenure implication of slavery, interest will be concentrated in both the direct and the indirect influences of slavery on tenure. Slavery and the sharecropping system it engendered as its successor were, of course, tenure institutions themselves, and they had various direct tenure consequences. But slavery and its concomitant institutions also had important indirect influences on farm-tenure phenomena. This was through their effect on the whole socio-economic fabric of Southern life, which is the context of tenure arrangements and practices in that region. These general influences of slavery on Southern life will be considered first.

Slavery was a " way of life " for the South and for both its races. On the economic side, it was a labor system; it reinforced and was reinforced by the pattern of labor-intensive, one-crop plantation agriculture; it was the foundation of the Southern aristocracy; and it discouraged the development of a diversified economy. On the social side, it was conducive to a high degree of stratification: There were slaves, the poor whites, and the planters, but scarcely any numerous and influential middle class. Where the plantation economy and its slave-labor system prevailed, population was sparse and scattered; and towns and cities were conspicuous by their infrequency.[1]

Until lately the prevalent view has been that slavery would have declined and disappeared even without the Civil War because it was an inefficient and unprofitable system for supplying and utilizing labor.[2] Careful research, however, has demonstrated that slavery was quite profitable for plantation operators and the whole South, that there was nothing necessarily self-destructive about the profits of the slave economy, and that slavery was an economically tenable institution in the ante bellum American South.[3] The conclusion that slavery was a reasonably viable institution may also be deduced as a simple inference from the following considerations: The number of slaves increased steadily during the last six decades of slavery in America; one does not expect practices that are unprofitable to the entrepreneural class to continue for long in a free-enterprise economy.

The system was probably inefficient, however, in a different and larger sense. To begin with, slavery and the one-crop plantation system resulted in the rapid deterioration of soils and the westward movement of cotton production as new lands came into production.[4] It was also inefficient with respect to diversified economic development. The stultifying influence of slavery and the one-crop plantation system on the economic development of the South was, however, probably more a matter of the various values and aspirations held respectively by plantation operators, poor whites, and slaves than it was a matter of narrow economic profitability.

Besides its general influence on the whole socio-economic makeup of the South, slavery directly influenced the Southern farm-tenure situation in several particular and specific respects. First, because it was a system of supplying and using unskilled labor, it did not encourage—

[1] Charles A. and Mary R. Beard, *The Rise of American Civilization* (Rev. and enlarged ed., 4 vols.; New York: Macmillan Co., 1937), II, 3–51; Max Lerner, *America as a Civilization* (New York: Simon and Schuster, 1957), 15–19; Chester W. Wright, *Economic History of the United States* (New York: McGraw-Hill, 1941), 369–79.

[2] See especially the works of the Southern historians, C. W. Ramsdell and U. B. Phillips.

[3] Alfred H. Conrad and John R. Mayer, " The Economics of Slavery in the Ante Bellum South," *Journal of Political Economy*, Vol. 66 (April, 1958), 95–131; Lewis C. Gray, *History of Agriculture in the Southern United States to 1860* (2 vols.; Washington: Carnegie Institution, 1933), I, 462–80.

[4] *Ibid.*, 474–80.

even necessarily discouraged—the process of raising the level of the skill, competence, motivations, and aspirations of human labor.

The second direct and specific tenure consequence of slavery was that slavery tended to destroy the small independent farmer.[5] This process was eloquently described in a contemporary comment found by Frederick Law Olmstead in an unnamed country newspaper and quoted in *A Journey in the Back Country*, published just prior to the Civil War:

> The cotton-growing portion of the valley of the Mississippi, the very garden of the Union, is year by year being wrested from the hands of the small farmer and delivered over to the great capitalists. . . .
>
> All the great cotton lands were first opened up by industrious settlers, with small means and much energy. No sooner is their clearing made, and their homestead growing in comfort, than the great planter comes up from the East, with his black horde, settles down on the district, and absorbs and overruns everything. This is precisely the process which is going on, day by day, over the greater portion of Louisiana and Mississippi. The small farmers, that is to say, the mass of the white population, are fast disappearing. The rich bottom lands of that glorious valley are being concentrated in the hands of the large planters, with one hundred to one thousand negroes.[6]

It is therefore not surprising that, to this day, the aspiration of climbing the agricultural ladder to attain the ideal of the family farm is less widely held in the South.

The third tenure consequence of slavery, closely related to the second, is that the tenure institution of sharecropping was a lineal descendant from the plantation slave-labor system. The same economic conditions and forces that, prior to the Civil War, had made slavery profitable also fostered the development and spread of sharecropping after the abolition of slavery.[7]

---

[5] *Ibid.*, 444–48, 462–80.

[6] Quoted by Frederick Law Olmstead, *A Journey in the Back Country* (New York: Mason Brothers, 1960), 329–30.

[7] Louis M. Hacker and Benjamin B. Kendrick, *The United States Since 1865* (New York: F. S. Crofts, 1932), 170–73; Mathew Brown Hammond, " The Extension of the Cotton Belt in the New South," reprinted in *Readings in the*

## Public Policies with Secondary Labor Implications

Of the various public policies that have to some degree had an effect on farm labor, the ones with the greatest impact were probably our policies on land settlement, general and technical education, and immigration.

In an earlier chapter it has been pointed out how public policies on land settlement, together with the relative abundance of arable land, meant a scarcity of labor relative to land that was conducive to a high return to labor as a factor of production and to a high percentage of owner-operatorship.

It has also been shown how public policies on technical agricultural research and education made American farm people individually, and American agriculture as a whole, more productive. Paradoxically, however, these improvements in the efficiency of farm production have resulted in a continuing " cost-price " squeeze, such that technological progress has benefited farm people more as consumers than as farmworkers.

Our system of public general education has, of course, had a profound influence on all aspects of American life. The consequences of public general education that relate to farm labor are such tendencies as: (1) to improve an individual's labor productivity in secondary respects, such as greater initiative and increased general knowledge and understanding, (2) to raise a person's vocational aspirations, and (3) to increase his vocational mobility.

The policies of the United States on immigration have changed during our history and have doubtless reflected the stages of economic development of this continent. During the period that parts of our country were unsettled or only sparsely developed, the United States imposed almost no restrictions on immigration. However, by the early years of this century immigration regulations became increasingly restrictive. This was, among other things, a reflection of the widespread popular feeling that unrestricted immigration would depress the returns and living levels of American workers both on the farms and in the cities. In a general sense, this popular view has doubtless had considerable economic validity.

*Economic History of American Agriculture*, eds. Louis Bernard Schmidt and Earle Dudley Ross (New York: Macmillan Co., 1925), 425–35.

*Agricultural Employment Under General Labor and Welfare Legislation*

Persons engaged in farm production are excluded from most of the general labor legislation of the federal government and the states but are covered by some federal and state welfare legislation.

The two main components of the farm labor force—(1) farm operators and other unpaid family workers and (2) year-round and seasonal hired farmworkers—are excluded from most general labor legislation but for different reasons. Farm operators and unpaid family workers belong to the " self-employed " category which, by its nature, is largely outside the scope of legislation affecting the employer-employee relationship. Hired farmworkers have been specifically excluded from most general labor legislation. The ostensible reasons given for this exclusion have been the following: the peculiar nature of farm production, the small number of hired workers per farm employer, and the difficulty that would be experienced in administering labor regulations in agriculture.

During the last decade farm operators and hired farmworkers have become eligible for Old Age and Survivors Insurance coverage under Social Security. They must, of course, meet certain minimum eligibility requirements.

*Minimum wages:* Agricultural workers are specifically excluded from the wage and hour provisions of the Federal Fair Labor Standards Act. The only federal legislation at present concerned with the wages of farmworkers is the Sugar Act of 1937. It requires producers of sugarcane and sugar beets, who wish to qualify for conditional government payments, to pay a minimum wage which is determined by the Secretary of Labor after a public hearing.[8]

The minimum wage laws of Hawaii and Puerto Rico specifically apply to agricultural workers. In two other states minimum wage rates for women and children have been established by administrative order under legislation broad enough to apply to agriculture.[9]

*Old Age and Survivors' Insurance under Social Security:* Initially, all farm equipment was excluded from Social Security retirement and

[8] *Status of Agricultural Workers under State and Federal Labor* (Washington: Bureau of Labor Standards, USDL, April, 1961), 3; Wayne D. Rasmussen, *A History of the Emergency Farm Labor Supply Program, 1943–1947* (Agriculture Monograph No. 13 [Washington: Bureau of Agricultural Economics, USDA, 1951]), 8.

[9] *Status of Agricultural Workers under State and Federal Labor Laws,* 3.

survivorship benefits. During the last decade, however, this coverage has been extended to hired farmworkers and self-employed farm operators. A hired farmworker, to be covered, must be paid by an employer $150 or more in cash during the year or have worked for an employer on twenty or more days a year for cash pay figured on a time basis. To accrue coverage, a self-employed farmer must make a net profit of four hundred dollars or more a year.[10]

*Child labor:* Two federal laws affect the employment of children in agriculture. The Fair Labor Standards Act establishes a sixteen-year minimum age for agricultural employment *during school hours.* Under the Sugar Act, if the producers are to obtain maximum benefits, they may not employ children under fourteen, or permit those of fourteen and fifteen to work more than eight hours a day in the cultivation and harvesting of sugar beets or sugarcane.

Only nine States, Puerto Rico, and the District of Columbia expressly provide a minimum age for employment of children in agriculture *outside of school hours.* For agricultural work *during school hours*, a minimum age expressly applies in fifteen states, Puerto Rico, and the District of Columbia.[11]

*Workmen's compensation:* Only seven states require workmen's compensation coverage for hired farmworkers in the same manner as other workers, and in another state workers are so covered unless the employer " elects " not to come under the act. Agricultural workers engaged in specific farm occupations (usually operating certain machinery) receive compulsory workmen's compensation coverage in five additional states and in four other states such coverage is elective at the discretion of the farmer-employer.[12]

*Unemployment insurance:* The federal Social Security Act of 1935 provided for, among other things, a system of unemployment compensation by and through the states. Only one state—Hawaii—provides compulsory unemployment insurance coverage for agricultural labor. The other states all exclude agricultural labor from compulsory unemployment insurance coverage. Most of these permit voluntary coverage of excluded occupations, but agricultural employers have made little use of this option. Puerto Rico covers agricultural workers in the sugar industry. The four states that provide for temporary disability benefits have specifically exempted agricultural workers.[13]

*Labor relations acts:* The federal Labor Management Relations

[10] *Ibid.*, 7.　　　[11] *Ibid.*, 1.　　　[12] *Ibid.*, 2–3.　　　[13] *Ibid.*, 6.

(Taft-Hartley) Act specifically exempts agricultural laborers. Of the fourteen state labor relations acts (in effect in early 1961) which recognize the rights of employees to organize and to bargain collectively, only three appear to be broad enough to cover all agricultural workers. Ten specifically exempt all agricultural workers from coverage and another exempts certain dairy-farm workers.[14]

## The Farm Placement Service

The Farm Placement Service is concerned with employment in agricultural and food processing industries. Its program is operated to benefit both hired workers seeking employment and farmer-employers needing workers by bringing individual employers and workers into communication with each other. It is " neutral " labor policy in the sense that it is not operated altogether for the benefit of either group. The Farm Placement Service is an affiliation of farm placement staffs of state employment services, coordinated by a national office and regional staffs in the United States Employment Service of the Department of Labor's Bureau of Employment Security.

The United States Employment Service was created by the Wagner-Peyser Act of 1933. Among other things, this act directed that a farm placement service be maintained within the uses structure, thus giving recognition to the problem of balancing supply and demand among agricultural workers.

The Farm Placement Service was set up as a specialized service concerned only with farm placement. One reason for this arrangement was the need for an agricultural labor force adequate in its composition, size, and availability to cope with the characteristics of modern agriculture—its large size, the variety of our crops and of their response to differences in climate and weather, the wide distance between crop areas, and the northward progression of the national harvest from April to December. The second reason was the trend toward large-scale agricultural operations, together with the willingness of workers to migrate to and through agricultural areas during harvest periods.

The planning of farm labor activities suitable to the individual states and to the nation as a whole occurs at both state and federal levels. The farm placement staffs of the state agencies have the responsibility of working with the users to shape their activities to fit into a larger pattern, according to geographical and crop-area con-

[14] *Ibid.*, 4.

siderations. Thus, the efforts of each state to fulfill its own farm labor requirements have the further goal of meeting the national interest.

The program of the Farm Placement Service is operated largely through local employment office farm placement staffs supplemented by a smaller number of volunteer farm placement representatives. The Farm Placement Service program includes the following activities: the Annual Worker Plan, which schedules migratory workers to help provide a dependable labor supply to farm employers and to increase the migrants' employment opportunities by arranging successive job referrals; the " day-haul " programs, which refer local workers to seasonal job opportunities nearby; the " youth program," which places youth in seasonal farm employment; " information stations," to assist migrants while they are traveling; a program for Puerto Ricans who come to do seasonal farm work in the United States; and a " harvest machine " program, which schedules small-grain harvest machines and their skilled crews for custom harvest work.

### Programs for the Importation of Foreigners for Seasonal Farm Work

A public policy of recent years that has related explicitly to farm labor and has aroused considerable controversy is the policy of permitting the temporary entry into this country each year of foreign workers for seasonal farm employment. The most important such program in terms both of its inducements to foreign laborers and also in numbers of foreign migrants is the Mexican Farm Labor Program. Foreign workers also legally come here for seasonal farmwork under the provisions of the Immigration and Naturalization Act (Public Law 414 of 1952), which permits the temporary admission of otherwise inadmissible aliens in certain labor-shortage categories. In recent years seasonal farmworkers have come to the United States from Jamaica, the Bahamas, other islands of the British West Indies, and even from Japan and the Philippines. Under less formal arrangements Canadians also do seasonal farmwork in the states along the northeastern border.[15]

These programs grew out of the World War II policy of encouraging the importation of foreign nationals for seasonal farm work to increase wartime agricultural production while many American farmworkers were in the armed forces and in industrial production. Foreign

[15] *Farm Labor Fact Book* (Washington: USDA, 1959), 155–58.

workers, however, have been employed in this country for more than half a century. For many years prior to World War II large numbers of Mexican workers crossed the border as illegal so-called " wetbacks " to work in states near the border during the spring and later during the harvest season. The incentive for use of Mexican and other foreign workers in the American farm-work force with its higher wage levels is apparently strong, both from the point of view of foreign workers and American farmers who employ them. Even after the Mexican Farm Labor Program made legal entry of Mexican workers possible, large numbers of illegal entries of " wetbacks " continued for a time. For example, during the intensified drive against illegal entry from January through May, 1954, the number of deportations of illegal Mexican aliens by the Immigrations and Naturalization Service was 248,000. But this number afforded little clue to the number actually employed, for the same individuals were often apprehended over and over, and the border seepage of re-entries and new entries for a time continued at a rate that seemed to exceed deportations. However, the Immigration and Naturalization Service campaign against and roundup of illegal Mexican aliens eventually made their employment more impractical, so that after 1954 greater use was made of the Mexican Farm Labor Program.[16]

The Mexican Farm Labor Program is authorized by Public Law 78, 82nd Congress, as amended, and is operated under the Migrant Labor Agreement of 1951 between the governments of the United States and Mexico. Before any Mexican nationals may be brought into any particular area under this law, the Secretary of Labor must certify to the following: (1) that qualified domestic workers cannot be found to perform seasonal agricultural work in the area in question, (2) that the wages offered the imported workers in the relevant area and occupation are not less than the prevailing wages of domestic workers in the relevant area and occupation, and (3) that the wages and working conditions of domestic workers will not be adversely affected by the proposed employment of imported workers.

The law also authorizes the Secretary of Labor (after the governments of the United States and Mexico have reached agreement on details of the program) to recruit Mexican workers, operate reception

---

[16] " ' Operation Wetback '—Impact on the Border States," *Employment Security Review* (Washington: USDL, March, 1955), 1–6; *Report of the President's Commission on Migratory Labor, Migratory Labor in American Agriculture* (Washington: Government Printing Office, 1951), 69–88.

centers, provide transportation from migratory centers in Mexico to the reception centers near the border, give subsistence en route from the former to the latter, and supervise the contracting of individual laborers to individual employers or employer-associations. Each American employer contracting with Mexican workers must pay a fee into a revolving fund to cover the cost of such things as transportation, food, shelter, and medical services while the worker is in process of being contacted.

When an American farmer-employer enters into the required Standard Work Contract with a Mexican worker, he guarantees to the worker the opportunity for employment for a specified number of work days during the contract period. If the worker is afforded less than this employment, he is paid the amount he would have earned had he worked the guaranteed period. The worker's transportation and meals to his place of employment, between places of employment, and on the return journey to Mexico are also paid by the employer. The employer agrees to supply housing accommodations with utilities and fuel according to prescribed standards. The standard work day is eight hours, but workers may and usually do voluntarily work the hours normal for the season and the community. The United States Government guarantees the wages due a Mexican worker under his contract with an employer and inspects housing and transportation facilities provided workers to see that minimum standards are met.[17]

From 1955 through 1959 the number of foreign contract workers admitted into the United States for seasonal farm production was well over 400,000 each year, with peak employment at any one time during each of these years between 250,000 and 300,000 workers. Use of foreign contract workers fell by about one-fourth during 1960. In order of numbers the states in which the most foreign farmworkers were employed in 1960 were Texas, California, Arkansas, Arizona, New Mexico, Michigan, and Florida, although some foreign workers were employed in all but eleven states. They constituted from 20 to 45 per cent of the peak seasonal employment in the production of cotton, sugar beets, citrus fruit, tomatoes, and cucumbers, and 80 per cent of the peak seasonal employment in lettuce production.[18]

[17] *Farm Labor Fact Book*, 162–73; "The Mexican Farm Labor Program," *Employment Security Review*, Vol. 28 (Washington: USDL, January, 1961), 36–42.

[18] *Hired Farm Workers in the United States* (Washington: Bureau of Employment Security, USDL, June, 1961), 36–42.

The programs for the importation of aliens for contract seasonal farmwork have been controversial because of the difficulty of objectively determining what has been the impact of these programs on the wages and employment opportunities of American farmworkers and because the small number of American farm operators who employ foreign contract workers believe that such workers are indispensible to their future farm production. Although the foreign contract labor programs doubtless benefit the individual foreign workers and the economics of their nations, this consideration has received relatively little emphasis in public discussion of these policies.

American employers of contract foreign labor maintain that a sufficient number of domestic workers is simply not available for the seasonal farm work that is necessary, and these employers affirm that under the protective provisions of Public Law 78 the use of such imported alien workers does not prejudice the interest of American farm laborers. This point of view is explained in detail in various testimony at the 1960 committee hearings of the House of Representatives on the Mexican Farm Labor Program.[19] The general argument of critics of these programs is that bringing several hundred thousand foreign farm laborers into the country each year cannot fail to have a depressing effect on the wages and working conditions of American migrants. These critics detail such difficulties in the administration of the program: (1) Considerable ambiguity attaches to the idea of the " prevailing wage " in an area. If the contract wage rate for foreign migrants one year is based (at least in part) on the prevailing wage in the previous year during which foreign seasonal laborers were also used, then the previous year's prevailing wage was probably already lower than what it would otherwise have been without foreign workers. (2) If higher wage rates had prevailed in a situation in which foreign farmworkers were *not* competing with American farmworkers, then a larger number of Americans might have been available for farm work. (3) Inasmuch as domestic workers are not offered the minimum employment guarantees, workmen's com-

[19] *Extension of Mexican Farm Labor Program*, 1960 and 1961 hearings before the Subcommittee on Equipment, Supplies, and Manpower of the Committee on Agriculture, House of Representatives, 86th Cong., 2d Sess., on March 22, 23, 24, 25, and 31, 1960 (Washington: Government Printing Office, 1960), and 87th Cong., 1st Sess., on March 6, 7, 8, 9, and 17, 1961 (Washington: Government Printing Office, 1961). In the 1961 hearings, see especially the testimony of Mat Triggs, pp. 2–17, and of A. W. Langenegger, pp. 37–47.

pensation insurance, and other benefits that foreign workers secure under their contracts, it is not possible to know if a shortage of domestic workers does in fact exist. And are we doing what needs to be done to make effective use of our domestic labor supply? (4) Is the importation of foreign laborers consistent with national immigration policy of protecting American living and working standards from foreign labor competition.[20]

## Tenure Implications of Labor Policy in Agriculture

The general characteristic of public policy for labor in American agriculture has been the absence of programs explicitly directed toward improving the material welfare of hired farmworkers, considered by traditional American standards the lowest farm tenure status. Hired farmworkers and their families did, however, benefit to some extent from various other public programs. The scant attention given in public policy to hired farm laborers as such has doubtless been in part the result of our country's emphasis on helping farm people achieve the aspiration of owner-operatorship by climbing the agricultural ladder and in part the result of a feeling that our country has a high degree of occupational and social fluidity, at least compared to that of other societies. But whatever its basis, public policy has given little explicit attention to the persons and their families who spend most of their working years as hired farmworkers.

Convincing arguments have been made for the point of view that more federal and state legislation is needed to improve wages, terms of employment, and working conditions of hired farm laborers.[21] Doubtless, more such legislation would help to improve the lot of persons presently working in that category. But there is also a danger that insufficient attention and emphasis will be given to slower working and less dramatic *long-run* policies to improve the material welfare of hired farmworkers and their families by raising the labor productivity and improving the employment alternatives of farm people for

[20] *Migratory Labor in American Agriculture*, 56–57; *Mexican Farm Labor Program—Consultant's Report to the Secretary of Labor* (Washington: USDL, October, 1959).

[21] Harry S. Kantor, *Problems Involved in Applying a Federal Minimum Wage to Agricultural Workers* (Washington: USDL, 1960); *Migratory Labor in American Agriculture*, 173–86; Robin Myers, *The Position of Farm Workers in Federal and State Legislation* (New York: National Advisory Committee on Farm Labor, 1959).

both farm and nonfarm employment. Among such long-run policies are the following: better general education, improved vocational and technical education, both better private health services and improved public health programs, a reduction in discrimination against racial and ethnic groups in matters of employment, and expansion of public employment services to offer to all farm people (including farm laborers and their families) more vocational counseling and greater information about nonfarm as well as farm job opportunities, especially full-time regular employment in other areas as well as in a person's present area of residence.

# CHAPTER SEVEN

# Tenure Patterns and Trends in the United States

HISTORIANS AND WRITERS of fiction have emphasized such factors as religious persecution, political oppression, the desire to evade the penalties of law, and various types of economic pressure as the basic reasons for early migration to the United States. Although these are important factors, they are perhaps no more important than the desire to own land. Many documents and much historical material give evidence that the " promised land " pulled immigrants to this country in large numbers. For illustration, G. S. Dow lucidly describes the role that the promise of land had in moving Irish and other immigrants to the United States. Concerning the former, he wrote:

> The chief reason for the coming of this element (to the United States) was the expiration of their one hundred year leases in Ireland. When the English had overrun and laid waste the northern part of Ireland during the days of Cromwell, it was made an almost uninhabited waste and to settle it up migrants were tempted over, chiefly from Scotland, by the promise of free land in the way of one hundred year leases. Here they were prosperous and built up industries, especially the linen industry, and successfully tilled the soil. Although these settlers had looked upon their leases as perpetual, they were evicted from their homes; America was their only refuge. It offered them a new home, where they could be sure of the future. It was a place where the land was either free or very cheap . . . so they migrated in large numbers from Ireland to America, where they have been known as Scotch-Irish.[1]

[1] See G. S. Dow, *Society and Its Problems* (New York: Thomas Y. Crowell Co., 1923), 103–108.

**103**

## Post-Revolutionary Land Policies

Colonial land policies varied from colony to colony in the United States until after the Revolution. It may be noted that the system of feudal land tenure which England tried to enforce played an important part in kindling the colonial rebellion against that country. In view of this, it is not surprsing that an attempt was made by the founders of the new nation to sweep away all traces of feudal land tenure at the conclusion of the Revolution.

One of the first acts taken by the leaders of the fledgling nation related to tenure. Steps to validate property rights were taken, the first being a declaration that the disposition of land up to the time of the Revolution would be recognized. Land which was unoccupied or unsold at this time was considered the property of individual states. However, individual states ceded these lands to the federal government, and the vast public domain of the United States was thus constituted.

Several attempts were made to settle the question of how and under what conditions land was to be distributed during the ensuing years. Various plans were presented to Congress in 1781 and 1784, with no definite action being taken. Finally, a land ordinance was passed in 1785. It was never implemented but did provide the foundation upon which the famous Ordinance of 1787 was built. The Ordinance of 1787 was most important since it put in effect a policy of guaranteeing full ownership of land with freedom of transfer and inheritance. Under this ordinance the federal government was empowered to transfer titles of land to settlers without reservations or qualifications, at the same time honoring old French and Canadian customs which had been previously established. Also under this ordinance new land holders were to be entitled to hold their land in fee simple.

Between 1787 and 1862 the land policy of the American government was expressed in many other Congressional acts. In general, from about 1787 to 1841 public lands were sold into private ownership chiefly for the revenue that accrued to the federal government. Then from 1841 to 1862 public lands were sold not so much to obtain revenue but rather to encourage land settlement.

Under the Pre-emption Act of 1841 a settler had first claim to land he had settled and cleared. Thus many settlers gained possession of 160 acres of land at $1.25 an acre. When federal auctions were held, the pre-empted lands were not open to competitive bidding.

The Homestead Act of 1862, as modified in 1864, provided for the granting of up to 160 acres virtually free to any settler who would occupy and improve the land according to law for a period of five years. Around 1891 the federal government changed its policy and practically stopped its disposal of public lands.

By the turn of the century, as a result of rather liberal land policies and a rapid westward migration, practically all of the available public lands were occupied.

## Factors Accounting for Different Systems of Land Tenure in Different Regions of the United States

The two basic factors accounting for different systems of land tenure developing in different parts of the nation are: (1) land policies at the time a particular region was settled and (2) soil and climate which in turn had an important bearing on the type of farm enterprise and the relative size of farms.

*The South:* At the time Virginia and Maryland and some of the other Southern states were first being settled the feudal plan of organization was uppermost in the minds of the holders of colonial grants. From the beginning one land company in Virginia (The London Company) adopted a policy of retaining ownership of the land and having it cultivated by farm laborers and tenants. Later, certain individuals built up huge estates through the " head right " system.

Experience taught the settler that there was economy in large scale cultivation. Vast tracts of fertile soil and ideal climatic conditions resulted in bountiful harvests of cotton, rice, and tobacco. All of these crops, however, required large amounts of labor, which was partially alleviated by the growth of slavery. After the Civil War former Negro slaves found themselves free but without jobs. Thus, it was natural that they returned to farming under varying tenant-type arrangements with their former owners. Through the years, then, a system of large holdings and tenant labor prevailed in the South.

The mechanization of agriculture in the South in more recent years has not changed this picture of large holdings.

*New England:* Fertile lands were limited in the New England region, and severity of climate did not encourage agriculture on a large scale. As a result, the New England area developed as a region of small farmers, where each possessed his land in fee simple. Each farm was traditionally a family farm, and tenancy never became a serious problem.

*Midwest:* By the time settlement began in the Midwest, certain land policies had been established which led to the adoption of a family-size farm system. Land was available at either a low cost or no cost, and it was parceled out in relatively small lots. The climate and soils of the region were influential in keeping the farms reasonably small as compared with those of the South and far West. Farm tenancy has never been a serious problem because of the type of farming carried on and agricultural policies followed. Where tenants operate land, they have worked in reasonably close partnership with the landlords. The combination of soil, climate, types of crops, and land policies thus promoted the development of family-sized farms, which have been maintained until today.

*Northwest and Far Western:* As the Western region of the United States developed, it was found that land distribution policies were not compatible with the needs of agriculture there. In semiarid areas the 160-acre, or even the 320-acre, tracts were inadequate for family-sized farms. When it became evident that many sections of the West were better adapted to grazing than for crop farming, the doom of small-sized farms was sounded. Under these combinations of circumstances the West developed an agriculture of large, owner-operated farms and ranches.

## Tenure Situation in the United States

The land tenure situation in the United States may be approached from several standpoints. The items reviewed below are considered to be the most important on the subject. Persons interested in more detail than can be given here are referred to the several cited references.[2]

[2] For example, see U. S. Department of Commerce and U. S. Department of Agriculture Co-operative Report: *Farm Tenure, A Graphic Summary, 1950* (Special Report, Vol. 5, Part 5 [Washington: Government Printing Office, 1952]); *A Statistical Summary of Land Tenure, 1954* (Agriculture Information Bulletin No. 200 [Washington: Agricultural Research Service, USDA, 1958]); and Frank Maier, S. T. Maitland, and Gladys K. Bowles, *The Tenure Status of Farmworkers in the United States* (Technical Bulletin No. 1217 [Washington: USDA, July, 1960]).

## Land in Farms

Perhaps the most basic fact related to land tenure is the amount of land in farms. In 1959 the total land in farms was 1,120,088,729 acres, or about 59 per cent of the total land area of the United States.

The proportion of land in farms has been increasing gradually since 1850. Of course, the development of new farm land has varied a great deal in different sections of the nation. The West has continued its expansion of farm land practically without interruption, while the Northwest region has experienced a steady decline in percentage of land in farms.

In connection with the amount of land in farms it is interesting that recently some writers have expressed alarm over the amount of farm land and potential farm land being taken over by highways, urban expansion programs, and other such developments. They argue that the continuation of such practices will result in future shortages. Others point out that technology has already developed to the point where huge surpluses of farm products are one of agriculture's major problems and that science and technology are destined to increase further the nation's productive capacity.

## Ownership of Land

Of the total land in the United States in 1954, approximately one and one-third billion acres (71 per cent) were privately owned. The federal government controlled 408 million acres (21 per cent), state and local governments owned 97 million acres (5 per cent), and 55 million acres (3 per cent) were designated as Indian lands.

Although federal, state, or local governments own more than one-fourth of the total land area, less than 4 per cent of the farm land is publicly owned. Of the total amount of land privately owned, only 5.0 per cent is held by corporate groups.

## Current Tenure Classes

The most widely used and accepted tenure classification in the United States is that of the Bureau of the Census. This classification includes all operators of farm land and is based on the total land owned, total land rented from others, amount of land managed for others and rented to others. The 1954 and 1959 Censuses of Agriculture give the following classifications and definitions:

*Full owners* own land but do not retain any land rented from others.

*Part owners* own land and rent additional land from others.

*Managers* operate farms for others and are paid a wage or salary for their services. Persons acting merely as caretakers or hired as laborers are not classified as managers.

*Tenants* rent from others or work on shares for others all the land they operate. Tenants are further classified on the basis of their rental arrangement as follows:

*Cash tenants* pay cash as rent, such as $10 an acre or $1,000 for the use of the farm.

*Share-cash tenants* pay a part of the rent in cash and a part as a share of the crops or of the livestock or livestock products.

*Share tenants* pay a share of either the crops or livestock or livestock products, or a share of both.

*Crop-share tenants* pay only a share of the crops.

*Livestock-share tenants* pay a share of the livestock or live-stock products. They may or may not also pay a share of the crops.

*Other tenants* include those who pay a fixed quantity of any product; those who pay taxes, keep up the land and buildings, or keep the landlord in exchange for use of the land; those who have the use of the land rent free; and others who could not be included in one of the other specified subclasses.

*Croppers* are crop-share tenants whose landlords furnish all work power. The landlords either furnish all the work animals or furnish tractor power in lieu of work animals. Croppers usually work under the close supervision of the landowners, or their agents, or another farm operator, and the land assigned them is often merely a part of a larger enterprise operated as a single unit.

The above classifications include all farm operators.

Another group deriving its livelihood from working on farms but not having property rights in the land is classified separately as farm laborers. Ordinarily farm laborers are further classified into subgroups, including regular, seasonal, and unpaid family laborers. Laborers are classified as regular if their period of actual or expected employment amounts to at least 150 days a year on a given farm.

Although some writers have long been critical of certain items being included in the different tenure classes,[3] on the whole the Bureau of the Census classification appears to be basically sound and to fit the various tenure arrangements found in the United States fairly well.

According to the 1959 Census of Agriculture, about one-third of the land in farms is operated by full owners. Operators who own part of their land and operate additional rented land account for about two-fifths of the farmland. Tenants, who rent all of the land they operate, use about one-sixth of the farmland, and only one-tenth of the land in farms is operated by managers.

Although full owners controlled only about one-third of the farmland, they owned about 57 per cent of the farms in the United States. This signifies that full owners are concentrated on the smaller farms. Full owners operated slightly more than half of the farms in the north central and southwest regions, but in the south and west, full owners held about two-thirds of the total number of farms, and in the northeast the proportion was slightly more than three-fourths.

At the other end of the scale we find that tenants are operating 20 per cent of the farms in the United States. Their importance varies considerably by regions, however. In the northeast and west tenants operate only 6 to 12 per cent of the farms, but in the north central and southern regions tenancy operation occurs on about one-fourth of the farms. Of the existing tenancy in the south, however, it is well to note that almost half of the tenants are sharecroppers.[4]

## Trends in Number and Tenure of Farm Operators

In 1959 there were approximately 3.7 million farm operators in the United States. This figure represents the smallest number of farm operators in our nation since the 1900 census indicated some 5.7 million. The largest number on record occurred in 1935, at which time there were 6.8 million. Since 1935, however, the trend in number

[3] The chief objection to this classification is the inclusion of croppers in the farm operator group. The contention is often made that croppers exercise no managerial functions, do not make major decisions concerning the operation of a farming enterprise, and therefore should be properly classed as laborers.

[4] *A Statistical Summary of Farm Tenure, 1954* (Agricultural Information Bulletin No. 200 [Washington: Agricultural Research Service, USDA, 1954]), 6–7.

of farm operators has been downward, with a decline of approximately
600,000 recorded between 1950 and 1954 and over 1,000,000 from 1954
to 1959. The number of farm operators has declined in every tenure
category between 1950 and 1954 with the exception of part-owner

LAND IN FARMS, BY TENURE OF OPERATOR, FOR THE UNITED STATES: 1954

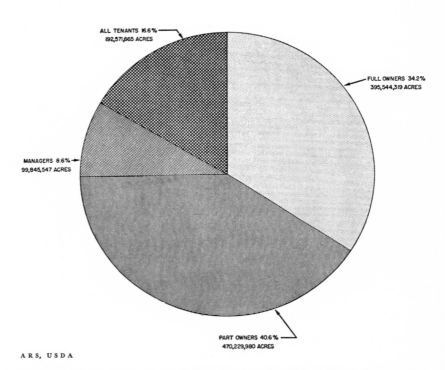

ARS, USDA

FIG. 2. Note the extent to which farm land in the United States is controlled
by owners and part-owners.

operators, which increased by some 44,000. Of course, it must be
recognized that owners became part owners by renting additional
land, hence the decline in number of owners is partly the result of an
increase in number of part owners.

   The first data available on tenancy are for 1880, at which time
25.6 per cent of all farms were operated by tenants. This high percentage can be explained by the large number of younger farmers

working toward becoming farm owners. Tenancy was being used by them as a stepping stone to land ownership. Another factor related to the high percentage of tenancy was the classification of croppers as tenants after the Civil War.

The percentage of farms operated by tenants increased steadily after 1880, reaching a peak of 42.4 per cent in 1930. Factors involved in these increases were higher prices of land, higher capital investments needed in farming, and the closing of the western frontier which practically stopped the development of new farms. Furthermore, established owners preferred to lease rather than sell under economic conditions at that time.

Much was written about the farm tenancy situation in the United States in the 1930's, and research studies in the field of land tenure increased at a rapid rate during this period. Since the 1930's the percentage of the nation's farms operated by tenants has steadily declined, until in 1959 only 20.5 per cent of the farms were tenant operated. Instrumental in these declines were a number of developments. Among these were the federal farm programs such as the Federal Farm Loan Act, the Farm Credit Administration, the Farm Mortgage Act and Commodity Credit Corporation. These programs provided for more favorable systems of credit for beginning farmers and helped tenants and owners alike with financing farm operations. Mechanization of farms and increased off-farm opportunities also encouraged a large number of tenants to move out of agriculture.

As previously stated, much concern was expressed over the tenancy problem in the United States in the 1930's. At the present time, however, with only one-fifth of all farms operated by tenants, there is no great concern over the situation.

Becoming a farm owner today is much more difficult than in the past. Not only is the capital requirement exceedingly high but the number of farms available for purchase have constantly dwindled, especially since the period immediately following World War II.

In the period 1945–1954 only 16 per cent of the farms in the thirteen north central states became available to beginning farmers, even though 31 per cent of the farms were vacated by older farmers. Farm enlargement or consolidation of farm units accounted for a 15 per cent decrease in number of farms in that region during the same period.[5]

[5] Don Kanel, *Opportunities for Beginning Farmers* (Neb. Agr. Exp. Sta. Bul. No. 452 [Lincoln: A. E. S., University of Nebraska, 1960]).

Only one-third of the farm boys remained on farms, the other two-thirds entered nonfarm occupations. The gradual decline in number of farmers required to supply market needs reflects the increased output per man that has improved at a rate far in excess of the rate of population increase.

Lack of capital continues to be a problem for most young men interested in becoming farmers. In Virginia a family-sized farm, either beef or dairy, costs about $30,000. This is fairly representative of the capital investment in a family-sized farm in other regions also. To meet this capital requirement it is invariably necessary to borrow money. Some people turn to commercial credit agencies for help, but by far the greatest number rely on family financial help. In fact, a study in Virginia indicated that two-thirds of the present farm owners received family financial assistance in the purchase of their farms.[6]

In the old days new farming opportunities were constantly being created. There was the westward movement to open up new territories; homesteading developed new farm units; and the agricultural ladder helped bridge the gap between the hired man and the farm owner. Today, the westward frontier and homesteading have about disappeared. The agricultural ladder still remains, but the capital required to achieve the final step has become almost prohibitive.

*Contract farming:* It is worthwhile mentioning briefly a type of tenure which seems to be assuming prominence in the United States. This practice, known as contract farming, has not been too important in the past. As a matter of fact, only recently has much research attention been directed to this practice and not too much is known about its social and economic implications.[7]

Contract farming is an important feature of so-called vertical integration in agriculture. Farming operations are said to be vertically integrated when the farm operator shares his managerial decisions in exchange for services or supplies. Most commonly agreements are made with feed, seed, and fertilizer suppliers; processors of food and meat; and distributors of the packaged product.

Contract farming appears to be an adjustment to rapidly advancing

[6] Frank D. Hansing and W. L. Gibson, Jr., *Becoming a Farm Owner, Is It More Difficult Today?* (Va. Agr. Exp. Sta. Tech. Bul. No. 473 [Blacksburg: Virginia Polytechnic Institute, 1955]), 30.

[7] For a well done summary report on contract farming in the U.S., see *Contract Farming and Vertical Integration in Agriculture* (Agriculture Information Bulletin No. 198 [Washington: USDA, 1958]).

technology. Its advantage, apparently, is a better co-ordination of the functions of the farm and farm related industries.

Contract farming has certain advantages for individual farmers, including more capital, improved facilities, and larger scale operation. However, some disadvantages also come about when the operator gives up a part of his decision-making prerogative. Also, although vertical integration tends to increase efficiency, it seems to increase competition.

What effect contract farming on a large scale may have for social organization is not now apparent. Should widespread integration develop, it is probable that urban and rural ways of life will come closer together.

Students of the future should be alert to the possibility that contract farming may emerge as a major form of tenure.

## The Tenure Ladder

Students of land tenure in the United States have made consistent use of a theoretical construct which represents vertical social mobility in agriculture. This construct, commonly known as *the tenure ladder* or the agricultural ladder, subsumes a series of positions occupied by an individual on a socio-economic continuum, ranging from a wage-earner in agriculture at the lower extreme to the owner-operator at the upper extreme. These positions are theoretically represented by successive rungs in a ladder, which farmers in the past have systematically been able to climb.

One writer recognized seven stages of progress in land tenure as early as 1923.[8] Arranged in the usual order or progression, these were: (1) farm wage laborer; (2) cropper, especially in the South; (3) tenant other than cropper; (4) part owner, mortgaged; (5) part owner, free of mortgage; (6) owner-farmer, mortgaged; and (7) owner-farmer, free of mortgage.

Of course, writers have long recognized that in general each succeeding step represents progress in independence of control and higher financial standing. It is also possible that several rungs might be skipped.

Some social scientists have described a different type of tenure ladder. John Kolb and Edmond Brunner describe a tenure ladder in

[8] L. C. Gray, *et al.*, "Farm Ownership and Tenancy," *Agriculture Yearbook, 1923* (Washington: Government Printing Office, 1923), 548.

which the first rung begins with 4-H Club youths who become involved in a project.[9] The next step is an apprenticeship which calls for monthly wages or allowances for the son from the father. The third rung is attained through a partnership arrangement under which the son assumes increasing responsibility. The final step is the assumption of full ownership by the son.

[9] John H. Kolb and Edmond de S. Brunner, *A Study of Rural Society* (4th ed.; New York: Houghton Mifflin Co., 1952), 93–94.

# Part 3: Theories, Legal Aspects, and Problems of Land Tenure and Transfers

TENURE ARRANGEMENTS OF all kinds involve written or oral agreements between individuals and groups. Part III, which comprises a major part of this volume, is concerned with the more important questions which have been faced in working out tenure arrangements in the United States.

Chapter 8 is devoted to a discussion of the theory, principles and problems of leasing, and provides information necessary for working out a good lease contract. The special terminology used in connection with water rights and the problems which stem from water tenure arrangements are taken up in Chapter 9. Chapter 10 follows through by discussing the nature of tenure and problems related to subsurface rights. The special tenure considerations which are necessary if the land is to be conserved are discussed in Chapter 11. The final chapter in Part III, Chapter 12, goes into the procedures and problems related to the transfer of land ownership in the United States.

# CHAPTER EIGHT

# The Theory, Principles, and Problems of Leasing

TENURE ARRANGEMENTS OTHER than ownership are formalized through some kind of leasing or renting agreement. The theory, principles, legal terminology, and problems relating to such agreements are discussed in the present chapter. Although leases are important to all tenure relations, the two forms of tenure which are directly concerned with leasing are part owners and tenants. The importance of these forms on the American scene has already been noted. By way of review it may be stated that during the past century no less than 42 per cent of the farms of the nation have been operated by either part owners or tenants. If land in farms is used as a measure, the records reveal that although part owners and tenants operated only 38 per cent of the total land in farms at the beginning of the century, they have operated more than 55 per cent since 1930. These two classes of operators have had under lease no less than 35 per cent of the total land in farms, and between 1935 and 1940 it was equal to at least 44 per cent. Today (1959) the total operating farm units of these two types of tenure represent approximately 2 million farms, over 650 million acres and a value of $54 billion invested in land and buildings. Thus a knowledge of lease forms and practices are vital to those interested in the study of land tenure.

## The Theory of Leasing

Inherent in an economic system which recognizes private ownership in property is the possibility of a differential rate of productivity and accumulation of savings to achieve ownership and control of non-human resources. Because ownership is not a single relationship between man and the right to control and use land but rather a "bundle of rights," it is possible for these rights to be shared with others. (See Chapter 1.) One man-made technique which is employed for sharing in the bundle of rights is known as leasing. This implies a separation of possession and use.

Before leasing as such is discussed, it should be recalled that exclusive rights are not held by the owner of land. The public holds four rights—the rights of escheat, eminent domain, police, and taxation. Private rights are concerned with relationships between or among private parties. They include the rights to buy, sell, transfer, mortgage, subdivide, consolidate, lease, use, occupy, possess, hold, and many others.

Tenure rights in land specify the conditions of possession and use over time. Generally, when land is leased there is a transfer of rights from the owner to a renter. The owner as lessor or landlord retains ownership rights and for some form of remuneration transfers use and possession rights to the renter or lessee. The transfer is usually for a stipulated period of time and for a determinable amount of compensation. Use and possession is not restricted to surface rights but may apply to subsurface and above surface rights as well.

The role or purposes of a lease may be multiple in nature. For example, its use can prevent conflicts among people in the control and use of land. It can also facilitate communication. An equally important role is as an aid in the orderly and efficient use of land for the production of goods and services.

## Basic Elements of a Lease Contract

In research, confusion can arise if the researcher does not distinguish between the positive—what is—and the normative—what ought to be —approach.[1] Likewise, the role of leasing can be confused if the writer does not make clear in his discussion the approach he is using.

Statements of the principles of leasing usually are statements using the normative approach, or statements of what ought to be. The statements themselves can only be in general terms, and the person who is looking for short, crystal clear, definite statements of law or principle will be disappointed. Nevertheless the content and intent of the principles are no less real or desirable nor do they detract from the utility of a lease.

Being rather arbitrary in discipline delineation, the principles of

---

[1] Milton Friedman, *Essays in Positive Economics* (Chicago: The University of Chicago Press, 1953), 4.

leasing can be divided into three subgroups: legal, economic, and sociological. The basic elements of each of these areas are as follows:

## Legal requirements

1. The lease as a deed or conveyance should transfer from the landlord or lessor to the tenant or lessee the right to possess for a fixed period of time in exchange for promised rental payments.

2. The parties to a written lease provide in the contract part the law for their own tenancy. In general, minimum requirements include proper identification and designation of each party to the contract and their signatures, a definite length of time for the contract to be effective, a description of the property being leased, and provisions for payment of rent.

## Economic considerations

1. The lease should provide for the combining of resources possessed by the landlord with those possessed by the tenant. Such combination should promote optimum economic utilization of resources over time. The resulting combination should provide for the enlargement of an operating unit if economies of scale are realized by such combination. It should provide for continuity of tenure, which is basic to security of tenure, because in most cases optimum returns from technology require time.

2. The lease should provide for an equitable division of total farm costs and returns between the landlord and the tenant.

## Sociological considerations

1. The lease should facilitate communication and understanding between or among the parties involved.

2. The leasing of land should resolve conflicts between farm family goals and community goals and minimize social waste. Change is normal; therefore, adjustments are the rule rather than the exception. Community goals such as churches, schools, roads, etc., can be aided or abetted by the technique of leasing.

It is possible to draw up a more elaborate list of principles, but it is believed that this list includes the basic essentials. If all leases were written and contained the elements necessary for the fulfillment of these principles, it is believed that considerable progress would be made toward improved tenure arrangements.

## Considerations Affecting Rental Rates and Lease Contracts

There may be a great deal of difference between what is done in actual practice and what should be done from the standpoint of attaining desired goals in leasing. In this section no attempt will be made to contrast current practices with recommended practices. Instead, the major considerations in the determination of working and equitable arrangements will be reviewed.

### The Findings of Research Studies

Prior to a discussion of the more general considerations for drawing up sound leases, it might be helpful to review some of the tenure research relating to lease practices. A great deal of effort was devoted by the Southwestern Land Tenure Research Committee to a regional study initiated in the late 1930's and the early 1940's. A number of recommendations resulted from this study which related specifically to leasing. It is appropriate to list these recommendations here:

1. Improved lease contract forms (for example, the United States Department of Agriculture farm lease or state experiment station leases) should be available for study and adoption where suitable by landowners and tenants. (County agricultural agents have improved lease forms available and are able to advise in their use.)

2. In order to establish a greater measure of security for both owner and tenant, enact legislation to insure adequate notice of lease termination or automatic renewal of leases where such notice is not given. A progressive and prosperous agriculture requires at least three months' termination notice, so that both tenant and owner will have time to make new arrangements.

3. Provide for voluntary arbitration of landowner-tenant problems, when questions arise between the two parties. In some states arbitration legislation may be adequate, but in others the procedure is too indefinite.

4. Encourage landowners to improve farm home living facilities on tenant-operated farms. At the same time tenants should assume the responsibility for maintaining these facilities, once they are improved. State statutes regarding standards of housing and family living facilities on rented farms are inadequate for the purpose. Legislation on minimum housing and other facilities on rented farms may be one answer.

5. As a means of encouraging more conservation, consider a payment for minimum standards of good leasing, through present agricultural programs that make direct payments for conservation practices. (The suggestion here is that the tenant be recompensed in some way for carrying out recommended conservation practices which bring him no immediate return.)

6. Continue group meetings by educational agencies in counties and communities to discuss lease matters of mutual interest to landowners and tenants. Emphasis in tenure education should be on a positive basis, proposing good practices that are mutually satisfactory.

Many present leases unwisely discourage improvements for better farming and for better living. Note the wording in the following excerpt from a lease form: " But it is expressly understood and agreed that party of the second part shall make no improvements, repairs or additions to the fences, buildings or any tenements whatever upon said lands situated, except at the will and pleasure of said party of the first part."

Favorable lease agreements usually have a long notification period. A good model states: " This lease shall run one year, beginning ―――――, 19― but shall continue from year to year thereafter unless either party gives written notice to the other at least ―――― months before the expiration date of any contract year."

An arbitration provision in a lease contract may help in easily solving misunderstandings. Such a provision might read: " If parties to this lease cannot reach an agreement on any matter, the difference shall be submitted to an Arbitration Committee. The Committee shall be composed of three disinterested persons, one selected by each party hereto and the third by the two others thus selected. The findings shall be binding on both parties."

Generally, important improvements will not be made unless a definite understanding for payment or removal exists. This problem may be handled by a statement like the following: " Party of the second part may, at the termination of this lease, remove any and all improvements placed on soil lands by party of the second part, and at his own expense, during the term hereof."

A further adjustment in this situation is possible. This is a statute requiring that all agricultural leases, whether written or oral, and regardless of their length, be automatically continued from year to year. Such a lease should provide for termination only by notice from either party several months before the end of the term.

7. While many problems in leasing are recognized, more adequate research is necessary before definite recommendations can be made. Among such problems are these:

a. What kinds of improvements can rented farms afford?

b. How can a tenant be assured of adequate compensation for unexhausted improvements when he leaves the farm? What is the life of improvements and practices?

c. Similar questions apply to compensation to the landowner in case of deterioration and due destruction by the tenant.

d. What rental rates are appropriate for new crops and practices that do not fit the mold of the " third and fourth " system?

e. What is the role of the landlord in the farming venture? What contributions does he make? What are his responsibilities? What does he receive from landholding over and above income from the farm? Why does he own land? What are his relationships with the tenant and to the land? [2]

### Legal Considerations for Determining Terms of a Lease Contract

Standard lease forms and statements of legal considerations are no substitutes for competent legal counsel. Parties to a lease must have some appreciation for legal consideration before they can obtain the maximum utility legal counsel has to offer in attaining their primary goal.

Legal rights and obligations of the parties to a lease are determined by the provisions of the lease. These provisions, to be binding, must not conflict with constitutional and statutory law nor with decisions of the state Supreme Courts. Landlord-tenant law, in practice, reflects the influence of the habits, customs, and traditions of the rural areas.

The legal relationship between a landlord and tenant is generally created by an expressed or an implied contract. The contract or lease agreement creating the relationship may be in writing, or it may be oral, or it may be implied by law from the conduct of the parties.

In some states oral leases are binding for a term not to exceed one year. To be enforceable for a term longer than a year, it must be in

[2] *Tenure Improvement for a Better Southwest Agriculture* (Ark. Agr. Exp. Sta. Bul. No. 491 [Fayetteville: A. E. S., University of Arkansas, November, 1949]).

writing. However, in some instances performances under an oral lease may constitute good and sufficient grounds for the courts to grant the renter an extension beyond a year.

If written, it should be stated in such a way as to show that the agreement is a lease, entered into by the landlord and the tenant whose names and addresses are clearly designated. The statement should contain a description of the property and the length of time the lease is to be effective. It may provide for an extension of the term of the lease, including the date when the extension should be agreed upon. It is probably wise to spell out in some detail the rights and responsibilities of each party. This would include the method of sharing costs and returns of not only items which would affect the productivity of the current year but also those practices or improvements that influence income in future years. It is also generally desirable to make provisions for arbitration of differences that might arise. If the contributions and the returns of each party are to be shared, it is desirable to provide for records and how and who is to keep such records.

Any other provisions may also be included in the agreement. Finally, it should be signed by all parties concerned.

## Economic Considerations for Determining Terms of a Lease Contract

The economic considerations for determining the terms of a lease could vary a great deal. A landlord, who is the father of the tenant, may have noneconomic goals which influence the economic considerations. He may be willing to make much greater contributions to the costs of operating the farm unit than his proportionate share of the returns. A city dweller who wishes to retire on a rural residential location may make investments in conveniences and appearances not warranted by expected economic returns. These and many other examples could make the determination of economic considerations complicated. A logical starting point, however, has been well outlined by Earl O. Heady in an article entitled " Economics of Farm Leasing Systems." [3] As he points out, the person who works out a lease agreement with the hope of making it as equitable as possible for a particular situation might well use as his point of departure the theoretically perfect lease.

---

[3] *Journal of Farm Economics*, Vol. 29 (August, 1947), 659–78.

The assumptions regarding the economic setting within which the perfect leasing system would operate Heady outlines as follows: " (1) Competition, except for imperfections growing out of leasing systems and the private ownership of resources, prevails, and (2) the pricing system is looked upon as the appropriate means for expression of consumer preference and hence for allocation of resources in the most efficient manner." The results of a perfect leasing system operating in such an environment would be " (1) the most efficient organization of resources on the farm relative to consumer demand as expressed in market prices and (2) an equitable division of the product among the owners of the various resources employed in production."

Heady then describes conditions under which perfection could be achieved. If the goal for economic considerations of a lease is that a firm act rationally in respect to the maximization of profits from resources which it controls, one may then use the four criteria which Heady outlines:

(1) A combination of products (choice of enterprises) which will equate marginal returns on resources employed in production of each.

(2) Substitution of factors (methods of production) such that the ratio of their marginal productivities is equal to the ratio of their prices.

(3) Combination of variables with fixed resources (where resources are fixed by conditions falling outside the leasing arrangements) such that marginal returns and costs for the farmer are equated.

(4) An over-all scale of operations which equates marginal cost and returns at a level consistent with the cost price relationship and normal uncertainties of the market. (These relationships must hold for all resources employed by the firm irrespective of ownership.)

In numerous situations, of course, the environment does not lend itself for complete perfection of a leasing arrangement. One author has pointed out the justification of the marginal-productivity concept, if the landlord and tenant enjoy relatively equal bargaining power when their alternative opportunities are about equal and when each is able to earn an adequate return from the resources he has to invest.[4] He concludes, however, that such conditions do not exist in too many cases.

Most researchers have attempted to use as their guide the continued application of joint inputs to the point where marginal factor costs and marginal value product are equal. The division of the returns are then based upon the proportion which each party contributes to the marginal factor cost. Such an analysis is not too difficult if factor costs can be readily determined by the market. A more difficult problem arises, however, when values cannot be so determined or when at best it is difficult to obtain mutual agreement regarding such values. For example, the " equilibrium price " in a perfect market for the landlord's and tenant's labor, land, and management may be difficult to ascertain. In such cases it is not difficult to realize why the parties to an agreement resort to custom or have attempted to work out an arrangement that takes into consideration all relevant factors rather than resort to a refined technique that would enable them to measure the marginal factor costs.

If the lease is based upon the principle that the landlord and the tenant should share in the farm income in proportion to the value of their contribution to the business, the cash-rent lease must be made adjustable. The reasons for making such adjustments would be because of wide variations in prices and costs and in production resulting from causes beyond the control of either party. If the parties do not wish to make adjustments for minor changes, they could agree on a rate of charge before adjustments are to be made. If historical data are available, a base rent can be agreed on and adjustments made from this base.[5]

If the participants use a share lease, the principle is more easily applied and the adjustments due to changes in prices, costs, and production can be made somewhat automatically. The contributions made by the landlord in the form of fixed factors, such as land and

[4] Raleigh Barlowe, *Land Resource Economics* (Englewood Cliffs, N. J.: Prentice Hall, Inc., 1958), 434.

[5] For examples of this concept see W. L. Gibson, Jr., and K. E. Loope, *Equitable Farm Leases* (Va. Agr. Ext. Ser. Bul. No. 254 [Blacksburg: Virginia Polytechnic Institute, January, 1958]), or Walter E. Chryst and John F. Timmons, *Adjusting Farm Rents to Changes in Prices, Costs and Production* (Iowa Agr. Exp. Sta., Special Report No. 9 [Ames: A. E. S., Iowa State College, April, 1955]).

capital, and by the tenant in the form of labor and machinery are determined first. The sharing of the other operating expenses such as fertilizer, costs of irrigation, special harvesting methods, etc., has generally proved somewhat more difficult. In general, however, it has been found that, if the landlord did not share in the increased expense of items such as fertilizer in the same ratio as he shared in the increased income, maximum farm income would not be realized. If the tenant paid for the total cost of fertilizer but received only a share of the crop, he would have an incentive to apply fertilizer only to the point where *his* marginal factor cost is equal to *his* marginal value product. This, of course, would fall short of the point where the two are equal for the firm as a whole.

Walter Chryst and John Timmons studied rental arrangements in Iowa, with one of their objectives to analyze the division of net income between landlord and tenant over a period of years in order to determine the rapidity with which it reflected cost, price, and production changes. They did not study the relationship between the share of the expenses of each party of the business to the share of the income. They accepted the ratio of rent to net returns resulting from the original agreement between landlord and tenant—a " rent norm." The basis for this acceptance was the apparent satisfaction with these ratios over time. Interviews with ninety landlords and tenants revealed that variations in both the shares and direction of trends of the shares could be explained by five major factors. In summary they were: (1) Shares become fixed by custom and lack needed flexibility; (2) changes in prices, costs, and production have a differential impact upon landlord and tenant because of different rates of contribution; (3) duration of contract does not coincide with the period of time when income changes; (4) unpredictable changes in prices, costs, and production are basic difficulties in keeping rents up to date; and (5) laws relating to liens in connection with rental payments tend to reinforce inflexibility in rentals.

Several proposals had been advanced to meet needed adjustments. One was called a " base and bonus " idea. An escalator clause advanced rents above a base as prices of farm products went up. A second was a " cash and share option " which permitted the tenant a choice up to a cut-off date of September 1 for each crop year. The third was referred to as a " commodity price adjustment " idea which started with a base rent and adjusted up or down in line with the price of the major commodity produced on that farm. None of these ideas were perfect nor had they been subjected to periods of time when rather drastic adjustments might be considered necessary. They were, however, attempts to provide needed flexibility. They also pointed out the need for starting with a " rent norm " that is readily acceptable to both parties and is well understood.

An examination of land tenure research in the Southwest concerned with economic considerations reveals several areas of imperfections. For example, in Caddo County, Oklahoma, the adoption of irrigation resulted in the need for new considerations in lease agreements.[6] A number of the installations were powered by electric motors which had a standby charge of eight dollars per rated horsepower of the motors in addition to the cost of electricity consumed. This standby charge was treated as an operating expense in the analysis of irrigation expenses. The authors of the report concluded that classifying the standby charge as an operating expense prevented both owners and tenants from recognizing the opportunity cost of a limited resource, as these leases used more water per acre than returns justified.

The method of sharing the cost of investment in the irrigation equipment also influenced the use because of its influence on marginal returns to the landlord and to the tenant. When investment capital was shared, the tendency was to spread investment cost by irrigating other crops.[7] The first use of the system was for irrigating peanuts, but it could also be used for cotton. There were indications that neither the lessors nor the lessees considered that cotton should be charged with any of the annual fixed costs. On the basis added cost and added returns from cotton in the area, the authors also determined that cotton could utilize a larger percentage of the irrigation water to the mutual benefit of lessors and lessees.[8] The conclusions of the authors were that the leases did accomplish the general objective of permitting owners of capital, labor, and management to combine their resources for mutual benefit. However, returns were not always in proportion to contributions.

A study of leasing practices which had to be worked out when irrigation was started in the High Plains of Texas revealed a lack of

---

[6] K. C. Davis and Harold Liles, *Rental Arrangements and Resource Contributions on Irrigation Leases in Caddo County, Oklahoma* (Okla. Agr. Exp. Sta. Bulletin B–558 [Stillwater: A. E. S., Oklahoma State University, July, 1960]).

[7] *Ibid.*, 15.  [8] *Ibid.*, 20.

information available for the parties to use as guides.[9] The authors found that in the absence of an established source of lease information, local custom is followed almost exclusively in deciding on rent to be paid and on the division of costs. They concluded that custom was not a completely satisfactory basis for rental agreements; it could be inequitable and discourage better farming methods. A thorough study of leasing practices was needed to analyze the equitability of share-patterns and to evaluate as far as possible the important items of management and risk.

Despite the difficulty of determining the value for some of the factor costs, landlords and tenants are experimenting with different leasing arrangements in order to be able to incorporate the latest technology into their farming operations. Our best guide may still be the model in a perfectly competitive economy against which we may test what landlords and tenants who are innovators are doing. Additional research on the determination of values can strengthen such comparisons and possible recommendations. Such would include a more precise measure of risk as well as the relationship between short-run and long-run costs and returns. Even though the task is difficult, the need is no less great.

### Social Considerations for Determining Terms of a Lease Contract

Private property is an institution created by society. The basis for establishing private property is apparently broader than economic efficiency. For this reason many in our society feel that the sharing of rights in property—leasing—cannot be based exclusively on economic considerations. One of the more important of these other considerations is sometimes referred to as the distributive justice in the allocation of returns between landlord and tenants; another is the overall impact of social-justice and welfare considerations.[10]

Most noneconomic social factors cannot be measured as precisely as economic efficiency, but they are no less real to our well-being. A few of these considerations would include the availability and quality of our institutions, such as schools, churches, cultural centers, and roads;

[9] William G. Adkins and Cecil A. Parker, *Form Leases on Irrigated Farms on the High Plains of Texas* (Tex. Agr. Exp. Sta. Progress Report 1434 [College Station: A. E. S., Texas A & M, February, 1952]), 8.

[10] Barlowe, *Land Resource Economics*, 424–25.

and the stability of our population concomitant with economic, aesthetic, health, and other considerations.

Generally, of major consideration to the landlord is the level of management of the tenant. And of major consideration to the tenant is the security of operatorship of the farm. As J. L. Charlton and others have found, owners and part owners have a higher level of living, as indicated by housing, household, and cultural possessions and participation on the community and county levels.[11] But this need not exist if leases could provide security of operatorship to the qualified tenant. Leasing terms which provide for the rapid adoption of proven technology, equitable division of returns to owner and to operator, and a sense of security to the tenant could create an improved situation for both the individual farm families and the community as a whole.

If improvements in leasing arrangements provided greater security of operatorship for a renter, they would also provide this advantage for those whose rights in land are more limited than the renter. This would include the sharecropper. " Although the share cropper is not considered to have legal rights of land tenure, once having started a crop he is protected by accepted and morally supported practice in the right of continuing the tenure until the end of the crop year." [12]

The insecurity of work is even greater for the farm labor and the migratory workers. In the words of the President's Commission on Migratory Labor: " The migratory workers engage in a common occupation, but their cohesion is scarcely greater than that of pebbles on the seashore. Each harvest collects and regroups them. They live under a common condition, but create no techniques for meeting common problems." [13]

Although sharecroppers, farm laborers, and migratory laborers possess few or no tools or livestock, to the extent that these may represent steps in the agricultural ladder, they should be of concern both in terms of the welfare of the individual and of the community. To the extent that improved leasing will stabilize and secure competent

[11] J. L. Charlton, *Social Aspects of Farm Ownership and Tenancy in the Arkansas Coastal Plain* (Ark. Agr. Exp. Sta. Bulletin 545 [Fayetteville: A. E. S., University of Arkansas, June, 1954]).

[12] *Ibid.*, 81.

[13] *Report of the President's Commission on Migratory Labor, Migratory Labor in American Agriculture* (Washington: Government Printing Office, 1951), 3.

operatorship, it may also improve the individual and the community aspect of those tenure classes more limited than the renter.

The extent to which social considerations will be reflected in the lease agreement will depend on the kinds of values in which our society believes and the spirit of cooperation and dedication of our landlords and tenants. If it is a privilege granted by society, it will need to be more than a device for the maximization of individual profit.

## Provision for Adjusting Leases in a Dynamic Agricultural Economy

Rapid adjustments are taking place both within and outside of agriculture. Some of the main impacts of technology upon agriculture have been the reduction in the number of farms, the increase in the size of farm, the increase in the investment in the total unit, and the level of competence of management. Because of the magnitude of the investment in an economical farm unit and the apparent continued trend toward even greater investments, we can expect greater separation of ownership from management. This will place more emphasis on leasing as one means of bringing ownership and management together. Therefore, the lease and terms of the lease will not become less but will become more significant in the foreseeable future. To facilitate desirable economic and social adjustments, leases will have to be flexible, and guides for incorporating changes will have to be kept current. Research should provide the facts which landlords and tenants will need in order to make the needed adjustments. Chryst and Timmons suggest six rules for making rent adjustments: (1) provision be determined ahead of the crop year and set forth in writing, (2) provision to encourage efficient use of resources, (3) provision made for changes in prices, (4) provision made for changes in costs, (5) provision made for changes in production, and (6) provisions be easily workable.[14] In addition, such provisions must be socially acceptable and must meet all tests of legality.

Lessor and lessee should make a concerted effort to adjust leasing provisions to facilitate adoption of proven technology. Research should provide the facts for equitable sharing of costs and distribution of returns. Education must spread this knowledge as rapidly as possible. If these things are done, leasing can continue to be a tool used to serve the best interests of a society, based upon the institution of private property.

[14] Chryst and Timmons, *Adjusting Farm Rents*, 37–38.

# CHAPTER NINE

# Tenure Aspects of Water Rights

TENURE RIGHTS AND relationships apply to water as well as to land. However, the terms and concepts used with reference to rights in water are quite different from those used for land. Land tenure terms and concepts developed during the Middle Ages in feudal Europe. By contrast water tenure concepts, except for the relatively unsophisticated riparian doctrine, did not evolve until the movement of settlers into the water deficit areas of the United States. The major difference in land tenure concepts and water tenure concepts is that the latter are largely of legal origin.

Tenure in water, like tenure in land, may be quite complex. This chapter is an attempt to describe the classes of water, to define rights in water, to illustrate how these rights are held and to discuss some of the problems arising in the competition for water.

## Early Concern Over Water Tenure Problems

As the successive waves of settlers moved westward across the North American continent, they carried with them cultural patterns and institutions used in the East. These customs, habits, and practices concerning the use of land and water were applicable in the West as long as the settlers were in a climate belt similar to the one they left behind. However, with each movement westward, changes in topography and ecology required the pioneers to make changes and adaptations of their customs and practices. For example, as the average annual rainfall declined, many practices designed for a more humid climate became inapplicable. Just as the Homestead Act with its provision of 160 acres did not fit the arid conditions of the western states, so the practices concerning water appropriation, holding, and use which served in the East were inadequate in the West.

About the turn of the century it was officially recognized that problems of water tenure involved economic and social considerations as well as law. This is evidenced by the studies of water rights made by government economists. Richard T. Ely, a land economist, was one of the first to be hired to make a special study of irrigation problems. Ely's report, dated September 19, 1904, was entitled " Economics of Irrigation." Two paragraphs from his report will illustrate the new concept of the problem of water rights which was developing at that time.

> The investigation which I have to conduct concerns property rights. As I understand it, I have to trace the origin and growth of property in water. It is necessary to describe the different doctrines of property which are the result of the common law, of statutes, and judicial decisions. The conflicting and incompatible nature of these doctrines must be fully described. . . .
> It is necessary to examine legal and economic treatises for the light that they may throw on this problem of property in water. A discussion with men of experience in irrigation is essential. Men who approach this problem practically from different points of view should be consulted, as farmers, lawyers, judges, engineers, and business men.[1]

Subsequently, lawyers, economists, irrigation specialists, and engineers studied rights in water and means of adapting them to the needs of arid land, with the result that several water doctrines were developed. There was also an evolution of existing informal customs and rights with regard to water use. Gradually the system of water rights and water-use patterns which is discussed in the following pages was evolved.

## Classifications of Water Sources

Rights in water vary according to the source and nature of water. Half a dozen major types of water sources provide the basis for water tenure concepts.

A *surface water* course consists essentially of a definite natural stream that is flowing in a definite natural channel and originating from a definite source of supply. A surface water course also includes

---

[1] Henry C. Taylor and Anne Dewees, *The Story of Agricultural Economics in the United States, 1840–1932* (Ames:  The Iowa State College Press, 1952), 830 *et passim.*

the underflow of the course. The rights to water in water courses are covered by the riparian and appropriation doctrines discussed in the pages which follow.

Waters that originate from rain and melting snow, that flow vagrantly over the surface before being concentrated in water courses or before sinking into the ground, are termed *diffused surface waters.* Generally, the owner of land on which such water is found is entitled to capture and use it while it is still on his land. Since this water is more often a nuisance than a benefit, there is a considerable body of law concerning problems of disposal of such water but very little concerning rights of using it.[2]

A *definite underground stream* has the essential characteristics of a surface water course except that it is under the ground. In disputes concerning underground streams, the problem of proof of the physical aspects is always difficult. Some states insist on establishment of all elements with reasonable inference. The rights to use water of definite underground streams is governed by the laws that govern water courses—by the riparian and appropriation doctrines, or both of them concurrently.

Another kind of ground water consists of the *underflow of surface streams.* Underneath the surface stream there is usually an underflow or subflow. This consists of water in the sands, gravels, and other subsoil over which the surface stream flows, moving in the same direction and in intimate contact with the surface stream. The boundaries may extend laterally for considerable distances beyond the banks of the surface channel. From a legal as well as a physical standpoint the surface stream and the underflow are not two separate rivers but are complementary parts of a single water course. Rights to the use of the underflow are governed by the law of water courses—riparian rights, appropriative rights, or combinations of the two.

*Percolating water,* a third class of ground water, is usually considered to be subsurface water that is free to move by gravity and hence to supply wells but is not concentrated in a definite underground stream or as underflow of a surface stream. As in the case of water courses, the right to use percolating waters falls into two general doctrines:

[2] In a Louisiana case the court upheld the right of the landowner to use diffused surface water on his land, but it also implied that there could be a cause of action if the lower owner could show injury. See Chandler v. Scogin, 5 Louisiana Appelate 484 (1926).

rights inherent in contiguous land—the riparian doctrine—and those based on priority of diversion and use—the appropriative doctrine.[3]

*Impounded water* is any water that is stored or impounded by reservoirs or dams. The nature of rights in impounded water is determined by the applicable principle—riparian principle or appropriation principle. The costs of using impounded water, however, are generally attached to the costs of constructing and maintaining the retardation structures.

*Navigable waters* in general are those rivers, lakes, seas, or other bodies of water that are navigable in fact without regard to whether they are tidal. Bodies of water are navigable in fact when they are used, or are capable of being used, in their ordinary condition as highways for commerce over which trade and travel are or may be conducted in the customary modes of trade and travel on water.[4] What this legal phraseology means specifically varies from state to state. Under some state laws streams navigable for pleasure boating are classed as navigable stream. The term " *public waters* " is often used to mean " navigable water " as distinct from " private waters," which are nonnavigable waters.[5]

## Nature and Origin of Water Rights

The ownership or proprietary rights of water rest with either the federal government or the state governments. The federal government owns all of the water on federal land while the state governments own water in other navigable water courses, streams, and lakes.

The rights to use water, called *usufructuary* rights, may be held by individuals or by subdivisions of the state government. Use rights consist of riparian rights, appropriative rights, correlative rights, and littoral rights.

The doctrine of *riparian* rights is one of the oldest water tenure concepts. According to this doctrine, the owner of land that borders a water course has certain rights in the flow of the streams. He may divert the water he needs for domestic use. For irrigation and other commercial purposes, each riparian landowner's use of water must be

---

[3] Wells A. Hutchins and Harry A. Steel, " Basic Water Rights, Doctrines, and their Implication for River Basis Development," *Law and Contemporary Problems*, Vol. 22 (Durham: School of Law, Duke University, Spring, 1957), 277–78.

[4] 65 *Corpus Juris Secundum* S 5.                    [5] *Ibid.*, S 1.

reasonable with respect to the requirements of all other riparian owners. The riparian principle applies to the ownership of land that overlies any underground stream or the underflow of a surface stream.[6]

The riparian doctrine was introduced to the United States from the Roman law by several different lines of descent. It was introduced into Texas by Spanish and Mexican governments. Here, in many instances, grants of land included rights in waters flowing through or adjacent to the grants. Thus the new world acquired the riparian

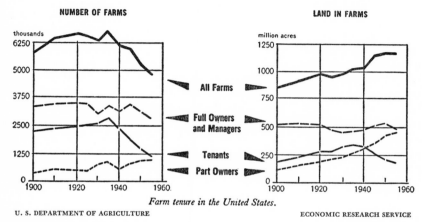

**NUMBER OF FARMS**                                        **LAND IN FARMS**

*Farm tenure in the United States.*

U. S. DEPARTMENT OF AGRICULTURE                           ECONOMIC RESEARCH SERVICE

FIG. 3. The changing tenure situation in the United States may be seen in the trends in number of farms and land in farms by type of ownership.

philosophy of the Spanish civil law and the Roman law from which it was derived. The policy of granting land, together with rights in adjacent waters, was continued by the succeeding governments of the republic and state of Texas until late in the nineteenth century.

The riparian doctrine as based on French civil law, which also had its origin in the Roman law, was imported to the Atlantic seaboard by two eminent jurists, Joseph Story and James Kent, in the early part of the nineteenth century. After Kent and Story advanced the riparian doctrine in keeping with the French Civil Law, the courts of England adopted it as part of their common law. Thereafter, this

[6] A comprehensive discussion of riparian rights and related court decisions pertaining to use, ownership, and dispersal of waters is contained in a publication by Mark E. Borton and Harold H. Ellis, *Some Legal Aspects of Water Use in Louisiana* (La. Agr. Exp. Sta. Bul. No. 537 [Baton Rouge, A. E. S., Louisiana State University, June, 1960]), 15–32.

doctrine became part of the law of many American states when they
adopted the common law of England as part of their legal system.

The riparian doctrine is generally followed in the eastern states. It
is also followed to a great degree in the six states that extend from
North Dakota to Texas, on the one hundredth meridian, and in the
three states that border the Pacific Ocean. In other western states
it has been replaced by the appropriation doctrine.

The *appropriation* doctrine rests on the proposition that the basis
of rights in water consists of putting the water to beneficial use. The
first corrolary of this doctrine is that the first in time is the first in
right. The appropriation doctrine developed in California among
miners. When miners wished to assert their rights in a stream which
they were using for washing gravel, they posted notices similar to
those used for mineral claims. In order to further advertise their
claims many miners also recorded their claims in the county record,
long before they were required to do this by legislation. The practices
of the Mormons in Utah and the Spanish and Mexican settlers in the
Southwest also contributed to the development of this concept. The
appropriation doctrine is a part of the water law of each of the seventeen western states and some application of this doctrine is also made
in the statutes of a few eastern states. In several states both riparian
and appropriation doctrines are in effect concurrently.

The appropriation doctrine is a combination of statutory law,
judicial law, and common law. It was first based on the customary
practices of miners which, in absence of appropriate legislation, the
courts in the region recognized. The earliest statutes passed by state
legislatures essentially codified the prevailing local customs, rules,
regulations, and practices which had grown up in the appropriation
and use of water. Later, as development progressed and complications
ensued, there came the enactment of longer, more detailed, more comprehensive statutes supplemented by hundreds of court decisions as
well as state constitutional provisions. Each of the seventeen western
states has a statutory procedure under which water courses may be
appropriated. Twelve western states also have ground-water appropriation statutes.

The appropriation doctrine has been applied to surface water, underground streams, and percolating ground water.

The doctrine of *correlative* rights is peculiar to California, where
it developed in response to an immediate problem of rights in ground
water during a period of scarcity. According to this doctrine, each

landowner is entitled, in time of shortage of water, to a reasonable proportion of the common supply of water that underlies land belonging to him and neighboring land owners. This doctrine is an extension of the concept of riparian ownership to underground water. Like the riparian doctrine it conflicts with the doctrine of appropriation and the claims of prior appropriators.[7]

*Littoral* rights concern the rights of owners of land along the shore of seas and great lakes. Littoral proprietors on a sea or lake correspond to riparian proprietors on a stream or small pond. The term " riparian " is often used coextensively with " littoral."

## Some Important Legal Aspects of Water Rights

Although all property rights are ultimately vested in the sovereign authority of the state, the state may delegate certain rights to public or private agencies, or to individuals.

The principal types of laws delimiting water rights are constitutional law, statutory law, common law, judicial law, and administrative regulations that carry all the force of law. The nature of each type of law is outlined below, and one should have no difficulty in making application to water tenure questions.

*Constitutional rights* and *statutory rights* (those established by the enactment of a law by the properly constituted legislature of a sovereign government) are well known to everyone. Both the federal and state legislatures enact law concerning water rights within the framework of the authority granted to these bodies by the respective constitutions.

*Common law* is a term used to distinguish an important body of law from laws created by acts of legislatures. Common law comprises the body of principles and rules of actions relating to governments, persons, and property which have their origin in usages and customs of immemorial antiquity and in the judgments and decrees of courts recognizing, confirming, and enforcing such usages. In the United States the common law refers particularly to the ancient law of England.

*Judicial law* is a phrase used to indicate the law established by

[7] J. Russell Whitaker and Edward A. Ackerman, *American Resources— their Management and Conservation* (New York: Harcourt Brace & Co., Inc., 1951), 163.

judicial decisions. Constitutions, statutes, and common practices may establish rules of actions of a general nature. Conflicts arise when there is disagreement and confusion concerning just how these laws should be applied in a specific instance. The judge, in applying the law to a specific case, is interpreting the meaning of that statute and so making law. Judicial law also consists of law established by judicial decisions in subject matter areas not covered by legislation.

*Administrative law* refers to the decisions of government administrators which have all the force of law (unless nullified by the courts). Any administrator of a government agency in charge of water or land, of which the government is the proprietor, is called on to make day-to-day decisions concerning the allocation and use of that resource. In some situations these decisions may constitute a small but significant development of the nature of law.

### Public Rights in Water

The proprietary (ownership) right of the government as the representative of the public and usufructory (use) right of individuals is extended, amplified, and detailed by the laws developed by constitutional conventions, legislatures, courts, administrators, and acts of individuals. Public rights and public tenure have been developed primarily by laws which draw their authority from references to powers of government stated in the Constitution.

One of the principal powers of the national government that influences the public rights in water is the right to regulate commerce. Article I, Section 8, Clause 3 of the federal Constitution states that power was delegated to the Congress to regulate commerce with foreign nations and among the several states and with the Indian tribes. This authority of the federal government to regulate commerce was challenged several times and interpreted various ways until it was finally settled in 1824, when Chief Justice John Marshall handed down a decision in the case of *Gibbons* vs. *Ogden* in which he said, " The power of Congress . . . comprehends navigation within the limits of every state in the union, so far as that navigation may be in any manner connected with commerce with foreign nations, or among the several states or with the Indian tribes." This declaration clarified the rights of the federal government in controlling all aspects of interstate commerce. Later decisions extended this concept specifically to cover navigation in all its interstate aspects. This federal commerce authority may also be used to permit the federal government to concern itself with the upper nonnavigable reaches of a navigable waterway and also concern itself with nonnavigable tributaries if the navigable capacity of the waterway is thereby affected, or if interstate commerce is otherwise affected.[8]

Another right of the federal government is that of adjudicating disputes between states and approval of interstate compacts. The Constitution of the United States provides that " no state shall without the consent of Congress . . . enter into any agreement or compact with another state." The Supreme Court has original and exclusive jurisdiction over all controversies between two or more states. The Supreme Court has passed on a number of water controversies between states, most of them involving disputes concerning the diversion and use of water from interstate streams. In these decisions the Supreme Court has attempted to adhere to the principle of equitable apportionment and to divide the water in equitable manner without quibbling over formulas.

The powers granted the federal government in the Constitution (or so interpreted by courts) have provided the basis for the large scale involvement of the federal government in water resource development projects during the 1930's. Some examples include the work of the Corps of Army Engineers in levee construction, flood control, dam construction, and improvement of rivers and harbors for navigation. The Bureau of Reclamation of the Department of Interior built dams for irrigation. The Soil Conservation Service of the Department of Agriculture established and administered programs for upstream watershed planning to reduce erosion. The Federal Power Commission engaged in power production. The Tennessee Valley Authority, a world famous and widely imitated multiple-purpose regional development, was initiated. Although all of these government agencies have accomplished great works, the narrowness of the objectives of all but the T.V.A. has been recognized, and the present trend is to set up agencies which can consider not only power, irrigation, erosion, flood prevention, and navigation but also recreation, pollution, and conservation of fish and wildlife.

[8] *Water Resources Law, The Report of the President's Water Resources Policy Commission* (3 vols.; Washington: Government Printing Office, 1950), III, 15–16.

## Patterns and Practices in Private Water Use and Tenure

It has been shown that the use and holding of water in North America developed on the basis of local climates, needs, and supply of water, as well as by legal precedent and historic accident. Although most of the states share a common heritage in common law derived from the British system, there has been wide divergence in codes, statutes, and in court interpretations. To illustrate the variety of combinations and interpretations of the various water rights, a review of a few of the patterns of water use found in a few representative western states is in order.

**WATER RIGHTS IN THE UNITED STATES**

DOTTED STATES: **Appropriation**          RULED STATES: **"California Code"**          WHITE STATES: **Riparian Rights**

*Directory and Buyers Guide,* AUGUST 31, 1956

Fɪɢ. 4. The prevailing doctrines relative to tenure rights in water, by states.

An example of variations in the application of a water-tenure doctrine is found in regard to right by appropriation. This water right which depends on appropriation and continuity of use of water requires a system for the registration of claims. In the early days of the California Gold Rush this system varied from mining camp to mining camp.

The state of Wyoming was one of the first to provide a more general and rational system of recording. The Wyoming legislature established a Board of Control consisting of the State Engineer and super-intendents of the four water divisions of the state. To appropriate water in Wyoming a person must file an application for a permit with this board. After the appropriation has been completed, the board issues the applicant a certificate of appropriation. Findings of the board are subject to review by the courts. This general method of supervising appropriate rights has been adopted in all western states except Colorado, Montana, and Texas. In Colorado a water user starts constructing the necessary water control works and then files his claim with the State Engineer. In Montana the control of appropriative rights rests with the counties. In Texas an improved system of administering appropriative rights is now being devised.

The state of Colorado pioneered the techniques of controlling the distribution of water to right holders. The system works so well that it has been said that each drop of water has the name and address of its user and the time of delivery engraved upon it.

The patterns and practices relating to riparian water tenure also vary considerably among the states. Some states have reduced the scope of riparian rights, while others have defined them. In Oregon and South Dakota the vested rights of riparian owners are restricted by legislation to the amount actually applied to beneficial use. The courts have interpreted this legislation to reduce riparian rights almost to a legal fiction.[9]

In Washington riparian rights may be preserved only if the landowner uses the water beneficially within a reasonable time. If he fails to do this, the water may be appropriated for use on nonriparian land. In Nebraska riparian rights have been reduced by court protection of appropriative rights against riparian owners who commence use of the water after the appropriative user. In case of a conflict the riparian right is recognized only if the riparian user proves damages by the earlier user.

In California the riparian rights are limited by statute to the quantity required for beneficial use under reasonable methods of diversion and use.

Practices relating to the use of percolating ground water have also varied widely. In Texas the English common law rule of absolute ownership is recognized. Under this rule ground water tenure is similar

[9] Interesting court decisions on repudiation of the riparian doctrine and recognition of the appropriation doctrine in New Mexico are contained in Wells A. Hutchins, *The New Mexico Law of Water Rights* (Agricultural Research Service Technical Report No. 4 [Washington: USDA, 1955]), 8–36.

to land tenure and the owner of overlying land may withdraw any quantity of water from an underground reservoir—even though his withdrawal drains neighboring lands. In reaction to the extremes of this practice many states adopted the American rule of reasonable use, which recognizes a landowner's right to pump water for useful purposes but restrains him from exporting it, wasting it, or injuring others.

California has adopted a modification of the American rule. This doctrine gives landowners rights of reasonable beneficial use of any ground water in connection with their overlying lands. Any surplus above this " reasonable " amount is subject to appropriation by others.

Problems concerning the use of ground water have led to adoption of ground water codes by a number of western states in recent years. An example is found in the Arizona code adopted in 1948. Its main objectives were to protect the ground water supply and to promote rational development of water. These goals would be encouraged by requiring the registration of wells, the issuance of permits for well drilling, requirement of reports from well drillers and well users, and the establishment of an enforcement procedure.[10]

The state of Arkansas provides a good example of an enlightened approach to the changing nature of water tenure practices. The Arkansas Water Study Commission, established in 1955, made a study of water resources and recommended that the legislature establish a water-tenure system based on beneficial use, to be administered by a Board of Water Commissioners with all necessary technical assistance.

## Conflicts and Problems in Water Tenure

Water tenure, similar to land tenure, consists of a bundle of rights and obligations which may be held by different holders. Yet water tenure differs significantly from land tenure in a number of ways. Water is transient; individuals use it while it passes by. Ownership, like the ownership of other elusive things, rests with the state. Water is indispensible to life, becomes a mortal threat when oversupplied, and can be harnessed for multiple purposes through large public investments. The sum effect of these characteristics is that conflicts in water tenure take a variety of forms. They may be interpersonal, intergroup, interregional or interagency.

[10] Obed M. Lassen, Land Commissioner, *A Summary of Ground Water Law of Arizona and the Rules and Regulations of the State Land Department*

*Interpersonal conflicts* are most frequent where a new use is being developed or an old use is being applied to a new area, as in the expansion of irrigation. Existing laws are inadequate to regulate the new situation. As mentioned, the appropriation doctrine was developed in California as an answer to the conflicts among miners over water sources used in mining. Interpersonal conflicts also arise where the applicable water law is not clear and definite as in the lower Rio Grande Valley, where aspects of both the appropriation and riparian doctrines apply simultaneously. Interpersonal conflicts usually result from uncertainty concerning the legal nature of the rights of the individuals involved and are usually resolved through legal processes. In many irrigated areas interpersonal conflicts have been reduced by the establishment of ditch companies. Joint efforts were required to capture, transport, and apply the water. Companies were formed requiring detailed agreements and mutual understanding of the rights and obligations of each member to reduce conflicts among individuals.

A large number of water tenure problems arise from conflict and competition among various special interest groups in our economy. These may be ditch companies, consumers of electricity, producers of electricity, fishermen, sailors, water skiers, etc. Others may be interested in future economic values such as the higher property values resulting from reservoir development. Municipalities may be concerned with providing constituents with services such as water, electricity, sewage disposal, freedom from floods, or recreation. Other government agencies may be carrying out the will of the people as outlined in legislation authorizing flood control, water conservation, or irrigation. Conflicts among these many groups are often inter-regional as well as local in nature.[11]

A common type of conflict arises between the people who live at the headwaters or upper basin where the streams are fed and the people in the lower basin where the water is used or allowed to flow unrestrained to the sea. For example, in Colorado a natural intrastate

---

*Concerning Ground Water—1957* (Arizona State Land Dept. Bulletin No. 302 [Phoenix: Arizona State Land Dept., 1957]).

[11] The numerous state and local organizations that have responsibilities and powers over water resources in Louisiana are briefly described by Mark E. Borton and Harold H. Ellis, *Some Legal Aspects of Water Use in Louisiana* (La. Agr. Exp. Sta. Bul. No. 537 [Baton Rouge: A.E.S., Louisiana State University, June, 1960]), 77–114.

competition for water developed between the few people on the west slope, where the clouds were made to give up most of their burden, and the populous water-deficit eastern slope. This natural geographical-based conflict was resolved through statesmanlike action by the governor and resulted in the Big Thompson multiple-purpose project.

Interwatershed conflicts arise whenever there is a critical disparity between demand and supply of water. The city of San Antonio, Texas, supplied by a small stream, flood run-off, and a few wells, looks enviously over the watershed divide to the Guadalupe river valley, where an ample supply of water runs little used down to the Gulf of Mexico.

The city of Houston with nearly a million inhabitants is located on the tiny San Jacinto watershed, just outside the valleys of the Trinity and Brazos rivers. To obtain water for continued growth, Houston must negotiate with the directors of the Trinity or Brazos River Valley Authorities.

The Brazos River Authority provides a variety of examples of conflicts in water tenure. Irrigators in the lower valley prefer water of low mineral content from the lower tributaries and wish to see additional dams built in this area. People in the middle section of the long valley want development to take place near them, as they hope to benefit from increases in land values and the secondary benefits of a large multiple-purpose water development.[12]

People in the upper valley, where water is scarce, are more interested in ground water development, evaporation reduction, and water recreation development.

Interagency conflicts in water resource development are legion. Unfortunately a number of government agencies have been established to implement separate aspects of water development. Each of these government agencies has its own supporters and pressure groups whose representatives work to get Congress to make appropriations for the favored projects. Several ways out of this complex and confused pattern of public interests in water have been tried or are being attempted. The Tennessee Valley Authority, a quasi-governmental corporation, is a widely copied (in foreign lands) method of bringing ordered development from the array of competing government agencies. Another attempt to harness the government agencies for team-

---

[12] Frederic O. Sargent, " Criteria for Appraisal and Planning Water Resource Development Agencies in Texas," *Land Economics*, Vol. 36 (1960), 43–51.

work has been to form a study commission that embraces all of them. This method is an improvement over the previous chaos and may work well with strong leadership.[13]

International conflicts over rights to the use and development of water resources present an especially difficult problem, as there exists no routine pattern for negotiation and compromise. Each body of water must be dealt with as a separate and unique case with the establishment of a special commission. Interregional and international conflicts of interest delayed the development of the St. Lawrence Seaway for a score of years after its engineering and economic feasibility were clearly understood. The Columbia River in the Northeast is undergoing the same slow process of negotiation. The rights of each country and especially of certain economic-interest groups within each nation must be considered, protected, and enhanced.

With the continued growth of large metropolitan areas, new and expanding industries, and increasing demand for water, the interregional problems of water rights, water use, and water development are becoming more critical. The Potomac River Commission is an example of the type of multiple agency, multiple use, long-range development planning that must come as per capita and total water demand continue to rise.

[13] *Id.*, " The U. S. Water Supply Commission for Texas," *Southwest Social Science Quarterly*, Vol. 41 (September, 1960), 156–62.

# CHAPTER TEN

# Subsurface Rights in Land Tenure

WITH NEARLY 385 MILLION acres in the United States under lease for oil and gas in 1959, no study of land tenure in the United States would be complete without a discussion of the impact that commerce in subsurface rights has upon land value and use. This is particularly true of the Plain states and perhaps even more pertinent in the Southern Plains where traffic in mineral rights is more intensive and of longer duration.

It is the purpose of this chapter to discuss why and how both the real and the speculative aspects of subsurface rights directly and indirectly affect land tenure.

## The Nature of Subsurface Rights

In the early history of the United States the utility of land was generally considered as lying in the surface stratum, and length and breadth were considered its important measurements. Little or no significance was attached to the third dimension, depth, until the discovery of valuable resources below the surface. The first settlers in the Great Plains states ascribed no significance whatever to the English common law doctrine that land includes not only the face of the earth, but everything over it and under it. It was only with the discovery of oil and gas in these states that landowners became conscious of the possibilities of income from the subsurface. As exploration and discoveries spread, the economic and legal significance of this hitherto ignored third dimension soon came to be of paramount importance.

It was soon after the discovery of " rock oil " in Pennsylvania in 1859 that certain legal questions began to arise. Unlike coal and other solid minerals, oil and gas are not confined to underground areas outlined by surface property lines. Instead, they are confined under

146

pressure in subsurface traps which seldom coincide with property boundaries. The fluid and migratory character of petroleum permits it to flow in the direction of the lowest pressure. Any penetration into the trap results in a lowering of pressure at that point.

The above characteristics of oil and gas deposits early raised the legal question, not only of ownership, but of control. Common law held that the surface owner's boundaries extended to the center of the earth. Through the years legal decisions flowed from the courts, with different courts holding somewhat different views on ownership of oil and gas. Finally, however, the doctrine that oil and gas could not be owned " in place " came to be widely accepted, and these minerals became property only upon capture.

In view of the fact that the use of the surface is necessary in exploring for, and capturing, oil and gas, the landowner, even though he cannot own these minerals in place, has a valuable property right in the subsurface by virtue of his control of the surface. This property right he can lease to others. The lease not only provides for a rental consideration to be paid by the lessee but further provides that if oil is found the landowner will receive a share of the value of the oil produced. This share, or " royalty," usually amounts to one-eighth of the total value and, as will be shown later, the value of the royalty can be very high.

As landowners' incomes from oil began to increase, speculators sought a method of acquiring a share in this income. In the infancy of the industry the method usually employed was to purchase the land itself. But the landowner would not always sell, or for other reasons fee purchase might not be practical. Other methods were sought whereby more than one person might benefit from subsurface income or by which one could speculate in minerals without acquiring the fee simple title. The method finally adopted, and the one which became common, was for landowners to sell a mineral deed or a royalty deed to all or a part of his mineral rights.

The holding of mineral rights separately from the fee simple title has now become widespread. A new type of ownership has developed; an ownership whose only interest in the surface is in its use for developing mineral interest. What is true of the mineral rights owner, is therefore only slightly less true of this type of fee simple owner whose primary interest in land is its subsurface value.

In most countries of the world subsurface rights in minerals belong to the state. The principal exception appears to be those countries whose laws and legal institutions are based upon the English common law. In the United States, with a few exceptions, fee simple ownership of land implies all the rights to the subsurface. The exceptions include some former public domain lands which passed to private ownership with part or all the mineral rights specifically excepted in the deed, some individual states which have sold state-owned land with mineral exceptions, and some Indian lands where the mineral rights were reserved to the tribe as a whole rather than to individual surface owners.

There is little question but that state ownership of subsurface rights has, in some countries, added vast wealth to the treasury. In some states of this country public ownership of subsurface rights results in a substantial flow of income into the state treasury.

## The Impact of Subsurface Rights on Tenure Relations

The extent of the impact of subsurface rights on tenure and other aspects of the agricultural economy is difficult to measure in definitive terms, but there is no question that the impact has been felt in many areas of the United States. The extent of leasing of subsurface rights, however, may be useful as one guide in measuring the impact.

On January 1, 1959, an estimated 382.6 million acres were under lease for oil and gas in the continental United States. Of this acreage, 286.8 million were found in the thirteen states referred to as the Great Plains states. Thirty-one of the forty-eight states had land under lease for oil and gas and about 25 per cent of the total land area of those states was leased.

In the southwestern states about 38 per cent of the total land area was under lease or in production on January 1, 1959, and in the northern Great Plains states about 34 per cent. Whenever that high a proportion of the land area is deemed to have value in addition to its ability to produce agricultural commodities, conflicts in tenure and the use of space are likely to arise in the competition for land.

The acreage under lease in 1959 or during any one year, however, does not reveal the full impact of subsurface values on the agricultural economy. For example, in 1956 nearly 384 million acres were leased for oil and gas as compared to 383 million acres in 1959. Only a portion of these acres were the same during both periods. It would be nearly impossible to determine the total number of acres which have at one time or another been under lease. In states where oil has been produced for many years the acreage which has at some time been leased probably would equal, if not exceed, 75 per cent of the total land area of these states.

If we translate the leased acreage into dollar values, it becomes more apparent why subsurface activity has an impact on the surface use and tenure of land and perhaps why it might very well take precedence over agriculture.

Income from nonproductive leases in the thirteen Great Plains states probably has averaged no less than $405 million per year for the past ten years. This assumes $1.00 per year for delay rentals on an estimated average of 225 million acres per year. While a one dollar per acre delay rental has been practically universal during the 1950's, the dollar is paid only four years in five. In addition, the "bonus" paid the mineral fee owner as an inducement to him to sign a lease probably would average no less than five dollars per acre for a five-year lease. This would result in an average annual income of $1.80 for each leased acre ($1.00 average per year for the bonus plus four years of delay rentals at $1.00 per year).

Income from leasing oil and gas rights, while substantial, relatively reliable, and widely dispersed, is not so spectacular as the income that subsurface rights owners have received from produced oil and gas. For example, the total value of oil and gas produced in the southwestern states since production first began approximates $107 billion. Of this amount, subsurface owners have received about one-eighth or $13.5 billion. There are about 8.7 million productive acres in the area indicating that each of these acres has yielded an average income of about $1,550 to the mineral owner. The fact that this amount is net to the mineral rights owner and that he pays federal income taxes on only 72.5 per cent of his oil income encourages speculation in subsurface rights.

The prospect of the relatively reliable returns from leasing plus the prospects of much higher returns from produced oil are strong inducements either to purchase land for the mineral rights or to purchase mineral rights separately. This added demand for land, or for subsurface rights, is reflected in land values. Farmers have increased difficulty in purchasing land. Speculative owners, because of the incompatibility of mineral exploration and production, are reluctant to rent to a surface operator or, at best, are willing to give only a short term surface lease.

## Major Agricultural Problems Associated with Subsurface Rights

### Land Use

An owner of a subsurface lease or a mineral deed has the right to use the surface of the land to exploit his interest. If this right is not explicitly stated in the conveying instrument, the courts hold it to be an implicit right. He has the right not only to sink a well or wells but also to construct such other facilities as may be necessary to develop his interests. The mineral developer may build power houses, storage tanks, dwellings for personnel employed on the lease, lay pipelines, power lines, roads, and paths.

While reasonable care must be exercised by the subsurface leases in the development of his interests, conflicts between the surface operator and the subsurface operator arise. And because of the greater possibilities for high income from subsurface operations as compared to agricultural operations, these conflicts usually are resolved in favor of the subsurface interests.

An owner of both the surface and subsurface usually is quite willing to suspend agricultural operations while the leasehold is being developed for oil and gas. The prospect of immeasurably higher returns from the subsurface makes such a decision an easy choice. After the mineral lease is developed, structures located, and rights-of-way established, these owners may again resume surface operations if subsurface returns prove to be modest. If they do resume such operations, the farming system may have to be altered because roads, wells, and other structures have segmented the farming area. If well spacing is close, then it may be completely unfeasible to use the surface for any kind of agricultural production.

The total acreage actually occupied by structures used in developing the subsurface depends on the well-spacing pattern. There is a growing tendency to drill only one well on each forty acres. If one includes lease roads, the area occupied by the well and service buildings, probably something like five acres of the surface, would be used in each forty acres. In fields where closer spacing prevails—such as 10-acre spacing—a much higher proportion is unavailable for agriculture.

The chances are, therefore, that subsurface exploration and development will cause a change in surface utilization of land. The change occurs not only because of the physical difficulty of farming around the obstacles mentioned above but also because of the change in the economic position of the landowner.

It has been observed that, even before actual subsurface operations begin, there is a tendency for landowners who have received substantial bonus payments for an oil and gas lease to shift to operations of a more leisurely nature, to use the surface less intensively. This frequently means shifting to something which might be termed " hobby farming."

Another tendency is for landowners to leave the farm whenever income from the subsurface becomes substantial, whether from oil lease bonuses or the actual production of oil. This results in either the abandonment of the land for agricultural purposes or the renting out of the land to an agricultural tenant.

If a tenant tries to farm where oil is being produced, he is at a disadvantage, because his desires and the rent he pays are secondary to the desires of the mineral producer and the income from subsurface operations. When land is rented to an agricultural tenant before exploration actually is begun, he usually is in an inferior position to that of the mineral lessee.

Agricultural tenants ordinarily can expect nothing more than a year-to-year lease in a " hot " area. To the mineral developer the surface tenant is an unwelcome intruder who, if his crops or livestock are damaged, must be compensated. While crop compensation normally can amount to no more than the value of one year's crop, the mineral lessee often finds it to his advantage to buy up the surface tenant's lease. The surface tenant might well be agreeable to this, for he knows that crop damage may recur and that after the payment for damage to one year's crop he continues to farm at his own risk, especially if reasonable care is being exercised by the subsurface operator.

There are areas where land is purchased primarily for its mineral value. Extensive purchases of this nature seem to be fairly well confined to the less desirable agricultural lands, where purchase fees would be little more than the cost of mineral rights alone. Farmers in those areas find it increasingly difficult to find a farm to operate or, if already farming, to expand operations.

Land held primarily for its mineral possibilities may also suffer greater surface deterioration. Lack of esteem for the surface value may result in neglect of even the most elementary efforts to conserve it. On the other hand, many speculatively owned tracts of marginal quality have, through abandonment of the surface, returned to native vegetation. The speculative owners, therefore, have accomplished, though perhaps unwittingly, what some agricultural programs are designed to do.

### Land Transfer Problems

A second major agricultural problem associated with subsurface activity has been that of transferring land. Because the mineral right is a valuable property right and because this right to the subsurface can be separated from the surface, problems both legal and economic in nature raise barriers to the transfer of land ownership.

Separate property interests in mineral rights have become so numerous in some areas of the Great Plains that the landowner who has complete title to his property is the exception rather than the rule. In all areas of the Southwest some " splitting of the fee " occurs.

Separate ownership of the mineral rights in a tract of land usually makes that tract undesirable as security for a loan. As a general rule most lending agencies will refuse to lend on a tract unless half the mineral rights are still owned by the borrower. Lenders probably are justified in their caution. The mineral developer who has the right to use as much of the surface as is necessary to develop his interest might very well prevent the borrower from meeting his loan obligations. If the borrower has half the mineral rights, however, income from the subsurface interest is likely to counteract losses in surface income.

Title clearance problems and increased abstracting costs also impede land transfers and prevent desirable readjustments in land tenure patterns.

A large number of individuals owning an interest in the same tract of land pose a problem in title clearance which is likely to grow in direct proportion to the number of owners. Where there are a great number of owners of mineral rights—and there may be hundreds of owners of the mineral rights in a single tract—there is frequently the problem of locating all the owners.

Mineral deeds pass to heirs in the same manner as other types of real estate, thus creating co-ownership of a deed to a small share of the mineral rights. In such cases it may be impossible to find all the owners, particularly if the mineral interest has lost its value and the owner has, in effect, abandoned it. Frequently the only solution to the case is a suit to quiet title, which necessarily entails costs and delays.

Another title problem sometimes arises out of the obscure language which granted a share in the mineral interest. There is doubt as to what proportion of the mineral rights the deed was meant to convey. The remedy to the problem may be a long and expensive court proceeding.

In addition to title difficulties, abstracting costs increase with an increase in the number of instruments recorded on any particular tract. Since each instrument so recorded must be copied or briefed in the abstract, costs are bound to increase as the number of transfers of mineral deeds increase. The number can reach fantastic proportions.

There is no limit to the division of the shares of mineral rights. Numerous instances have been found of ownerships of less than 1/1000 of an acre interest in the mineral rights. Abstracting costs sometimes amount to more than the value of the land for agricultural purposes. One case was found in which an abstract on an 80-acre farm cost $1,800. The agricultural value of the land probably did not exceed $1,200, but the fact that it also had subsurface value justified the expense of abstracting. While an $1,800 abstract is exceptional, $400 to $600 for an abstract is not unusual in areas where speculation in the subsurface has occurred.

Another problem in land transfers, that of the increase in land values above the value for agricultural purposes, arises in areas where minerals have a potential or real value. The hope, or fear, of oil discovery influences the prices set by land buyers and land sellers in all areas where they have become conscious of land's third dimension. Not only does the possibility of discovery influence price, but it also has an influence on the proportion of the mineral rights which will follow the surface in a land transfer.

Landowners, for fear of later oil development, often will refuse to sell unless they are allowed to retain a proportion of the mineral rights. Some prospective buyers will not even consider a place unless they can get all the mineral rights. In some areas the proportion of the mineral rights to be transferred may be more subject to bargaining than the price to be paid.

Studies in North Dakota, Oklahoma, and Texas show that the selling price of land is directly related to the proportion of minerals trans-ferred. The relationship is most apparent in areas where there is considerable oil activity, less apparent in areas where there is less consciousness of mineral values.

In Oklahoma, for example, data compiled on more than 2,100 land sales occurring in 1941 and 1942 showed about 28 per cent more was paid for land with all the mineral rights as compared to sales where there had been some mineral separation. The surface alone sold for only about one-third as much as the complete title and for about one-half as much as land with half the mineral rights.[1]

Some, but not all, of the difference found in price probably can be attributed to the quality of the land, for it appears that buyers of the better quality land are more insistent on an unencumbered title or at least insist on a substantial proportion of the mineral rights. The better the land, the greater the chances of loss in surface income if oil is found. Moreover, buyers of the better quality land are more likely to need credit, which means that in most instances they must also own at least half the minerals.

When good land sells without the mineral rights, the dollar discount usually is much greater than in the case of poor quality land. In one county in Oklahoma the best quality land with none of the mineral rights averaged nearly $51.00 per acre less in price than did similar land with all mineral rights. Poor quality land sold in the same county showed a difference of only $7.50 per acre between all minerals and none. A much higher proportion of the poor land sold with no mineral rights than was the case for the best land.

## Methods of Holding Subsurface Rights

Interest in oil and gas may be held in three ways: (1) mineral rights incident to the ownership of land, those conveyed by mineral deed, and those retained by mineral reservation; (2) oil and gas leases granted by owners of mineral rights, and (3) royalty rights either assigned by the mineral owner or reserved by a former mineral owner.

### Mineral Rights

Mineral rights are sold in the same fashion as other real property. Part or all of these rights may be transferred by the same deed that transfers the land surface, or they may be sold by mineral deed separately from the surface. A landowner whose title to the land includes

---

[1] It is expected that these differences narrow considerably in later years, when land values for agricultural purposes greatly increased.

the mineral rights may create for himself subsurface rights in the land by a specific mineral reservation when he sells his land.

Title to the mineral estate or to any part of the mineral estate usually does not refer to specific acres. If one purchases, or reserves, half the mineral rights, he has in effect purchased or reserved a half interest in the entire mineral estate. Such conveyances or reservations commonly mention the right of ingress and egress in order to develop the mineral interest, but this right is held to exist even if it is not specifically mentioned.

While mineral deeds or reservations usually are in perpetuity, they may be granted for a term of years. Ten- to twenty-five-year terms are most common. Unless the term is mentioned in the deed, they are held to be perpetual in all states of the Southwest except Louisiana.[2] Here, if a separate mineral estate is created, it is limited by law to ten years unless exploration is being conducted or oil and gas are being produced at the end of the term. At the end of the term the mineral estate expires and reverts to the then owner of the land.

### Oil and Gas Leases

Another method of holding subsurface rights is by lease. An oil and gas lease is an agreement by which the owner of mineral rights (the lessor) grants the lessee the exclusive right for a stated period to enter upon the land to explore for oil and gas and to produce them if found.

A lease is drawn for a primary period of five or ten years and as long thereafter as oil and gas is produced from the land, or as long as the lessee is engaged in drilling operations. The usual wording in the standard lease form is such that the lease terminates at the end of one year unless the lessee has commenced a well or unless he pays the mineral owner the amount of annual rental stated in the lease.

Payment of rental on or before the agreed date (the lease anniversary) keeps the lease in force for another year. The payment of such rentals constitutes a payment by the lessee for the privilege of delaying the start of drilling operations; hence these payments are commonly termed " delay rentals." If the lessee neither starts drilling nor pays the delay rental, the lease expires.

A " bonus," mentioned earlier in connection with lease income, often is paid by the lessee to the lessor as an inducement to the latter to

[2] The laws of the states outside the Southwest have not been studied.

sign a lease. Where there is little or no competition for leases, the mineral owner can expect little or no bonus. If considerable competition for leases exist, the bonus may be substantial, frequently overshadowing the amount the mineral owner receives from delay rentals.

### Royalty Rights

Royalty rights refers to the share of production paid to the mineral rights owner under an oil and gas lease. The customary royalty is one-eighth of the value of the oil produced and marketed from the lease. This is a periodic payment and is calculated on the basis of the market price of crude oil on each day of production.

A mineral owner may transfer to someone else the right to receive a stated share of the royalty income, if and when minerals are produced from the tract. The instrument used to convey a royalty interest is known variously as a " royalty deed," a " royalty conveyance," or " royalty assignment." A royalty right also may be created by reservation in a deed granting land or mineral rights.

Some royalty interests run with an existing lease and expire when that lease expires. Others are granted for a specified term of years and expire at the end of the term unless oil or gas is being produced. In the latter instance it expires when production ceases. Still other royalty interests are perpetual, and owners or their successors participate in any future royalties.

A " mineral deed " includes more rights than does a " royalty deed." A royalty interest of any kind includes only one of the rights covered by a mineral interest; the right to share in produced oil. The holder of the royalty interest does not participate in oil and gas lease negotiations, nor does he share in lease bonuses and delay rentals.

### Combination Mineral Interests

Mineral interests of various kinds may be held by several individuals in the same tract. A landowner, for example, may sell one-fourth of his mineral rights through a mineral deed, then later sell his land and reserve one-fourth of the remaining royalty rights. The new landowner would be the owner of three-fourths of the mineral rights, subject to the outstanding one-fourth royalty interest. If the new landowner should then sell one-fourth of his mineral rights, there would then be four owners of mineral interests—there could as easily have been forty—in the tract. Three of these owners would participate in lease negotiation, and all would participate in any production found.

It is situations of this kind carried to an extreme which cause potential lessees to look askance at a tract. Too many interests must be contacted and too many instruments negotiated before the lessee feels free to commence drilling operations. If oil is discovered, there are too many participants whose interests must be protected. The usual solution in case of multiplicity of ownerships is to arrange for a central agency to distribute the royalty income to the participants. It may be extremely difficult to determine just what interest each individual has.

## Management of Subsurface Rights for Maximum Income

The landowner whose property lies in an area of leasing activity must sooner or later make certain decisions regarding his mineral rights. Usually the occasion for his decision is not of his own choosing. At any time an oil company may offer to lease his land or an investor may offer to buy some of his mineral rights. He has no alternative but to make a yes-or-no decision. Moreover, he usually must make these decisions in an environment of uncertainty.

Because of the uncertainties, a landowner might well base his management plans on two guiding principles: (1) avoid hasty decisions; try to obtain all possible information; (2) when a decision must be made, try to gain maximum returns in one form or another, regardless of whether oil is found.

When an oil company contacts them for a lease, many landowners immediately assume that oil will be found. However, a prudent landowner should assume that the possibility of oil under his land is still remote. Even when oil is discovered on an adjacent tract, he cannot be certain that the oil sand extends under his land. At the same time he should make his decisions in such a way that he leaves the way open for his participation in royalties if oil is discovered on his land.

### Decisions in Leasing

The first decision that a landowner may have to make is whether to grant an oil and gas lease on his mineral rights. Some landowners may have personal reasons for not wanting to lease their lands, but for most the real question is not whether to lease, but rather *when* to lease and to *whom*.

In rank " wildcat " territory the delay rentals offered may be only ten or twenty-five cents per mineral acre, with little or no cash bonus.

In this situation the landowner's chief decision is *when* to lease; that is, he must decide whether to accept the current offer or to hold out for possible higher rentals and bonuses later on. If he accepts this offer, he foregoes the chance of getting a larger bonus and higher rentals during the primary term of the lease. This primary term might be as long as ten years, if he is unable to negotiate a shorter primary term. If he decides to hold out for higher rentals, he may not get any kind of an offer later on, depending on whether an active lease play develops.

In short, a landowner has no clear-cut basis for deciding when to lease, if there is little or no competition for leases. As most landowners in wildcat territory are more interested in getting exploration started in their community than in getting higher rentals, a majority usually can be expected to sign leases at the first opportunity.

If competition for oil and gas leases is considerable, a landowner will have an opportunity to choose between two or more lessees; that is, his chief decision is to *whom* should he lease. To reach this decision he may compare (1) the merits of the prospective lessees, (2) the proposed lease rates, and (3) various provisions of the proposed lease.

In comparing the merits of prospective lessees, a landowner usually finds it advantageous to deal with a well-financed, well-managed company which has demonstrated its ability to carry out effective exploration and development programs. However, it is not always easy for a landowner to know with whom he is actually dealing. Many oil companies, for example, obtain leases through independent brokers. Sometimes the broker may not be at liberty to divulge the name of the company until the lease assignments are recorded. Generally, however, a landowner can protect his own interests by following four rules:

(1) Fractional mineral owners in the same tract should try to lease to the same broker or company. In so doing, they may avoid the problems that frequently arise when two or more lessees control fractional interests.

(2) A landowner should try to deal with the dominant lessee in the area; that is, with the broker or company that has leased the most land. If several companies hold intermingled leases, the plans of all may be hampered and development delayed.

(3) If possible, a landowner should avoid leasing to adventurous small promoters who may not have adequate financial backing for

exploration and drilling programs. From a landowner's standpoint there is danger that such ventures will fail. In these circumstances some leases are not canceled; the small promoter cannot be found to get a lease release; and a cloud is left on the landowner's titles, which may result in some expense and trouble to remove.

(4) The landowner should ask anyone who contacts him for a lease to show credentials and check these credentials before signing a lease.

The amount of rentals and bonuses offered depends largely on the competition for leases. In most areas a dollar per mineral acre is the usual annual rental. Seldom does competition push rentals above this rate; instead, competition is reflected in the cash bonus offered. Bonuses usually range from one to fifteen dollars per mineral acre, although in some instances they may amount to much more.

In comparing proposed leases a landowner should consider the following:

(1) A royalty clause that provides for one-eighth royalty on natural gas and casing-head gasoline as well as on oil is usually more advantageous than a clause that permits the company to pay an annual flat rate per well if gas alone is produced.

(2) A " shut-in " clause which permits the lessee to shut in wells that produce only gas generally is considered reasonable and proper in new areas where there is a lack of pipelines and other facilities for marketing gas. This clause should provide for an annual payment of shut-in royalties, such as fifty or one hundred dollars per well, during the shut-in period.

(3) A " dry-hole " clause is undesirable for the landowner, as it provides that if the first well drilled is a dry hole, the lessee can retain the lease for the rest of the primary term without paying rentals or conducting additional drilling.

(4) Under the usual type of lease, the lessee does not pay delay rentals on a lease anniversary if he has " commenced a well," which may mean merely digging a slush pit, developing a water supply, building a road to the well site, or simply staking out a well location. Leases more favorable to the landowner use the phrase " commence the drilling of a well," which means the " spudding in " or actual start of drilling operations.

(5) Most lease forms contain provisions that give some protection to the surface owner, such as a clause to the effect that the lessee will not drill a well within a stated distance from any building; a clause that requires the lessee to bury all pipelines below plow depth if so requested by the landowner, and a clause that provides that the lessee will pay for damages to crops and improvements caused by the lessee's operations. The wording of these clauses is more favorable to surface operators in some lease forms than in others.

Most brokers and oil companies prefer certain lease forms and do not like to change them. Nevertheless, they will sometimes make reasonable changes, especially if competition is sharp.

### Size of Tract Under One Lease

Under the usual oil and gas lease the lessee does not pay delay rentals if he is actually drilling a well anywhere on the leasehold on an anniversary date. Thus, the landowner may get more rentals if he divides his holdings into several leasing units. The lessee is interested in having large acreages under single leases. In addition to the possibility of paying less in delay rentals, larger acreages and fewer instruments mean lower initial costs for drawing up leases. Thus, the size of tract may be a bargaining issue for a large landowner, as the prospective lessee might be willing to pay a somewhat greater bonus for a single lease. The landowner's decision may turn on whether the additional bonus will more than offset the possible reduction of delay rentals in the event of drilling.

### Decisions in Selling Subsurface Rights

A landowner who sells mineral rights or royalty rights assures himself of an immediate cash return—though it may be low—in exchange for a highly uncertain future income from oil production. He also incurs certain future costs and disadvantages which are associated with separation of mineral rights. Thus, the selling price of a mineral or royalty right is of primary importance in sales.

A *mineral right* in an undrilled tract has two value elements: (1) lease value, based on the possibilities of earning rentals and bonuses in the future, and (2) royalty value, based on the possibilities of earning royalties in the event oil is produced. In contrast, a *royalty right* in an undrilled tract has only royalty value.

Royalty value of either mineral or royalty titles may be measured fairly accurately by petroleum geologists and engineer-appraisers in proved or producing areas. In wildcat territory, however, royalty value is highly speculative and cannot be appraised accurately. A mineral right has little or no *lease value* in the case of producing acreage, but in wildcat territory this is the chief element of value.

Theoretically, lease value is the sum total of all future delay rentals and bonuses, discounted to the present at some accepted capitalization rate. If a tract could be leased perpetually for an annual delay rental of one dollar per acre, its capitalized lease value at a capitalization rate of 5 per cent would be twenty dollars per acre. Experience in the older oil areas, however, indicates that few tracts are under oil and gas lease continuously for long periods and that, in any broad area, a large number of tracts are not under lease in any one year.

The ultimate royalty value of any particular tract varies from zero to $3,000 or more per acre, depending on whether oil or gas is found and in what quantities. For most tracts this value will be zero. As there is no way for a landowner to tell what the ultimate royalty value may be before drilling, he must rely on historical averages from other areas. A method for estimating *average* royalty value in advance of drilling is presented here.

Total yields from older oil pools in the United States have varied widely, from less than 1,000 to more than 400,000 barrels per acre. Because of this wide range and lack of accurate data, it is difficult to estimate average yields. One authority says that the average yield is not more than 5,000 barrels per acre. The royalty owners' share of 5,000 barrels would be 12½ per cent or 625 barrels per acre.

The 1946–1953 United States average price of crude oil at the well was $2.34 per barrel.[3] At this average price, the total income to royalty owners from average production would be $1,462 per royalty acre. This income would be received over a period of perhaps twenty-five to thirty-five years, with most probably coming during the first twenty-five years. In order to simplify the computations, it is assumed that $1,300 of the $1,462 total royalties per acre would be received in approximately equal annual amounts over a twenty-five-year period,

[3] This compares with the 1958 U. S. average price of $3.01 per barrel. Prices averaged $1.65 per barrel during the 1920's, $.98 during the 1930's, and $1.55 during the 1940's. However, it is not likely that crude oil prices will decline to those levels for the next few years because of the increasing degree of production control afforded by interstate compacts and state conservation laws.

with any royalties to be paid after the twenty-fifth year ignored. The present value of $1,300, under this assumed timing and discounted at 5 per cent, is $730 per acre.

This average royalty value of $730 per acre pertains only to the area that is underlain with oil pools. Oil pools seldom comprise more than 4 or 5 per cent of the total area of a sedimentary basin, and the average probably is nearer 1 or 2 per cent. Thus, the average royalty value of all land in wildcat territory would be within the range of 1 to 5 per cent of $730, or $7.30 to $36.50 per acre. The lower estimate of $7.30 per acre might well be used before exploration and drilling is done in any locality. The higher estimate might be more appropriate after drilling intentions are announced.

If a landowner is to sell any of his subsurface rights, he must sell the kind for which there happens to be a market. In wildcat territory buyers of subsurface rights are more interested in lease value than in royalty value, and so they discriminate against royalty conveyances. A broker or speculator, for example, may be willing to pay $15 to $20 per mineral acre for mineral rights, but only $3 to $5 per royalty acre for royalty rights in the same land. On the other hand, in and near areas where oil has been found, buyers of subsurface rights are interested primarily in the possibilities of receiving royalties.

Prices of royalty rights cannot be compared directly with prices of mineral rights. Thus, it may not be more advantageous to sell mineral rights even though the price is higher. By selling mineral rights, a landowner gives up more possibilities of future income than he would if he sold royalties. He also incurs greater risks of future disadvantages, such as the increase in abstracting costs which were discussed earlier.

The effects of fractionalization of royalty rights are less severe than is the fractionalization of mineral rights. For example, if no new leases are taken on the tract after fractionalization occurs, the effect on abstracting costs would be about the same for mineral right as for royalty right fractionalization. However, if a new lease is made after fractionalization, the increase in abstracting costs may be four or five times as large with mineral as with royalty rights, because of the additional lease instruments to be recorded. When a landowner sells subsurface rights, he should allow for these possible increases in future land title costs. A study in North Dakota, a relatively new area of development, indicates that in mineral rights sales an allowance of $1.20 per mineral acre might cover all except the more extreme situations of fractionalization. A similar cost allowance for sale of royalty rights would be about thirty cents per royalty acre. In older areas of development these costs might be considerably greater.

A landowner may make his own comparisons between mineral and royalty prices in order to decide which type of right to sell. Suppose a landowner has estimated the average royalty value in his area, following the method outlined above, at $7.30 per acre. Suppose further that he has estimated the lease value of his mineral rights at $7.00 per acre, based on the average length of time tracts remain under oil and gas lease and the average delay rentals and bonuses being paid in his community. The price comparisons under various situations may be summarized as follows, assuming the North Dakota costs apply:

(1) If the landowner were to sell *mineral rights* in advance of drilling on his land or on an adjoining tract, he should get at least $7.00 per mineral acre to cover the possible loss in future lease income, plus $1.20 to cover possible increases in future land-title costs, or a total of $8.20 per mineral acre. If the landowner were to accept less than $8.20, the chances are that he would suffer a net loss in the long run.

(2) To sell mineral rights for $8.20 per mineral acre would be equivalent to making the buyer a free gift of the speculative royalty value. If the landowner wishes to get the average speculative value for his *mineral rights* before drilling, he would have to get $8.20, plus $7.30, or $15.50 per mineral acre. Any price less than $15.50 would be considered low.

(3) If a landowner were to sell *royalty* instead of mineral rights, he would not need to figure on any loss of lease income and only thirty cents per royalty acre for future increases in land-title costs. Thus, the average value of royalty rights to the landowner before drilling would be $7.30, plus $.30 or $7.60 per royalty acre. That is, from the landowner's viewpoint a price of $7.60 per royalty acre for royalty rights is equivalent to a price of $15.50 per mineral acre for mineral rights. In this illustration, mineral rights are worth twice as much as royalty rights. However, this ratio varies depending on the assumptions that are made regarding future lease income and oil prices.

(4) If *mineral rights* are sold after a well is located on the land-owner's property or on an adjoining tract, the average value would

be $36.50 (speculative royalty value), plus $7.00 (lease value), plus $1.20 (land-title cost allowance), or a total of $44.70 per mineral acre. Any price less than this may be considered low.

(5) If *royalty rights* are sold after announcement of a well location, the average speculative value for royalty rights would be $36.50, plus the land-title cost allowance of 30 cents, or $36.80 per royalty acre. This price would be equivalent to the $44.70 per mineral acre for mineral rights.

In deciding on what rights to sell, a landowner can make his own computations, following the method illustrated above, using whatever assumptions he thinks realistic for his situation. The amounts used above are averages and may not reflect specific conditions. Under any assumptions, however, mineral rights have a higher value than royalty rights.

Usually, in selling subsurface rights an owner will find it advantageous to sell rights in specified minerals only. Most buyers are interested primarily in oil and gas. They would be unwilling to pay an additional amount for rights in other minerals. Thus, the landowner may be able to keep rights to other known and unknown minerals that have little current value, but which might have considerable future value.

In most instances a landowner will find it advantageous not to sell more than half his oil and gas rights. By keeping at least half, he will share in any future rentals and royalties. He also will maintain the loan-security status and sales value of his land. Moreover, he will retain the right to participate in future lease negotiations and so can seek lease provisions that will protect his surface rights in the event of drilling.

Likewise, in areas where strip-mining of coal or lignite is a possibility, it is unwise for a landowner to sell all rghts in these minerals because this type of mining almost completely destroys surface values. If he retains at least part of the mineral rights, he will be in a stronger position to bargain for adequate compensation.

Before a landowner considers selling any of his subsurface rights, he should know definitely what rights he owns and what rights have been separated by prior owners. It is believed that many instances of complete separation of surface and subsurface rights are the result of carelessness on the part of landowners. They sold 50 per cent of the subsurface rights without realizing that 50 per cent of the rights had been reserved by prior owners.

During the several weeks in which a well is being drilled, the prices for oil and gas rights on that tract and adjoining tracts usually rise rapidly. A landowner who wishes to get the greatest returns from his subsurface rights will watch the local market carefully. He will try to time the sale of part of his oil and gas rights when speculation is at a peak. Even if the well proves to be a dry hole, having sold when the market for oil and gas rights was high assures the owner of some return. If the well is a producer, the landowner who has retained part of the oil and gas rights may expect sizable returns from royalties.

One of the more difficult decisions a landowner may have to make is whether to accept a relatively low offer for his subsurface rights or to hold for higher prices. The wisest decision on this point is based on the landowners' debt position and need for ready cash. The heavily encumbered landowner can ill afford the uncertainty that is inherent in holding out for higher mineral prices. A debt-free farmer is in a position to consider holding for higher prices than those currently offered. If he does decide to hold for higher prices, he should recognize that he is speculating and that he may not receive any returns.

## Management of Subsurface Rights in Land Transfers

If there has been little or no mineral activity in a locality, buyers and sellers of land are not greatly concerned about subsurface rights and relatively few transfers contain mineral and royalty reservations. Where oil has been discovered or where leasing has been common, many of the land transfers contain reservations, and the amount of subsurface rights may be as important a matter for bargaining between buyer and seller as the price to be paid for the land.

Drafting of deeds that contain mineral and royalty reservations is a highly technical legal matter. It is said that more problems arise from mistakes made in subsurface reservations than in any other phase of transferring rights in land. In order to avoid possible mistakes and the resulting disagreements and lawsuits, buyers and sellers of land should obtain competent legal service for drafting deeds that contain mineral or royalty reservations.

### Decisions of Seller

Practically all of the adverse effects of separation of surface and subsurface rights, other than the effects on selling price, fall upon the buyer of the land rather than upon the seller. Thus, decisions of the seller can be based almost entirely upon the prices he can get for his land with various proportions of the subsurface rights attached.

Relationships between land prices and the proportions of subsurface rights that go with the land are complicated. Although the various price and reservation alternatives available to the seller depend on the particular situation that surrounds each sale, the following general tendencies will give prospective sellers some idea of what to expect:

(1) Subsurface reservations depress land prices more in areas where there have been lease plays and oil discoveries than in areas remote from mineral activity.

(2) Reductions in land prices associated with mineral right separations generally are greater for high quality than for poor quality land.

(3) The seller often can reserve up to half of the subsurface rights without sacrificing much on price. If he tries to reserve more than half, the selling price may be sharply lower. Land with all minerals may bring twice as much per acre as land with no minerals.

### Decisions of Buyer

One effect of oil discovery or of leasing activity is an increase in the prices of land as speculative mineral values are capitalized into land values. Frequently, a buyer can reduce his land investment costs by buying tracts from which part of all of the mineral rights have been separated. However, he should weigh the reduction of price against several disadvantages:

(1) The land may be harder to resell, because the market is restricted to the few who will consider buying less than a complete land title.

(2) Only in exceptional instances will lending agencies accept land as security for purchase-money mortgages if more than half of the mineral rights have been separated.

(3) The buyer will receive any future rentals and royalties only in the same proportion as his ownership of mineral and/or royalty rights.

(4) By owning at least part of the mineral rights, the buyer can exercise some control over oil and gas leases and thus may provide some protection for his surface rights.

Buying land without mineral rights may offer an opportunity to enlarge a farm at relatively low cost. The buyer can afford to forego the advantages of the mineral interest in an additional tract if the use of the tract is not vital to his main operating unit. The buyer of land should judge each prospective purchase on its own merits, weighing all the factors. He may be wise to put aside any prejudices against fractional mineral interests and examine the pros and cons from an economic standpoint.

# CHAPTER ELEVEN

# Conservation and Land Tenure

THE PRINCIPLE OF conservation is as ancient as life itself. Mother Nature has the ability to provide abundant supplies of plants and animals. If left to her own devices, the perpetuation of both is confidently assured. Trees, grasses, fish, and wild game are generously endowed with regenerative powers to perpetuate their kind. It is only with the advent of man that nature's balance has been tipped askew. Conservation practices and tenure status are closely bound together. This chapter explores the nature of this relationship and reviews the problems which have arisen and the policies which have been adopted in an effort to solve the problems.

## Definition of Conservation

Conservation has been variously defined, but all definitions incorporate one or more of the following concepts: (1) orderly and efficient resource use, (2) the elimination of waste, and (3) the maximization of social net returns.

Raleigh Barlowe suggests the following simple definition. Conservation is the " wise use of resources over time—or the when of resource use." [1]

E. W. Zimmermann in his definition emphasizes the buildup of future stocks. He states, " Conservation is a reduction in the rate of disappearance or consumption and a corresponding increase in the unused surplus at the end of a given period." [2] E. O. Heady and O. J. Scoville suggest that conservation is not intended to increase future supplies, but as a farm practice it is the " prevention of diminu-

[1] Raleigh Barlowe, *Land Resources Economics* (Englewood Cliffs, N. J.: Prentice-Hall, 1958), 284.

[2] E. W. Zimmermann, *World Resources and Industries* (Rev. ed.; New York: Harper & Bros., 1951), 790.

168

tion in future production on a given area of soil and from a given input of labor and capital. In other words, it is a problem of retaining a given production function over time." [3]

The thought was also expressed by R. T. Ely and G. S. Wehrwein that conservation, as far as timber is concerned, no longer means withholding the supply from the market to insure a future supply, but it is now a matter of replenishing the vanished resources and putting idle acres to work.[4]

## Historical Background of Conservation Movement in the United States

It is generally agreed by writers in the field of conservation that a certain social philosophy is necessary among individuals, community groups, and even nations before definite strides can be made toward conservation. In this regard the social philosophy of the group will often contradict the behavior of an individual. The individual is generally motivated by economic forces and a desire for personal gain. The social group, on the other hand, is motivated by social forces and welfare issues. Values related to conservation developed slowly in the United States, as will be shown in the discussions which follow.

### The Colonial Period

It was difficult for early settlers to develop a philosophy of conservation as they were floundering in an abundance of natural resources. Vegetation that interfered with cultivation was removed as quickly as possible, frequently by burning. Soils were rapidly exposed to the elements, and careless row cropping added to the extensive losses of soil fertility.

The first evidence of a conscious effort to conserve natural resources was displayed in early controls imposed on the cutting of timber by the British government. Representatives of the King cruised the New England forests and marked trees that were to be reserved for making ships' masts.[5]

[3] E. O. Heady and O. J. Scoville, *Principles of Conservation Economics and Policy* (Iowa Agr. Exp. Sta. Research Bulletin 382 [Ames: A. E. S., Iowa State College, July, 1951]), 365.

[4] R. T. Ely and G. S. Wehrwein, *Land Economics* (New York: Macmillan Co., 1949), 282.

[5] *Our Public Lands* (Washington: Bureau of Land Management, USDI, July, 1958), 6.

In 1626 the Plymouth Colony passed an ordinance which provided that no colonist could sell or export any timber from the colony without first obtaining permission from the governor. A Pennsylvania Ordinance of 1681 provided that, for every five acres of land cleared for farming, one acre was to be left in standing timber.

On May 20, 1785, the basic rectangular survey system was established and provided that Section 16 of every township in the western territories was to be reserved for the maintenance of public schools. This ordinance also included the reservation of one-third of all gold, silver, lead, and copper mines to be sold, or otherwise disposed of by the federal government.

The Ordinance of 1787 abolished entail and primogeniture, thus permitting alodial tenure, free transfer of title, and grants to settlers by the federal government.[6]

Conservation of trees for shipbuilding purposes was again emphasized in the Naval Stores Timber Act of 1799 which appropriated $200,000 for the purchase of lands containing live oak trees suitable for ships' masts and timbers. Under this act two purchases were made on the Georgia coast. One consisted of 350 acres on Grover's Island, costing $7,500, and the other a 1,600-acre plot on Blackbeard's Island at a cost of $15,000. Thus it can be clearly seen that little effort was devoted to systematic conservation during the Colonial period.

## Developments During the Nineteenth Century

A growing sentiment in favor of conserving timber resources was reflected in the birth of Arbor Day in 1872. In the spring of the same year Congress set aside the Yellowstone National Park and provided for administration of the park area by the Secretary of Interior. In 1873 Congress passed the Timber Culture Act to encourage the growth of timber on western prairies. Under this act any person " who would protect and keep in healthy growing condition for ten years, forty acres of timber, the trees to be planted not more than twelve feet apart, would receive title to the quarter section of which the forty acres was a part. Under this act also, homesteaders who had been on their lands for three years and had had one acre of trees under cultivation for the last two years of that time should be given patents." The act was amended in 1878 to reduce the required acreage in trees from

6 Ely and Wehrwein, *Land Economics*, 475.

forty to ten and prescribed 2,700 trees per acre at time of planting and 675 trees per acre at time of granting the patent.[7]

The encroachment, depredations, and removal of timber from public lands had become such a flagrant problem that Congress in 1878 prepared legislation to provide for classification and sale of timber lands. Thus, the Timber Cutting Act and the Timber and Stone Act were passed. The first act provided that bona fide settlers and mining interests could cut timber on the public domain for their own use without charge. The second act provided for the sale of surveyed lands, valuable chiefly for timber or stone and unfit for cultivation, in quantities of not more than 160 acres at the minimum price of $2.50 per acre.[8]

In fiscal year 1891–1892 President Harrison created six national forest reservations, and within another year nine more reservations were proclaimed, making a total of fifteen. By 1897 thirteen additional reserves were created. The chief proponents for this action were the strongly organized forestry associations found in many of the western states.

The nineteenth century might well be termed the maturing period for our nation. During this period free land and the abundant natural resources began to dwindle and arouse concern. A Frenchman, J. J. Jusserand, speaking before a timber resource conference in Washington, D. C., in 1905 stated, " To every nation as it approaches maturity comes the necessity of husbanding its resources." [9]

## The Conservation Movement Since the Turn of the Century

At the turn of the century the conservation movement was considerably strengthened through the efforts of President Theodore Roosevelt and Gifford Pinchot.

In 1907 Roosevelt appointed a commission on Inland Waterways and in 1908 the National Conservation Commission was established to make an exhaustive inventory of the nation's natural resources. The statements and recommendations included in the commission's report were of such far reaching importance that a brief summary of the report is given here:

A careful classification of public lands was recommended to deter-

[7] Roy M. Robbins, *Our Landed Heritage* (Princeton: Princeton University Press, 1942), 218–19.

[8] *Ibid.*, 287–88.

[9] Ely and Wehrwein, *Land Economics*, 472.

mine whether land was valuable for agriculture, timber, or minerals. Timber had been removed from sixty-five million acres of public land which was fit only for timber culture, but replanting was done on only one acre for each 10,000 that needed replanting. Stricter fire laws were recommended because an average of fifty million dollars worth of timber had been lost annually since 1870. But, in addition to fire losses, timber was being cut at a rate three and a half times its annual growth. The commission recommended that forest reserves not be restricted to the West but be extended to the East to preserve timber on the watersheds of the Appalachian and White Mountains for the prevention of floods and the preservation of water power. It was also mentioned that the government should control the use of grazing land to prevent removal of grasses and thus reduce the threat of erosion, also to provide for reforestation in regions where excessive wash had occurred.[10]

The crusade for conservation during Roosevelt's administration was well exemplified by the fact that in 1908 and 1909, forty-one states and fifty-one national organizations created conservation commissions. Not only was conservation tackled on a national scale but it was also considered on a continental and world-wide basis. A North American Conservation Conference was organized in 1909 in which the United States, Canada, Newfoundland, and Mexico participated. In the same year a World Powers conference at The Hague took up the matter of conservation of the earth's natural resources.

Although most of the conservation efforts in this period of development were directed to land, timber, and mineral resources, recognition was also given to the need for conserving water resources. In 1873 the American Association for the Advancement of Science sent a memorial to Congress asking for forest reserves in order to preserve favorable hydrologic conditions.[11] In 1902 the Newlands Act assigned receipts from the land sales in the arid states to the construction of reservoirs or permanent irrigation works. Water thus made available was to be distributed under the water laws of the respective states.

In 1909 John W. Weeks of Massachusetts introduced a bill " to enable any state to cooperate with any other state or states, or with the United States, for the protection of the watersheds of navigable streams and to appoint a commission for the acquisition of lands for the purpose of conserving the navigability of navigable rivers." The

[10] Roy M. Robbins, *Our Landed Heritage,* 357–63.
[11] *Ibid.,* 304.

bill provided for an appropriation of a million dollars the first year and two million each year until 1916 for the purchase of forest lands in the Appalachian and White Mountains.[12] The bill experienced much controversy but was finally passed two years later. This act proved to have far reaching consequences, for it brought the public's interest in conservation from the West to the East and served as the authority on which President Franklin D. Roosevelt, twenty years later, based his soil conservation and water power programs for the nation.

The importance of water conservation was aptly expressed in 1929 by the Secretary of the Interior, R. L. Wilbur from California, when he said, " Plant life demands water, from Nebraska west, water and water alone is the key to our future—there must be a great western strategy for the protection of our watersheds and the plant life on them." [13]

## Tenure Problems Relating to Conservation

It is generally recognized that conservation of natural resources is considered more seriously by resource owners than by those who may be privileged to use the resources through some contractural arrangement. Many works have been written on the merits of family farm ownership, and our national policies have been consistently directed toward sponsoring the development and perpetuation of family-owned and family-operated farms. Part of this emphasis results from the attempt to remedy some of the undesirable aspects of land-lord-tenant relations, an important one being the matter of conservation of resources.

### The Variant Goals of Owners and Tenants

Ownership of factors used in production does not in itself assure conservation of resources. The goals of the owner may or may not be the same as the goals of the tenant. If we accept maximization of income as the primary goal then, in the short run, it is logical to expect that both tenure groups would utilize available resources in much the same way. In a recent Iowa study, based upon marginal returns to different tenure classes, it was found that the " extent of deviations from optimum resource combinations for each tenure class are small and do not differ significantly between tenure classes." [14] The report

[12] *Ibid.*, 368–70.                    [13] *Ibid.*, 413.
[14] Walter G. Miller, Walter E. Chryst, and Howard W. Ottoson, *Relative*

further states that resource adjustment to approach optimum production levels varied according to tenure status, but observed differences could have been partly due to data limitations and applied analytical techniques. Nevertheless, the point to be emphasized here is that the three tenure classes (owner-operators, crop-share-cash, and livestock-share) were about equally as efficient in adjusting the use of resources to approach optimum production levels. Nothing, of course, is mentioned regarding the lack of conservation, or exploitation, of resources that may have occurred in the process of resource adjustment. It is assumed that owner-operators would have combined land, labor, and capital in somewhat different proportions than the crop-share-cash renters or the livestock-share renters. That is to say, owner-operators could have substituted capital for labor or land, while the tenant would have used more labor and less capital.

A class of tenure frequently overlooked when discussing conservation is the part-owner. The part-owner is in the enviable position of owning his own farm and renting additional acreage to enhance the size of his farm. It has been observed that the part-owner effectively displays two divergent attitudes regarding conservation of resources. He will usually apply conservation practices on his own farm and exploit the land he rents.

Sometimes tenants will rent additional land to adjust toward a larger farm unit, just as part-owners do. There is a difference, however. Landlords may object to their tenants spreading their resources too thinly and possibly encountering conflicts of interest between competing enterprises. In either case, the tenant's concern about conservation would normally be less than that of the owner.

Sharecroppers, as a tenure class, are more prevalent in the South. Since they obtain direction and supervision from the landlord and are not free to make management decisions they merely carry out whatever conservation measures the landlord dictates.

Perhaps the most important characteristic that differentiates the tenant from the owner-operator on the farm is that of security, or in a sense you might say stability. The attitude of the individual toward the natural resources surrounding him will hinge to a large extent upon the prospects of remaining in the same place for years to come. Insofar as the tenant has limited tenure, frequently of one

---

*Efficiencies of Farm Tenure Classes in Intrafirm Resource Allocation* (Iowa Agr. and Home Econ. Exp. Sta. Research Bulletin 461 [Ames: Iowa State College, November, 1958]) , 334.

year duration, he will naturally be less concerned about conserving resources for the unknown future.

Improvements in landlord-tenant contracts are constantly being recommended, and some changes are becoming effective. (See Chapter 8.) Written contracts are gradually replacing oral agreements. Many leases carry an automatic renewal provision, which extends the contract beyond the contract year, but this in itself does not engender a feeling of security because in most cases the renewal clause can be suspended by an appropriate notice from the landlord. A more significant improvement in tenant contracts is the provision which compensates the tenant for the unexhausted value of certain improvements left on the farm in the event the contract is terminated. In like manner many contracts contain reciprocal clauses which compensate landlords for damage or lack of maintenance to the rented property.

Insecure owner-operators react in somewhat the same way as insecure tenants. Those with life estates and those who have abandoned hope of surmounting mortgage indebtedness will tend to mine the soil, destroy timber, and neglect buildings and other improvements.

## Problems Arising from Other Social Conditions

Sometimes economic motives are not compatible with conservation motives. The constant clamor for larger farm units may be justified from the standpoint of providing a more adequate family income, but it does not necessarily follow that the larger unit will be treated with more favorable conservation practices. It has been stated, on occasion, that intensive farming mines the soil. This in itself is true, provided the operator fails to replenish the elements removed by the harvested crop. On the other hand, general observation would indicate that conservation was much more in evidence on intensively farmed small tracts than on large tracts where extensive farming prevailed. Deep gullies, idle fields, and scrubby underbrush are seldom, if ever, seen on intensively farmed small tracts but are quite commonplace on large extensively farmed areas.

Suburbanized rural farm lands usually have an air of neglect. These lands, in the process of transition from rural to urban, frequently suffer from lack of conservation measures. Here again the answer lies in the impermanence of tenure, but the problem in this instance may not be as serious. What does it matter whether city concrete is poured over fertile soil or over the denuded subsoil?

Another aspect of tenancy frequently overlooked is the relationship between the social environment and conservation. Tenants, especially in the South, are usually forced to live in squalid surroundings and denied the facilities which create community pride. The lack of well-equipped and comfortable homes tends to degrade the status of tenants and certainly fails to instill conservation incentives.

Also in the South there is evidence of rebellion against the consolidation of small land holdings to form large pine plantations. Southern pulp mills are constantly buying or leasing additional land for pine production. In the process of developing pine stands they remove hardwoods which, in the past, provided food for wild game as well as nuts and acorns for roaming hogs allowed to forage in wooded areas.

Pine plantations are the very essence of conservation of trees and soil but evidently not the type of conservation that native inhabitants will accept. There is strong resistance to changing the nature of land use. The feeling of rebellion is well expressed by the frequent fires and the following threat found posted along a country lane:

> You may cut out the hardwoods,
> And string up new lines
> But we'll tear down your fences
> And burn up your pines.[15]

### The Uncertainty of Economic Returns

In a study of costs and returns from soil conserving farming systems, E. O. Heady and C. W. Allen point out that gains or losses realized from the use of conservation practices may be due not to the process of production but to changes in economic environment. Net profits may be realized during a period of favorable prices, but losses would result during periods of low prices.[16]

The authors go on to state that costs incurred to change a crop and livestock farm with low conservation to an erosion control system of farming would not be covered until the fourth year of operation. Hence, the economic advantage of an erosion control system differs between owner-operators and tenants. It will be of little or no benefit

---

[15] Thomas Hansbrough, *A Sociological Analysis of Man-Caused Forest Fires in Louisiana* (Dissertation, Louisiana State University, Baton Rouge, 1961).

[16] E. O. Heady and C. W. Allen, *Returns from the Capital Required for Soil Conservation Farming Systems* (Iowa Agr. Exp. Sta. Research Bulletin No. 381 [Ames: A. E. S., Iowa State College, May, 1951]), 349.

to tenants who have no assured tenure beyond three years, but it has a good potential value for the permanent owner. Similarly, contouring and terracing provide more immediate results than crop rotations because these practices readily contribute to conservation of moisture and improved soil fertility.[17]

In the previous paragraph it was noted that a particular soil erosion control system would have to be in effect four years before any net returns would be realized. Barlowe suggests an eight-year planning period.[18] In another study, a budgeting analysis for a beef-breeding enterprise, R. H. Blosser indicates that, with investments made at 1951–1955 prices, the period of time required to finance soil conservation practices on certain Ohio farms would vary according to beef production per acre and price per hundredweight. In any event, if 195 pounds of beef were produced per acre of cropland and improved permanent pasture and then sold at $23.00 per hundredweight, about ten years would be required to finance the soil improvements which were imposed. If production were limited to 150 pounds of beef per acre and price was $25.50 per hundredweight, ten years would again be required to cover the cost of conservation. A higher price would necessarily shorten the time required, and a lower price would lengthen it. But, if price per hundredweight were as much as $2.50 less than the prices quoted above, it would be impossible to pay the additional costs associated with soil conservation practices assumed in the study.[19]

In view of the prolonged ripening period, from the time of initiating a conservation program to the time of realizing benefits therefrom, it appears necessary, for the benefit of society, to: (1) have leasing arrangements that compensate tenants for their investments in conservation, (2) provide credit and capital where assistance is justified, and (3) compensate individuals for loss of income during the ripening period.

## The Present-Day Approach to Conservation of Agricultural Lands

The history of the public domain is replete with examples of conflicting interests regarding the ownership, use, and control of natural

[17] *Ibid.*, 355.
[18] Barlowe, *Land Resource Economics*, 305.
[19] R. H. Blosser, "Soil Conservation on a Beef Farm," *Journal of Farm Economics*, Vol. 40 (August, 1958), 693–95.

resources. The conflict throughout appeared to be the individual and corporate desires for realizing quick, handsome profits, as opposed to the public interest which has traditionally leaned toward conservation and the welfare of society.

Public policy with regard to conservation vacillates in keeping with the trends of the times and in conformance with strong political forces that frequently sway public opinion in a direction that will provide special advantages to vested interests. At times conservation activities are carried out, not only to conserve natural resources, but also to fulfill other needs. For example, during the depression of the 1930's the Civilian Conservation Corps provided employment for many young men who otherwise would have been aimlessly wandering the streets. Similarly the Soil Bank Program and the Agricultural Conservation Program have aided in the agricultural price support program by taking land out of crop production and encouraging land-use practices which conserve soil and wild game.

Conservation policies have frequently been challenged because the policy that may benefit society is not always of benefit to the individual but, in general, society's interest is held to be paramount. A strong leaning toward government control was expressed in the policy advocated by Ely and Wehrwein as follows: "Insofar as land and resources are affected by the public interest, no landowner holds title to land to the exclusion of the rights of the public, including future as well as present generations. Our political philosophy must give meaning to the vague idea of public versus private rights to land. The right to control land use exists and lies in the sovereign power of the state and may be exercised through police power, eminent domain, and taxation." [20]

Another land economist, Raleigh Barlowe, maintains that "society's best interest is frequently to the best interest of the individual. Social controls are justified when they are used to prevent individual property-use practices that contribute to neighborhood blight, or that cause damage, erosion, fire, siltation, or soil drifting problems on other properties. Sometimes individuals must be compelled to help themselves." [21]

In the early stages of the conservation movement the primary goal was to conserve the forests. Today the objective is to promote the

[20] Ely and Wehrwein, *Land Economics*, 475.
[21] Barlowe, *Land Resource Economics*, 311–12.

highest level of multiple uses, taking into account water, forests, grass cover, wildlife, minerals, and recreational resources.

Conservation measures frequently accomplish much less than intended because fundamental problems relating to economics, social philosophy, tenure of property, and certain legal aspects are frequently overlooked. For example, when antitrust laws were put into effect, unbridled competitive forces were encouraged to exploit natural resources. At least this was the view expressed by large corporations. They maintained that, with proper control of the industry, they could follow self-imposed conservation measures, but if competitive forces were protected and encouraged they would be forced to retaliate by exploiting resources to the utmost in order to compete cost-wise. It is not intended in this discussion to weigh the merits of these two philosophies but merely to point out that, as a policy for conservation, some thought has been given to allowing industry to control competition by granting powers to fix prices yet maintaining legal controls to safeguard employees and consumers. There is no assurance, however, that giant corporations will be magnanimously conservation-minded. Their actions will invariably be profit motivated rather than conservation motivated.

Since economic factors tend to encourage exploitation rather than conservation and since society's best interest is frequently opposed to the best interest of the individual, it appears that the public has an obligation to help individuals meet the cost of conservation. If individuals destroy or seriously abuse a capital asset, a future public liability must be created.

According to Ely and Wehrwein, " If all individuals were willing to reduce the rate of consumption for the avowed purpose of benefitting posterity it would not be necessary to speak of a conservation policy." [22] Education, they say, is not the answer. Instead, a social philosophy, a desire to conserve, must be incorporated into the institutions, customs, and thinking of the people.

If education is not the answer to conservation, then more forceful measures must be employed. Zoning is one device for controlling the use of resources that generally has the support of most local citizens. Zoning permits the establishment of desirable resource-use practices and can be used to force the termination of undesirable uses.

Technological advances will also encourage individuals to adopt

[22] Ely and Wehrwein, *Land Economics*, 473.

conservation measures. The cost of carrying out practices such as terracing, ditching, building ponds, and planting trees can be considerably reduced through the use of newly developed equipment. Furthermore, new techniques in hay making and the development of improved pastures through fertilization are big steps in the direction of soil conservation.

In addition to lowering costs of conservation practices, technology can promote economic development by facilitating discovery of new resources and by making extraction or utilization easier and more complete. Even in the biological sciences technology has led to the development of improved breeds and species.

In a study of farmers' attitudes toward soil conservation it was found that the physical characteristics of the land and the apparent need for conservation did not mean that a greater effort was made to conserve the soil. In fact, the reverse seemed to be true. Those who followed conservation practices most readily were those with better farmland, more cropland, less forestland, and in general, the more prosperous farmers.[23]

Barlowe discusses a number of obstacles facing private efforts at conservation. These can be classified into three categories. First, there are physical obstacles such as location and the destructive forces of nature. Second, there are potent economic forces geared to lack of knowledge and foresight, proper evaluation of costs and benefits, and the lack of capital and risk of economic instability. Third, there are socio-cultural obstacles in the form of habits, customs, philosophy of the individual, the pattern of ownership, land policies, and the taxing structure.[24]

To overcome these obstacles he recommends the following list of remedies: education, subsidies, easier credit, more technical assistance, a favorable tax structure, public ownership, and more use of police power and right of eminent domain.

Although democracies generally frown on public ownership, there are a number of conservation advantages to be realized from this type of ownership. Ely and Wehrwein suggest the following arguments in favor of public ownership: [25]

[23] Julian Prundeanu and P. J. Zwerman, " An Evaluation of Some Economic Factors and Farmers Attitudes That May Influence Acceptance of Soil Conservation Practices," *Journal of Farm Economics*, Vol. 40 (November, 1958), 914.

[24] Barlowe, *Land Resource Economics*, 312–15.

[25] Ely and Wehrwein, *Land Economics*, 480.

(1) Time preference not limited to a decade but may extend over a century.

(2) Government ownership means lower carrying costs, no taxes, and money can be borrowed at low rates.

(3) By spreading costs over the total population, per capita costs can be insignificant.

(4) Income from public holdings will flow into the public treasury.

(5) Timber from national forests, royalties from minerals, and grazing fees from pastured lands may be shared with local units of government and may cover the costs of conservation.

Public ownership, however, provides no guarantee that resources will be conserved. Some public lands have been subject to serious wind and water erosion for years. Since wild game and waters in federal forests come under jurisdiction of the states, local interests frequently violate conservation practices by free grazing, indiscriminate hunting, and careless use of fire.

### Factors Relating to the Supply and Depletion of Natural Resources

Since resources differ as to supplies, durability, and replacement potential, a policy of conservation must be tailored accordingly. An exhaustible resource requires one kind of care and a recurring resource requires another. Thus, for purposes of conservation, resources have been classified into four types: fund resources, flow resources, biological resources, and a combination of the three.

Fund resources are those of limited supply which, when exhausted, are not replaceable—for example, minerals. Flow resources are those which recur naturally like rain, wind, and sun. Biological resources are those that may be either exhausted through exploitation, maintained at present levels, or increased through careful planning and management. Some resources may be difficult to classify because of their complex nature. Soil, for example, may be classed as a fund, flow, or biological resource because it has characteristics of all three.

Scarce supplies of a given resource can sometimes be overcome. Lumber for example has been replenished with second growth or replaced with substitute products. Just as substitutes were developed for wood products, they may also be developed for other resources. It is quite risky, however, to carelessly exploit existing resources with the hope that new discoveries and inventions will come to the rescue. The loss of resources not only accrues to the individual, but the loss of soil or forests can lead to a loss of community income, delinquent taxes, loss of population, and bankruptcy of local governments.

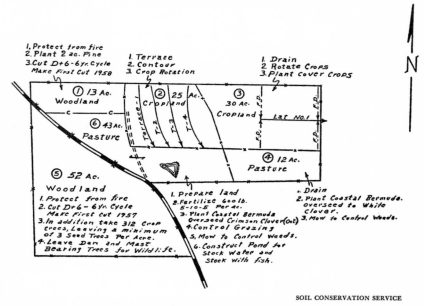

FIG. 5. The Soil Conservation Service provides technical assistance to land-owners in developing soil conservation plans.

## Land and Soil

Extensive measures have been taken to preserve our soil resources. The Soil Conservation Service has unquestionably provided a good and valuable service to farmers and to society in general. Yet efforts have been directed primarily to preventing soil erosion, without much thought given to the broader aspect of conserving the land for its best use. This has not been a serious problem in our young country where we can still boast of wide open spaces, but it has been a serious problem in countries where the supply of land must be rationed in accord with population needs. In England, for example, agricultural land is reserved for agricultural use. Land unfit, or less desirable for agriculture, may be used for highway, residential, or other nonagricultural development.

Some countries impose taxes to influence land use. In New Zealand and Tasmania, for example, tax rates are graduated according to size of land holding: the larger the holding, the higher the tax. In the United States, however, taxes are imposed primarily for gathering revenues, and land uses are directed primarily through other economic forces.

## Water

Even as the supply of land is fixed and the competition for its use growing steadily more severe, the competition for water is also becoming more acute. According to the 1955 Yearbook of Agriculture, the average daily use of water from United States public waterworks in 1900 was less than 95 gallons per person; the average use increased to 138 in 1950 and to 143 gallons per person in 1955. The total use, personal, agricultural, and industrial, amounts to about 1,200 gallons per person per day.[26]

It is expected that by 1975 the total demand for water will double and the per capita consumption will be about 175 gallons per day.

The average annual precipitation in the United States is about thirty inches. Of this amount, about twenty-two inches may return to the atmosphere through evaporation and transpiration. The rest flows into streams and underground supplies. The Geological Survey has estimated that present fresh water demand is about 4 per cent of total precipitation or 13 per cent of the surface and ground water supplies. About 3 per cent of the demand is supplied by surface waters and 17 per cent from ground waters.

## Minerals

Mineral resources are limited and exhaustible, thus conservation of minerals becomes a rationing process. Much of the concern expressed over the exploitation of limited supplies is alleviated by the possibility that new supplies will be discovered and that new techniques will reclaim wasted supplies. In the coal industry, for example, waste that occurred in the early mining of coal can now be reclaimed if needed. The demand for coal, however, has been largely replaced by the demand for substitutes such as gas, fuel oil, and electricity. Hence, the exploitation was not as bad as the conservationists predicted. The

[26] *Water, The 1955 Yearbook of Agriculture* (Washington: Government Printing Office, 1955), 651.

thought has also been expressed that smelted minerals, such as iron, lead, copper, and aluminum, are probably as durable (except for rusting of iron) above the earth as beneath it, and it is therefore desirable to continue mining and processing at a rapid rate. Since minerals are nonconsumptive, they will be available for both current and future use. Obviously there will be a continued need for scrap collectors and dealers, also a need for land treatment measures to heal the open wounds and scars left by the various mining operations.

### Forests

Timber is both a fund and flow resource. Supplies can soon be exhausted if greedily exploited, but they can also be increased through reforestation and natural growth over time.

Although the long-time trend of commercial forest land area in the United States has been downward, no appreciable change has occurred since about 1920. The latest (1953) estimate of 489 million acres compared to the 461 million acres estimated by the Forest Service in 1945 indicates a 28 million-acre increase in commercial forest land. The increase is attributed to (1) changes in land use, (2) changes in land classification, and (3) more accurate estimates. The largest addition to forest land occurred in the South, where ten million acres of farm land reverted to forest use.

## Implications

It should be evident that the economic and social aspects of conservation present a complex problem. It involves all the relationships in production and consumption for the present as well as for the future. In the use of our resources, particularly the fund and flow resources, there is a continuous process of investment and disinvestment. When economic conditions are favorable, there is a tendency to emphasize investment. When emergencies arise, there is a period of disinvestment or exploitation.

The chief deterrent to conservation is the cost involved, not only the immediate cash cost associated with the application of conservation measures as recommended by, for instance the Soil Conservation Service, but also the cost of holding resources for future use. The holding cost, comprised of deferred income and taxes on fund resources, provides a strong incentive to exploit resources to the utmost. In recognition of this cost of conservation, subsidies and tax concessions are frequently provided to ease the burden of individual landowners for the benefit of society and future generations.

Another cost of conservation frequently overlooked is the cost to the consumer. As the use of present supplies is restricted, current prices are necessarily increased, and the question arises, " Is the consumer willing to pay more today in order that future generations may also have trees, game, oil, and natural gas? " Impromptu answers will probably reveal that great sacrifices are not really necessary. Technological advances will help to reduce cost through increased efficiency and reduction of waste. Furthermore, technology will provide substitutes for scarce resources. Coal, oil, and gas are already being replaced by atomic power; lumber and wood products also have many substitutes. It is only the biological resources that seemingly must be husbanded with great care to assure bountiful future supplies.

Occasionally public policies are inconsistent. Antitrust legislation, for example, was designed to break up monopoly control of certain resources, yet it is readily admitted that conservation is impossible under a system of cut-throat competition. Very few individuals can accept present losses in hopes of future gains; hence, exploitation by one firm must necessarily encourage exploitation by a competing firm.

Education has been proposed as the first essential in developing a conservation consciousness among individuals. But how does education overcome the time barrier? As was indicated previously, there must be some compensation for deferring income today with hopes of increased future incomes. The uncertainty of the future is a great obstacle. The lack of investment in conservation practices hinges largely upon this uncertainty. There is the uncertainty of future need of the resource, the uncertainty of income, the uncertainty of future public policy toward the investor, and in the case of forest resources, the risk of loss from fire, disease, insects, and storm.

As mentioned previously, taxation policies can be designed to encourage conservation as well as discourage it. A high property tax encourages exploitation, since resources will be extracted as quickly as possible to avoid prolonged costs. Such a policy led to quick depletion of forests and mines. On the other hand, severance taxes and yield taxes have provided some relief to resource owners. Furthermore, certain soil and water conservation expenditures and depletion allowances are considered legitimate deductions in federal income tax returns.

Although there has been a constant clamor about the waste of land resources, agricultural productivity has improved in defiance to all lamentations. From 1940 to 1957 crop production per acre increased by 20 per cent, and total farm production in the United States increased by one-third; this was accomplished by only two-thirds as many man-hours and with the output per man hour almost double the output before World War II.

# CHAPTER TWELVE

# The Land Market and Transfer Process

TENURE HAS BEEN defined as encompassing man's relations to the land. In the light of this definition, the nature of land and the methods by which it may be acquired and disposed of become important. These matters are the concern of the present chapter.

## Definition of Land

In physical terms, land is the surface of the earth, embracing all natural resources down to the center of the earth and extending upward to include a column of air stretching from the earth to infinity. Permanent improvements in the nature of buildings, fences, and drains attached to the land are also considered part of the land. Vegetation such as grass, trees, and shrubs are part of the land only as long as they are rooted to the land.

Frequently the terms real estate, real property, and realty are used synonymously with land. Real, in this sense, refers to the lasting or permanent nature of the land as distinguished from a fictitious or imaginary existence. This characteristic of land makes it readily adaptable to ownership and control.

## Ownership and Control of Land

In addition to controls exercised by the individual landowner, there are a wide variety of controls imposed on land by given societies. These can be grouped into four categories: First, there are informal controls attributed to custom, tradition, religion, and education. Second, there are formal controls exemplified by zoning laws which place restrictions on the use of land; and third, there is the right of eminent domain by which the government, or duly authorized local government units, can expropriate or condemn private property to accomplish some public purpose (See Chapter 1). A fourth control measure, somewhat indirect to be sure, is the property tax. Generally the tax is used as a source of revenue, but it can also be used to direct acquisition and land use.[1] Private ownership, however, is most common and therefore warrants rather detailed treatment.

The most complete ownership is known as *fee simple* ownership, which legally implies an unrestricted right to sell or dispose of property without regard to time limits or use restrictions. Purchasers of farmland desiring unqualified control should make certain that the conveyance (deed) specifies a fee simple title, free from encumbrances and legal claims of others.[2]

Two or more persons may own the same tract of land as *tenants-in-common*. This means that each has an undivided and undesignated interest in the whole. One of the owners may sell or convey his undivided interest, in which case the newly designated owner becomes a tenant-in-common with the other. To sell or convey the entire tract requires the mutual agreement or consent of all of the tenants-in-common. There is no right of survivorship in this type of ownership. That is to say, the surviving tenant does not automatically acquire possession when another tenant-in-common passes away. Instead, the interest of the deceased tenant descends to his children or other relatives in keeping with inheritance laws.

Tenancies-in-common may be created in a deed or will, but they more generally result from the lack of these. For example, when a farmer dies without leaving a will, his farm, by virtue of inheritance laws, passes on to his wife and children, who are tenants-in-common. Tenants-in-common do not have to own equal shares. The dower interest of the surviving spouse may be one-third and the remaining two-thirds divided equally among five or six children. If, through the course of time one of the children marries and has children of his own, his surviving spouse and children will in turn inherit equivalent shares of an already fractionated ownership.

From the foregoing, it is readily evident that tenancies-in-common have several objectionable features:

[1] A comprehensive discussion of social control of landed property may be found in Roland R. Renne, *Land Economics* (Rev. ed.; New York: Harper & Bros., 1958), Chap. 16.

[2] A more detailed discussion of legal terms relating to land ownership may be found in H. W. Hannah, *Law on the Farm* (New York: Macmillan Co., 1952).

(1) They frequently result in disagreements over use and disposition of the land.

(2) They result in poor farm management due to inability of all owners to co-operate.

(3) If one tenant attempts to buy out the other interests, the burden usually becomes more than the farm will carry economically.

(4) Dividing up the land area to satisfy each tenant usually results in small uneconomic farm units.

Another type of ownership, somewhat similar to tenants-in-common is *joint tenancy*. The one important difference here is that this form of ownership carries with it the right of survivorship. This means that when a joint tenant dies his interest in the land reverts to the surviving tenants and not to his heirs. Money lenders are very cautious about accepting mortgages from joint tenants unless all of the joint tenants sign the contract, because upon the death of a joint tenant legal title to the land shifts to the surviving tenants.

The usual example of a joint tenancy is that of husband and wife, often referred to as tenancy by the entireties. The primary objective is to leave the property to the wife in the event the husband should die. It is well to recognize, however, that some states have inheritance laws with strict statutory requirements regarding joint tenancy and, if ignored, the resulting contract may be only a tenancy-in-common instead of a joint tenancy.

It is possible to place time and use restrictions on the land through deed or will. A farmer who wishes to assure that his wife will have the farm during her lifetime will generally provide her with a *life estate* and stipulate that after her death the property shall go to his children. In this case, the wife is the *life tenant* and the children are *remaindermen*. In like manner, a farmer who wishes the son to have the farm may deed the farm to him, reserving a life estate for himself.

A life tenant has the right to possession, use, and income from the farm during his or her lifetime but does not have the right to destroy buildings, trees, or permanent improvements, nor to develop and extract minerals in such a way as to deprive the remaindermen of real property.

The life tenant cannot sell the property unless the remaindermen join in the conveyance. When a sale involves a life estate, all related mortgages, deeds, or leases should contain signatures of all life tenants and remaindermen.

## The Land Market and Variability of Land Values

Although land is fixed as to location and not readily distributed like other commodities, its ownership is marketable and transferable. The land market, therefore, embraces those activities dealing with the transfer of land ownership. Before the transfer of ownership is discussed, however, it is important to recognize the variability found in land values and to acknowledge the many factors which contribute to this variability.

There are really two types of variability in land values. First, there is variability because of the different land uses within a given area; and second, there is variability within a given land use because of the interaction of physical, economic, and socio-cultural factors, as well as the influence of government policies and programs.

In the former case, it is recognized that land, when classified as to its primary use, can be normally arranged in ascending order of values, as follows:

1. Waste or idle
2. Forest
3. Farm

4. Rural-residential
5. Urban-residential
6. Urban-commercial

### Values by Types of Use

Waste or idle land includes the arid deserts, frozen arctic, flooded or marshy areas, and rugged mountains. The ownership of these lands rests primarily with the government. A fixed dollar value for wasteland does not exist, but values on the more isolated areas would certainly run at less than ten dollars per acre.

Appraisals on government-owned land are made by the Bureau of Land Management as requests for particular tracts are received from interested parties. Subsequently, the land is offered for sale on a highest bid basis. All mineral rights on vacant public lands are reserved by the federal government.

The value of forest land is steadily mounting in response to the increased demand for woodpulp, paper, and timber products, as well as for its aesthetic and recreational value.

Information on the market value of forest land is quite limited.

Sales of land devoted exclusively to forests are relatively rare. Forested areas, however, are frequently included in transfers of farm land and are considered part of a farm package; hence average values of farm land generally include value of forest land. In North Louisiana considerable forest acreage has been leased by paper and pulpwood industries. The leasing fever was raging in this area from 1947 to 1956. Practically all leases were drawn up for ninety-nine years, and the average price was twenty five-dollars per acre. A recent study of land

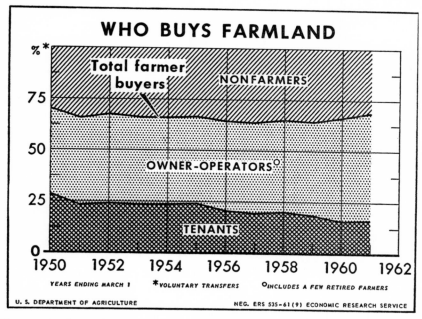

Fig. 6. An increasing proportion of the farm land sold in the United States is being purchased by farm owner-operators.

transfers (1954–1956), confined to tracts having more than 50 per cent of the land area in forest, indicated an average sale price of fifty-four dollars per acre. Farm land in this same area, in 1958, was selling for seventy-five to a hundred dollars per acre.

Farm land values are reported more frequently and openly than values of other types of land. The values as reported, however, generally apply to farm real estate, which includes the value of farm buildings and other fixed improvements as well as the land.

Reported values must be recognized as averages which may be used for regional comparisons. They conceal the wide variation in prices that usually exist within a state. The average does not necessarily represent the acreage value of a particular farm, nor does it differentiate between bare land and land containing costly improvements.

The averages for the various regions of the United States follow a rather distinct pattern. In the Rocky Mountain area farm-land values average near fifty dollars per acre. In California and the corn producing states of Iowa, Illinois, Indiana, and Ohio the values average $200 to $300 per acre. In the smaller states surrounding the city of New York (Connecticut, Rhode Island, and New Jersey) values average near $400 and $550 per acre. The remaining areas, particularly the southeast, south central and northwest regions, reflect average values of from $50.00 to $200 per acre. California differs from the rest of the western states in that population pressures and intensive farming have boosted farm-land values to an average of better than $300 per acre.

The variability of farm-land values provides a good illustration of the second type of variability, mentioned earlier, in which physical factors, economic factors, socio-cultural factors, and government policies and programs influence the price of farm land. The physical factors relate to geographic location, character of the soil, topography, and climate. The economic factors are those which enter into the cost of production and distribution of farm products. The socio-cultural factors are the less tangible factors relating to custom, tradition, education, and religion.

The influence of the socio-cultural factors on the land market is well illustrated among the Amish people. This religious sect represents a rural culture with social and religious attitudes tied very closely to farming and landownership. To these people the land is almost sacred. The thought of leaving the land is inconceivable. To them the occupation of farming has become almost an informal prerequisite for church membership. Tilling the soil and replenishing the earth are sanctioned by the Bible and represent the good life.[3]

Although the number of farms in the United States have been decreasing and the size of farms have been increasing, the Amish farming areas have experienced an opposite trend, namely more farms and smaller size units. This naturally results from the traditional

[3] Elmer Lewis Smith, *The Amish People* (New York: Exposition Press, Inc., 1958), 128.

adherence to farming as a way of life. New generations must be accommodated; hence the limited land areas are continually being divided into smaller parcels to provide farm units for the new young farmers emerging from the unusually large Amish families. A study in Lancester County, Pennsylvania, covering a fifteen-year period (1939–1954) indicated that Amish sons followed the occupation of their fathers 92.8 per cent of the time and, of this number, 92 per cent, at the time of marriage, were farmers.[4]

The rapid increase in population among the Amish sect creates a demand pressure for farm land that considerably bolsters land prices in the immediate area. Recent sales in the heart of the Amish section of Lancaster County, Pennsylvania, discloses that a thirty-four-acre farm sold for $44,622, or an average of $1,300 per acre. Another fifty-eight-acre farm averaged $1,338 per acre. In a non-Amish section nearby, during the same period, a 116-acre farm sold for $27,000 and a 122-acre farm for $12,800.[5]

Government policies and programs also affect values of farm land. Lands having acreage allotments, whether for cotton or tobacco, generally claim a higher price than land in the same area without a crop allotment. Similarly, price supports and soil conservation programs tend to boost or bolster existing land values.

Factors accounting for variability in values of urban-residential land hinge largely upon presence of utilities and the type of improvements or man-made facilities found thereon. In addition, however, the location relative to schools, shopping centers, and business districts are quite important. The nature of the terrain, landscape, drainage, and vegetation influence aesthetic values. Type of streets, density of traffic, and proximity to commercial nuisances are additional factors to be considered.

Since commercial areas thrive on communication and transportation facilities, the values of commercial properties are closely associated with the type and density of pedestrian traffic, parking areas, public transportation facilities, and extent of frontage and corner locations.

The value of urban land, whether it be residential or commercial, shows a variability even more pronounced than for farm land. There is one difference, however, in that urban land values are frequently measured in terms of dollars per front foot. A front foot is a foot along the sidewalk with a strip extending behind it to about 100 or 150

[4] *Ibid.,* 150.                    [5] *Ibid.,* 157.

feet. A foot of frontage on the right street can have a value far in excess of a whole farm. Along State Street in Chicago frontage sells for $30,000 a foot. Market Street in San Francisco has values up to $10,000 a foot. Fayetteville Street in Raleigh, North Carolina has frontage values of about $4,000 per foot.[6] A residential lot in Starkville, Mississippi, sells at a price of about ten dollars per front foot. An average suburban lot in Baton Rouge will normally sell for about $5,000, or $50.00 a front foot. In the more exclusive areas residential sites will sell for $250 to $500 per front foot. Apartment sites average even higher. Frontage along Lake Shore Drive in Chicago averages above $1,000 per front foot.[7]

Some subsidiary shopping districts sell for $1,000 a foot, and the best industrial sites in many of the larger cities will command well over $100,000 per acre.

Land along new superhighways, particularly near interchanges, was bringing several thousand dollars an acre in 1957. Potential sites for motels or shopping centers frequently are quoted at $10,000 to $50,000 an acre.

As urban areas become congested and horizontal expansion is unable to keep up with the rate of growth, vertical eruptions occur and skyscrapers appear on the scene. This development frequently places a premium on airspace. In New York City an option on airspace over the Pennsylvania Railroad tracks was priced at more than three million dollars an acre in 1955. A Times Square billboard brings $75,000 per year.[8]

In this country it is estimated that total urban land values exceed farm values several times over. In fact, it is quite possible that urban land values exceed farm values on a per capita basis. In any case farm property taxes are less per capita than nonfarm property taxes— roughly $54.00 compared to $72.00 in 1956.[9]

Industrial lands will vary in value mainly because of differences in extent of development. Factors similar to those of concern in commercial areas also apply to industrial areas.

The value of mineral lands rests upon the known or anticipated presence of minerals or related resources. Frequently, subsurface rights are separated from surface rights. As a result, surface values may be somewhat depressed but still subject to the same value-determining

---

[6] *Land, The 1958 Yearbook of Agriculture* (Washington: USDA, 1958), 503.
[7] *Ibid.*, 506.                    [8] *Ibid.*                    [9] *Ibid.*, 507.

factors as farm land. The value of subsurface rights are readily reflected by the rentals and royalties associated with mineral activities in a given area. (See Chapter 10.)

## Why Land Values Are Mounting

In keeping with general economic theory the interaction of supply and demand helps to determine the price or sale value of land. On the demand side the following factors are evident:

(1) Increasing population—need for more living room.

(2) Higher incomes and greater purchasing power.

(3) Improved communication facilities help conquer space and facilitate commuting over greater distances.

(4) New technological advances overcome problems of labor in isolated areas.

(5) Expanding utilities and services in the form of electricity, domestic water supplies, and sewage disposal.

(6) Anticipating future industrial needs—for example, wood-using industries obtaining and developing forest lands.

(7) Increased leisure time encourages search for recreational areas or quiet and privacy.

(8) Government policies and programs, particularly those which provide financial aid to landowners through share cost and cheap credit.

(9) Investment in land as a hedge against inflation and speculation by those who expect land prices to continue climbing.

(10) A means of tax avoidance by assuming responsibilities associated with a farm business.

(11) Existing farms demanding additional land to achieve economies of scale.

Although demand, as expressed by need and bolstered by purchasing power, is increasing, the supply of desirable land is decreasing. Some reclamation of land is recognized, but the net gain from drainage and irrigation is relatively small. What is of increasing concern, however, is the vanishing frontier. In the past the overflow of an expanding population was accommodated by moving westward. Homesteading was a popular way to gain possession of farm land. This possibility no longer exists, the frontier has now shifted to Alaska, but the climate, terrain, isolation, and more complex procedures for claiming possession of land do not provide the attraction to settlers that formerly prevailed in the westward movement.

Public ownership of land is frequently mentioned as one cause of the decreasing supply of land on the market. This may be somewhat

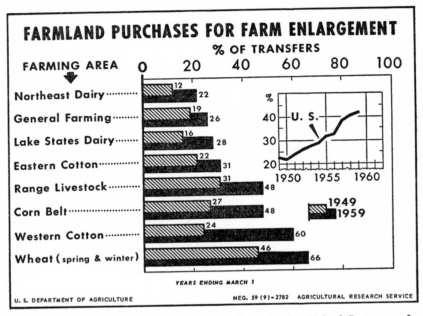

FIG. 7. Over 40 per cent of farm land purchases in the United States are for farm enlargement. This trend is more pronounced in the wheat, cotton, corn and livestock areas of the United States.

exaggerated. Federal ownership has been gradually decreasing. Of the 1,442 million acres of the original public domain, 1,031 million acres have been transferred to state and private ownership and only 411 million acres remained for public purposes, as of June 30, 1956.[10] Grazing districts and national forests account for about three-fourths of this acreage. The remainder is used for Indian reservations, military reservations, national parks and monuments, and miscellaneous needs. It is true, however, that states and local units of government are

[10] *Ibid.*, 48.

continuing to gain possession of additional lands to meet public needs, but the extent of public ownership, federal and local, does not exceed 5 per cent of the total land area.

## How Land Values Are Determined

Going land values may be determined in several ways. First, one may study transfer records to discover sale prices of properties which have been bought or sold in a given period of time. In some areas the actual sale price is recorded on the deed, but in many others it is not. Nevertheless, the sale price can be estimated from the value of federal tax stamps affixed to each deed. (Every fifty-five cents worth of stamps represents five hundred dollars of sale value, or fraction thereof).

Periodic reports from the United States Department of Agriculture serve as additional sources of information on land values. These are obtained by the Economic Research Service of USDA from two groups: (1) farmers who are crop reporters for USDA and (2) a sample of farm real estate dealers, lawyers, bankers, and county officials who are in contact with the local farm real estate market.[11] Both groups represent a total of 6,000 to 7,000 reporters who submit survey information. Questionnaires are mailed to the latter group two times a year and to the crop reporters three times a year. They are asked to report values for properties used primarily for farming. The prices or dollar values reported may be biased upward because of a tendency to report asking prices instead of sale prices. Then, too, crop reporters are found on the better farms and in better farming areas.

In the eastern states crop reporters provide separate estimates of value for good, average, and poor farm land. Since 1952 reports from Florida give separate estimates for citrus groves, pasture lands, and all other farm land. Since 1926 crop reporters in western states have provided separate estimates for irrigated, dry farming, and grazing land.

An index of farm values is computed by first obtaining simple averages of reported values for crop reporting districts, then these averages are weighted by acres of land in farms to obtain a weighted

[11] To understand better the statistics reported for real estate values see *Major Statistical Series of the USDA*, Vol. 6 (Agricultural Handbook No. 118 [Washington: USDA, October, 1957]).

average value for each state. An average of weighted values for the years 1947–1949 has provided the value which represents the latest base or index.

It is well to recognize some of the limitations attributed to the use of the index of farm real estate values when measuring changes in the land market:

(1) There is a wide variation of land values within small areas.

(2) The valuation process is of a subjective nature and easily biased.

(3) Special elements of supply and demand for a local area are concealed by state average figures.

(4) State averages have relatively little value for determining changes in value for an individual farm.

(5) The number of estimates is too small to overcome sampling variability.

(6) Averages to be meaningful should be limited to each homogeneous area within a state.

To determine the value of a property which has remained under one ownership for an extended period of time becomes a problem for an appraiser. If neighboring properties with similar attributes have been sold recently, the problem is one of comparing the subject property with those sold and making the necessary adjustments to arrive at an estimated value. If real estate sales have not occurred in the area for an extended period of time, the problem is more complex and would likely require a very detailed appraisal. A systematic appraisal will usually consider size of the unit, location, community, markets, climate, topography, drainage, soils, minerals, surface cover, right of ways, water supplies improvements, and layouts. The final estimate will usually be a composite value based on an average value per acre, replacement value of improvements, and a value on intangibles such as frontage, beauty, location relative to desirable or undesirable features, and carrying capacity in terms of its most likely use. In any event, it can at best provide an asking price which becomes the sales value only if a buyer takes it at the quoted price.

Another method of arriving at land value is to analyze its productive capacity. This is particularly true of land in specialized farming areas. A net return to land can be computed over a period of years to derive an average annual net profit which will represent both good and bad production years. By capitalizing the average net profit figure the productive value of land can be determined. For example: An average net return from an acre of corn during the past five years might amount to ten dollars per year. If an investor normally expects a 5 per cent return in his money then the ten dollars represents a 5 per cent return on a $200 investment ($10 ÷ .05 = $200), and the land which returns ten dollars profit per year is actually worth $200 per acre on the basis of its productive ability.

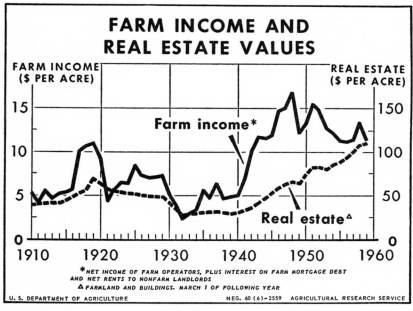

FIG. 8. Farm real estate values traditionally have fluctuated less than farm income on a per acre basis.

### Trends in Land Values

Land values in the continental United States have fluctuated in keeping with the economic conditions in the country. A peak in land values, equal to the 1947–1949 average, was reached in 1920 immediately after World War I. The low point during the past half century occurred in 1933. A very steep climb in land values has been observed during and since World War II. In 1948 and again in 1952 and 1953 there was a slight hesitation to an otherwise continuous climb which by November of 1958 had reached a value 58 per cent above the 1947–1949 average. Even more impressive is the 110 per cent increase in value since 1941. This represents better than a 4 per cent annual increase in average land values during the past twenty-seven years.

A wider fluctuation in land values was generally evident in the agricultural states and those states in the South and West which are experiencing new industrial development and attracting population from other areas. Fluctuations or changes in value were of less magnitude in the colonial states, particularly the New England states.

Although the price of land readily responds to general economic conditions, the swing to higher or lower levels is much more pronounced than for the average of all commodities as a group. The real price of land, which is the price index of land values as a percentage of the all-commodity price index, takes into account the general price fluctuation and indicates the price of land relative to the aggregate price of all other commodities. On this basis the real price of land during the past thirty-two years has been below the all-commodity average from 1933 to 1934 and again from 1947 to 1948. On the other hand, the real price of farm real estate in 1958 was 33 per cent above the all-commodity price index. An almost similar high occurred in 1931 when the real price was 29 per cent above the all-commodity index. Between 1931 and 1934, however, the real price of farm real estate had dropped thirty-nine percentage points or 13 per cent per year.

## Land Transfer Procedures

### Conveyances

Property ownership is usually exhibited in the form of a title, deed, or grant. These three terms are frequently used synonymously. A title implies a claim to ownership. A deed is a written document containing details of the contract in a transfer agreement. A grant is similar to a deed in that it is a written document conveying property ownership. It has been frequently used by the government in transferring ownership of public lands to private parties.

A few additional terms common to land transfers should be acknowledged. Two common types of deeds are the warranty deed and the quit-claim deed. The warranty deed carries a guarantee or protection for the buyer in that the seller remains responsible for a clear title to the property.

A quit-claim deed merely cancels any claim that an owner may have had to the property. It absolves the seller from any subsequent property liability.

An abstract of title is a copy of recorded conveyances and legal proceedings affecting title to a tract of land.

Title insurance is designed to insure the buyer against any future dispute arising from prior ownership claims.

A federal stamp tax is an internal revenue tax imposed upon land transfers since 1932. From 1932 to 1940 the tax was fifty cents per five hundred dollars or fraction thereof. Since 1940 the tax has been fifty-five cents per multiple of five hundred dollars. The tax covers only the cash part of the transaction, and the amount of any mortgage assumed by the buyer must be added when determining the total sale price. The seller pays the transfer tax, although both buyer and seller are legally liable for its payment.

## Types of Transfers

The transfer of land ownership may be broadly classified under three headings as (1) voluntary, (2) forced, and (3) administered. Voluntary transfers are those occurring in the normal course of buying and trading of property. Buyers and sellers get together to decide on an exchange value and proceed to complete the transaction.

Forced transfers are those in which the seller may be deprived of ownership against his will. Three common causes of this occurrence are (1) sale of property because of tax delinquency, (2) foreclosure of mortgage or bankruptcy, and (3) property taken by right of eminent domain. The first two procedures result when the owner fails to meet his financial obligations. The third, the right of eminent domain, comes into play when the property is needed for public use or to eliminate a public hazard. This power to take private property without consent of the owner is granted by the Constitution. The federal government exercises this privilege under provision of the Fifth Amendment which provides that " no person shall be deprived of life, liberty, or property without due process of law; nor shall private property be taken for public use without just compensation." States also abide by the " due process clause " of the Fourteenth Amendment, as interpreted by the courts. In turn, states may grant the power of eminent domain to local units of government, to semipublic and even to private groups, if the public welfare is served thereby. Railroads obtain rights of way, power companies flood land, and conservationists provide drainage or irrigation under this right.

Administered transfers are those resulting from inheritance or gifts. Here the seller is represented by an administrator, probably designated in a last will and testament or properly appointed by court order. The administrator presumably acts in the best interest of his client and negotiates the transfer of ownership in keeping with the circumstances of the case. It may only require the processing and recording of legal documents to designate the new ownership.

The recording of legal documents provides an element of protection to both buyer and seller. Official recording of land transactions was designed to prevent unscrupulous landowners from selling a given tract of land to several different parties. It is a well-established practice to have property transfers recorded at a central records depository, usually the county courthouse. Here the recorder transcribes or makes photostats of deeds and mortgage contracts. The recorded copy is then filed chronologically in one of the numerous volumes making up the book of deeds. The names of the buyer and seller are then listed in directories to facilitate future alphabetical reference. The deed may then be located by reference to either party engaged in the transaction. The ledgers containing the names of the sellers are those labeled grantors (vendors), and those with names of the buyers are labeled grantees (vendees). In like manner, there are books for recording mortgages and accompanying directories listing the mortgagors (borrowers) and the mortgagees (lenders.).

Transfer procedures relative to sale of public lands differ somewhat from ordinary land market transfers. Public lands are managed, and occasionally processed for sale, by the Bureau of Land Management with headquarters in Washington, D. C., and field organizations in three areas in the United States and one in Alaska.

The procedures for conducting a sale of public lands as outlined in a recent prospectus are summarized as follows: [12]

(1) Times, date, and place of sale is listed in the prospectus.

(2) Each tract offered for sale is identified as to location, acreage, brief description, and appraised values.

(3) Sealed bids are requested. Separate bids must be submitted

[12] *Prospectus For Public Domain Land Sales in Louisiana* (Louisiana Area Sale No. 3 [Russelville, Ark.: Bureau of Land Management, USDI, 1959]). Date of sale: February 24, 1959.

for each tract desired, and each bid must be accompanied by a certified or cashier's check, or money order, payable to the Bureau of Land Management for the full amount of the bid.

(4) The sealed bid must be for an amount not less than the total appraised price of the entire tract.

(5) Following the opening of all sealed bids, each tract will be offered at oral auction, the lowest acceptable oral bids must be greater than the highest sealed bid for the same tract.

(6) Preference rights are extended to fee simple owners of adjoining lands, who may purchase the offered tracts by matching the high bid or paying three times the appraised price, whichever is lower. Preference rights may be granted for thirty days following the date of sale.

(7) If no bids are received for a tract, there will be no sale and preference rights will not be honored.

The land market is unique in that it deals with a product of unlimited variability. What commodity, other than land, varies as much in shape, size, form, location, and value, yet has a universal appeal to all, regardless of age, sex, nationality, race, or creed?

## Descent and Inheritance

Who succeeds to property in the event of death of a landowner? If the owner has prepared a will the disposition of the property is predetermined. If the owner dies intestate (leaving no will), the laws of descent or distribution within the individual state will designate the persons having claim to the property as well as the fractional shares inherited by each.

If the deceased was married and a common property arrangement existed between him and his wife, she generally retains one-half interest in the property, and the descendants acquire the other half. Furthermore, some states provide that the surviving spouse enjoy the use and fruits of the share of property inherited by the children (similar to a life estate) until she should die or remarry.

If there are no descendants, but there is a surviving father and/or a mother of the deceased, one-half of the deceased's share is inherited by his parents and the other half by his wife. She thus would have three-fourths interest in the property under these circumstances. If there were neither father, mother, nor descendants, the surviving spouse inherits the deceased's share, hence acquires total ownership.

Generally the children are entitled to an equal division of inherited property, and descendants of a deceased child take the deceased child's share. In the event there are no surviving relatives, the land " escheats " or becomes property of the state.

The state has the right to impose inheritance and gift taxes as well as to alter the normal line of descent, if it is deemed in the best interest of public welfare. Furthermore, possession by virtue of inheritance may entail a responsibility on the part of the heirs to pay debts imposed upon the previous owner, and on occasion, possession may be lost when all of the property is used to pay outstanding debts.

When a property owner dies intestate (leaving no will), state laws will prescribe the order of property distribution among survivors. Frequently this order of succession is in keeping with the traditonal pattern of inheritance established by early landowners. Nevertheless, a landowner need not conform to the traditional pattern. In fact, it might be more desirable from a farm business standpoint to make sure that the farm remains intact as a functional business unit. Too frequently it is divided among surviving children and heir of children already deceased. The resulting multiple ownership of land usually restricts farm operations because mutual agreement from all parties is frequently required. It is more likely that the individual demands will necessitate either dividing the farm into smaller tracts or selling the farm and dividing the returns.

# Part 4: The Impact of Change on Tenure

Rural society in the United States is in a period of rapid change. Part IV is an attempt to focus attention on the important implications which rural social change has had for land tenure in the recent past and the trends which might be expected in the future.

Chapter 13 is concerned with the impact of technology on tenure arrangements and other farm characteristics. In Chapter 14 the overall pattern of changing human relationships, insofar as tenure is concerned, is discussed as an ongoing rural social process. The major changes in terms of the spatial location or ecology of tenure forms are treated in Chapter 15.

# The Impact of Technology on Land Tenure

The primary concern of this chapter is agricultural technology and its impact on the relationships of individuals and groups to the land. Many forces set in motion by technology relate to land tenure. These forces effectively change tenure arrangements by bringing about alterations in various institutional arrangements.[1] In studying the topic at hand, one must remember that changes are seldom brought about by a single factor. Thus, technology may be related to given tenure changes but may not be the single cause of such change.

## Technology Defined

Technology is a force for change. Technology *is* change. In agriculture, the application of new technology changes productivity and efficiency. Out of this change, new ideas, modes of living, and interacting patterns are developed that influence man's relationship to the land.

Agricultural technology is more than new materials and equipment —machines, buildings, fertilizers, and insecticides—which require investments of capital. Technology is new varieties of plants and breeds of animals, new ways of doing things—cross-plowing, crop rotation, and contouring, for example—which require little or no additional capital.

Technology acts as a substitute for land when it increases the productivity per acre. It may also remove the factors that make land submarginal for certain agricultural uses.[2] Thus, agricultural tech-

---

[1] For example, Social Security coverage for farmers, rural development programs, acreage-allotment programs, farm credit programs, state and federal tax laws, urbanization, and highway development.

[2] Orlin J. Scoville, Lewis B. Nelson, and Elco L. Greenshields, "Land and

nology applies not only to mechanical, chemical, and biological developments in agriculture but also includes changes in the methods of producing, harvesting, processing, transporting, and marketing agricultural products, which result either in the production of new or improved goods or services, or production of the same goods or services with fewer inputs per unit of output.

## Development and Adoption of Technology

Technological developments in agriculture become available at uneven rates. In addition, farmers do not adopt new technology at equal rates. The uneven development and application of new technology is important to tenure and other changes in agriculture. The processes by which changes are accepted are briefly discussed below.

### Process by Which Innovations Are Accepted

New Jersey farmers rejected the first successful cast-iron plow invented in 1797 in the belief that iron poisoned the soil and encouraged the growth of weeds.[6] At least one farmer considered manuring of land to be " a base and corrupting mode of forcing nature." [4]

Adoption of new technology is not based entirely on economic efficiency. The acceptance of new technology is a complicated process that often extends over a long period of time and involves a series of thoughts and actions.[5] In Iowa, for example, the average time span from awareness to adoption of hybrid seed corn was seven years.[6]

One of the most important factors in the increase in productivity of farm resources in recent years has been the increased rate of adoption of new technology. Hybrid sorghum seed, for example, has been adopted by farmers at a more rapid rate than was hybrid corn seed.

Advances in Technology," *Land: The 1958 Yearbook of Agriculture* (Washington: USDA, 1958), 480.

[3] Holland Thompson, *The Age of Invention, a Chronicle of Mechanical Conquest* (New Haven: Yale University Press, 1921), 112.

[4] Amos Alcott quoted in Gilbert Seldes, *The Stammering Century* (New York: The John Day Co., 1928), 208.

[5] Robert L. Greene and Nelson L. LeRay, " Development and Application," *Yearbook of Agriculture 1960: Power to Produce* (Washington: USDA, 1960), 331–32.

[6] *How Farm People Accept New Ideas* (North Central Regional Publication No. 1, Iowa Agr. Exp. Sta. Special Report No. 15 [Ames: A. E. S., Iowa State College, 1955]), 3.

About thirteen years passed after introduction of hybrid corn seed before two-thirds of the corn acreage was planted to hybrid seed. In contrast, little hybrid sorghum seed was planted in 1955, but in 1959 it was used to plant about two-thirds of the sorghum acreage.[7]

When an idea has been introduced into a given community and the process of acceptance has begun, people can be found in all stages of the acceptance process. These stages have been broken down into the five steps:

(1) Awareness: At this stage the individual learns of the existence of the idea or practice but has little knowledge concerning it.

(2) Interest: As the individual develops interest in the idea, he seeks more information and considers its general merits.

(3) Evaluation: The individual weighs the idea's merits for his own situation. He obtains more information about the idea and decides whether or not to try it.

(4) Trial: At this stage the individual actually applies the idea or practice—usually on a small scale. He is interested in how to apply the practice; in amounts, time, and conditions for application.

(5) Adoption: This is the point of acceptance leading to continued use.[8]

Adoption rates are influenced by individual, group, and community factors. The first individuals to adopt new ideas are seldom named as persons to whom to go for farming advice.[9] They are often referred to as " experimenters." " Community adoption leaders," on the other hand, do not test untried ideas, but they are quick to adopt tried and proved ideas. Usually, they are the larger commercial farmers of the area, and they have direct contacts with agricultural agencies. They have greater than average participation in formal organizations. The majority of the people look to " local adoption leaders " for information and ideas. These leaders are important in the adoption of practices because they are the informal leaders whom the majority expects to take the initiative within their groups. The majority of people in a community are " later adopters." They have less education, participate less in community affairs, and are older than the early adopters.

[7] *Changes in Farm Production and Efficiency* (Statistical Bulletin No. 233 (Rev. ed.; Washington: USDA, July, 1960), 10.
    [8] *Ibid.*, 3–4.                              [9] *Ibid.*, 9.

### Factors Determining the Extent of Use of Technology

A recent study conducted in the Delta area of Mississippi indicates that operators of large cotton plantations do not use their mechanical cottonpickers to the fullest extent possible.[10] Here are some of the factors that contribute to the limited use of mechanical cottonpickers: (1) If no hand picking were available, many of the resident laborers needed for chopping would be idle; (2) the resident laborers want to pick some cotton by hand; (3) skilled mechanics and picker operators are not always available; (4) machine picking is sometimes prohibited by adverse weather; and (5) machine-picked cotton does not grade as high as does hand-picked cotton. The study concludes that in the future the extent to which machines will be substituted for labor in the Delta will depend primarily on (1) availability and cost of new and improved machines; (2) prices received by plantation operators for cotton and other crops; (3) wage rates for hand chopping and picking; (4) availability of workers skilled in operation and maintenance of mechanical equipment; (5) opportunities in nonfarm employment; and (6) government agricultural programs.[11]

The study by William Adkins and William Metzler of tenure and mechanization of the cotton harvest in the Texas High Plains is revealing. It indicates that the share-rental arrangements in the area are an obstacle to the use of mechanized harvesting methods.[12] Landlords object to machine harvesting because it may result in grade loss and reduced income, while tenants stand to benefit from a reduction in harvesting costs.

The value orientation of a group toward farming and man's relationship to land is an important determinant in the development and adoption of technology. If, for example, land ownership is viewed as a means to an end (economic, political, social), new technology that promotes progress toward this goal will often be adopted at a relatively rapid rate. However, if land ownership is considered an end in itself, any technology that places this end in jeopardy may not be

[10] Nelson L. LeRay and Grady Crowe, *Labor and Technology on Selected Cotton Plantations in the Delta Area of Mississippi* (Miss. Agr. Exp. Sta. Bul. No. 575 [Starkville:  A. E. S., Mississippi State University, 1959]), 18.

[11] LeRay and Crowe, *Labor and Technology on Selected Cotton Plantations in the Delta Area of Mississippi*, 4.

[12] William G. Adkins and William H. Metzler, *Tenure and Mechanization of the Cotton Harvest, Texas High Plains* (Tex. Agr. Exp. Sta. Bul. 813 [College Station:  A. E. S., Texas A. & M., 1955]), 2.

adopted or, if adopted, will be introduced at a relatively slow rate. The important determinant is the value orientation.

## Technological Revolution in Agriculture

The practices and procedures for producing, harvesting, processing, transporting, and marketing agricultural commodities have undergone and are still undergoing revolutionary change.

Technology has an important influence on the proportion of a population that works on the land and its relationship to the land. In 1787, the year in which Jefferson and others framed our Consti-

TABLE 1—PERSONS SUPPORTED BY PRODUCTION OF ONE FARM WORKER, UNITED STATES, 1820–1959

| Year | Persons supported per farm worker | Total farm employment | Total United States population, July 1 [2] |
|---|---|---|---|
| | Number | Millions | Millions |
| 1820 ............. | 4.12 | 2.4 | 9.6 |
| 1840 ............. | 3.95 | 4.4 | 17.1 |
| 1860 ............. | 4.53 | 7.3 | 31.5 |
| 1880 ............. | 5.57 | 10.1 | 50.3 |
| 1900 ............. | 6.95 | 12.8 | 76.1 |
| 1920 ............. | 8.27 | 13.4 | 106.5 |
| 1940 ............. | 10.69 | 11.0 | 132.1 |
| 1950 ............. | 14.56 | 9.9 | 151.7 |
| 1959 [3] ............. | 23.69 | 7.4 | 177.1 |

[1] Persons supported include the farm worker. Thus, in 1820, each farm worker supported himself and 3.12 other persons.
[2] Includes persons in our military forces in this country and abroad.
[3] Preliminary.
Source: *Changes in Farm Production and Efficiency: A Summary Report* (Statistical Bul. 233 [Washington: USDA, Revised July, 1960]).

tution, it required the work of nineteen farmers to produce enough surplus agricultural products to feed one city person.[13] In 1959 each farm worker in the United States produced enough food, fiber, and tobacco to supply himself and almost twenty-three other persons, Table 1. From 1820 to 1900 the number of persons supported per

[13] National Resources Committee, *Technological Trends and National Policy* (Washington: Government Printing Office, 1937), 99.

farm worker increased by 2.83 individuals; from 1900 to 1950, by 7.61 individuals; and from 1950 to 1959, by 9.13 persons. The proportion of workers employed in agriculture to total population decreased from 25 per cent in 1820, to 17 per cent in 1900, to 6 per cent in 1950, and to 4 per cent in 1959.

The effect of changes in equipment and production methods on labor requirements is apparent when expressed in terms of man-hours required per unit of production. For example, labor required per acre

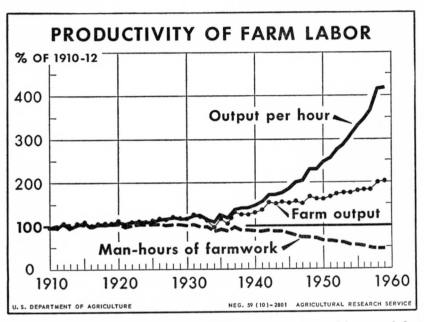

FIG. 9. Note the tremendous rate at which output per hour of farm work has increased within recent years.

of corn grown in the United States decreased from thirty-five man-hours per acre during the 1940–1944 period and dropped to ten man-hours per acre during the 1955–1959 period. During these same periods average production was 26, 32, and 48 bushels per acre, respectively. During the 1910–1914 period an average of approximately 116 man-hours was required per acre of cotton. With the use of new technology the man-hours required dropped to sixty-six per acre, and the yield of cotton increased from an average of about 200 pounds per acre in the

1910–1914 period to 428 pounds in the 1955–1959 period. Equally impressive gains were recorded in milk production. For example, average man-hours per milk cow in the United States decreased from 146 during the 1910–1914 period to 142 during the 1940–1944 period and dropped to 116 during the 1955–1959 period, while milk production per cow averaged 3,842, 4,653, and 6,138 pounds, respectively.

### Technological Revolution to Continue

Projections indicate that the technological revolution in agriculture will continue at a rapid pace. The following economic attainable yields

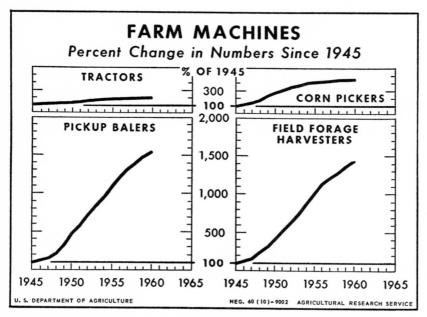

FIG. 10. Farm mechanization has increased rapidly since 1945.

per harvested acre have been projected for the year 2010: corn, 85 bushels; cotton, 805 pounds; and sugar beets, 34 tons, compared with 1951–1953 averages of 39, 291, and 16 respectively.

In the past, one of the main factors in the continuation of the upward trend in labor productivity has been the replacement of workstock by tractors, trucks, and other types of machines. Resources formerly used to feed and care for horses and mules were available as inputs for production of food and fiber for human consumption. Millions of acres of cropland and other resources were released for production of farm products for human consumption when farmers were able to replace horses and mules with gasoline engines.

Since relatively small numbers of workstock remain on farms, future increases in labor productivity will depend primarily on chemical and biological developments and adoption of improvements in farm machines and farm practices.

Changes of the magnitude outlined influence both the economic and the social organization of rural society.

### Relation of Technology to Tenure

The impact of technology may be seen in the population and the land, including the nature of property rights, the distribution of ownership and control of land, and the ways of extracting a living from the soil.[14] The extent and impact of technological change on tenure is influenced by the attitude of church, state, and other social systems toward tenure and technology as expressed in action and policy. For example, Jefferson's love of the land and his desire to see the widest possible distribution of rights in land can be seen in the Declaration of Independence, the Constitution, and the Land Ordinances of 1785 and 1787. For Jefferson, agrarianism and private property were not ends in themselves, but the means to democracy. Land was the typical form of private property, and farming was the typical use of land.[15] Joe R. Motheral credits Jefferson as being "the most influential carrier of the agrarian tradition into the American colonial setting, although the Jeffersonian adaptations were highly portentous of a modern and distinctively American brand of philosophy."[16] Jefferson expressed his admiration of the farmer in the following words:

> Those who labor in the earth are the chosen people of God,
> if ever He had a chosen people. . . . Corruption of morals in the

[14] Smith lists these points, along with systems of land divisions and settlement patterns, as the five important relationships between the population and the land. T. Lynn Smith, *The Sociology of Rural Life* (3d ed.; New York: Harper & Bros., 1953), 197.

[15] A. Whitney Griswold, *Farming and Democracy* (New Haven: Yale University Press, 1948), 18–46.

[16] Joe R. Motheral, "The Family Farm and the Three Traditions," *Journal of Farm Economics*, Vol. 33 (August, 1951), 516.

mass of cultivators is a phenomenon of which no age nor nation has furnished an example. . . . generally speaking, the proportion which the aggregate of the other classes of citizens bears in any State to that of its husbandmen, is the proportion of its unsound to its healthy parts, and is a good enough barometer whereby to measure its degree of corruption." [17]

The agrarian ideas of Jefferson have become history. Today many no longer consider agriculture the foundation of democracy. In fact, in some segments of society, agriculture is viewed as the problem of democracy.

## Socio-economic Changes Related to Technology

The major socio-economic changes in American agriculture that are related to technological change and man's relationship to the land are reviewed in the following pages.

*The proportion of the population living on the land has decreased:* In 1910 about one in three persons lived on farms. By 1950 the ratio had declined to one in six, and by 1960 only one in twelve persons lived on farms.[18] The movement of individuals from farms has been made possible through increased opportunities in nonfarm employment and adoption of new agricultural technology.

*The number of farms has decreased:* There were 1.5 million fewer farms in 1954 than in 1930. The total number of farms in operation in 1959, which was estimated at 4,641,000, was about 11 per cent less than in 1954.[19]

*The size of farms has increased:* Farm size can be measured on the basis of labor requirements, total acreage, acres in cropland, acres in major crops, amount of livestock, net farm income, and capital invested in agriculture. Some indications of changes in farm size are as follows:

[17] Quoted in Everett E. Edwards, *Jefferson and Agriculture* (Agricultural History Series No. 7 [Washington: Bureau of Agricultural Economics, USDA, 1943]), 23.

[18] *Farm Population* (Series Census-Agricultural Marketing Service No. 29 [Washington: USDA, April 18, 1961]), 27.

[19] *Number of Farms by States, 1910–56* (Report SpSy 3 [Washington: USDA, November, 1957]); *Number of Farms by States, 1957–59* (Report SpSy 2 [Washington: USDA, February, 1960]). The 1954 census definition of a farm is used in these estimates.

(1) The number of acres per farm has increased. The average number of acres increased from 174 in 1940 to 302 in 1959.

(2) The value of production assets per farm and per farm worker has increased. The amount of production capital per farm averaged $34,648 in 1959 compared with about $6,000 in 1940, while average value of production assets per farm worker increased from $3,413 in 1940 to $21,303 in 1960. However, changes in investment per commercial family-operated farm have varied by type of farm.

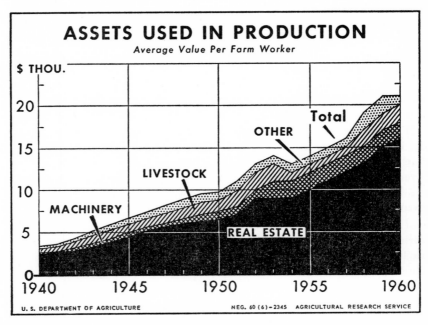

Fig. 11. Note the rate at which the average value of assets used in farm production has increased in the recent past.

(3) Realized net and gross incomes of farmers have changed. The average realized gross farm income (including government payments and realized nonmoney income) per farm in 1959 was $8,073 compared with $5,751 in 1950, an increase of 40 per cent. But total net farm income per farm increased from $2,479 in 1950 to $2,548 in 1959, an increase of only 3 per cent. In terms of purchasing power in 1947–1949 dollars, however, total net income per farm from farming decreased from $2,457 in 1950 to $2,152 in 1959.

*The proportion of land operated by part-owners has increased:* Full tenancy and full ownership are being replaced by part-ownership. Changes in size of operation necessary for commercial agriculture have made it increasingly difficult for farm youth to climb the traditional agriculture ladder from unpaid farm worker on the home place through the upward steps of farm wage laborer, farm tenant, owner-operator with mortgage, to full owner.[20] Many farm boys who want to own their own places and have not been able to obtain farm capital through marriage, inheritance, or gift must spend a large part of their productive lives working on farms they do not own and can never hope to own, or they must obtain nonfarm employment. Not only is it now more difficult to climb the agricultural ladder, but it is easier to slip down the ladder.

R. S. Crickenberger and W. L. Gibson conclude that farming as a part-owner is a solution to the young farmer's problem of achieving security of tenure with limited capital. Part-ownership permits a young farmer to achieve reasonable security of occupancy of a farm of efficient size rather than remaining a tenant for a long period of time or becoming an owner of a smaller, less efficient farm.[21]

*The relative importance of labor as an input item has decreased:* Farm labor accounted for approximately half of the total agricultural inputs in 1940 but dropped to less than 30 per cent in 1959. The relative importance of real estate remained about the same, but the proportion of inputs of power and machinery, feed, seed, livestock, fertilizer and lime, and other inputs increased.

*The share of farm land purchased for farm enlargement has in-*

[20] See Frank H. Maier, Sheridan T. Maitland, Gladys K. Bowles, *The Tenure Status of Farmworkers in the United States* (Technical Bulletin 1217 [Washington: USDA, July, 1960]), 5–33, for an appraisal of the functioning of the agricultural ladder from 1880 to 1950.

[21] R. S. Crickenberger and W. L. Gibson, Jr., *Farming as a Part Owner* (The Southeast Land Tenure Research Committee Publication No. 34 and Va. Agr. Exp. Sta. Tech. Bul. No. 504 [Blacksburg, A. E. S., Virginia Polytechnic Institute, April, 1959]), 41–42. For additional material on approaches to expanding opportunities for beginning farmers, see Don Kanel, *Opportunities for Beginning Farmers, Why are They Limited?* (North Central Regional Publication 102 and Nebr. Agr. Exp. Sta. Bul. 452 [Lincoln: A. E. S., University of Nebraska, May, 1960]); and Howard L. Hill and Sydney D. Staniforth, *A Modification of Leasing Arrangements to Expand Farm Opportunities* (Wis. Agr. Exp. Sta. Research Bulletin No. 213 [Madison: A. E. S., University of Wisconsin, August, 1959]).

*creased:* During the year ended March 1, 1959, more than 40 per cent of the transfers of farm land were for farm enlargement, while in 1950 purchases for this purpose constituted about 20 per cent of the transfers. This is another indication of the trend toward fewer but larger farms.

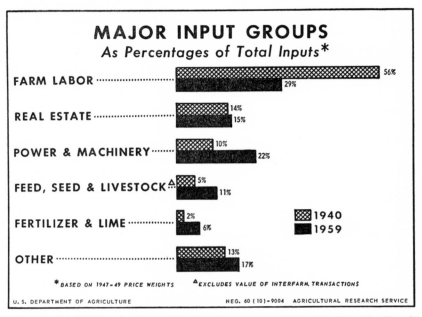

**FIG. 12.** The indicated changes in farm inputs reveal the drastic reduction in need for labor which has come about with the great increase in use of power and machinery.

*The proportion of farm land purchased by credit has increased:* The proportion of farm real estate transfers requiring credit has increased with increased investment in real estate.

*The proportion of land purchases made under land-purchase contract has increased:* [22] Land purchase contracts are instruments for obtaining control of land when the title to the land remains with the seller until all payments have been made, or until a specified percent-

[22] See also Lloyd K. Fischer, Richard Burkholder, and John Muehlbeier, *The Farm Real Estate Market in Nebraska* (Nebr. Agr. Exp. Sta. Bul. SB 456 [Lincoln: A. E. S., University of Nebraska, March, 1960]), 14–17.

age of the total price has been paid. This type of contract is attractive to buyers who lack sufficient equity to obtain mortgage financing and ordinarily involves more risk for the buyer than does mortgage financing.

*The number of farms operated by tenants has declined:* The number of farms operated by full owners and managers has remained about

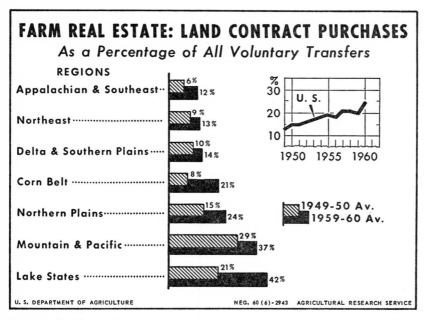

FIG. 13. Land purchases by means of land-purchase contracts are becoming increasingly important in this nation, particularly in the lake states and western states.

the same, while the number of farms operated by part-owners has increased.

*The number of hired and family farm workers has decreased:* Total farm employment in the United States decreased from 12.8 million in 1929 to 7.4 million in 1959, a decrease of 42 per cent. The number of hired workers and family workers decreased at about the same rate during this period. Between 1929 and 1954 the decrease in hired labor was at a greater rate than the decrease in family labor, but between 1954 and 1959 the number of family workers decreased at a greater rate than the number of hired workers. Alvin Bertrand comments that the decrease of farm laborers is one of the most significant effects of technology on agricultural systems. Farm laborers have been affected more by technology than any other major tenure group.[23]

*The number of migratory agricultural workers has increased:* In many areas the peak seasonal labor requirements for many crops cannot be supplied from local sources. Many farm operators can meet their labor requirements for land preparation, planting, fertilizing, and insect control with the use of new technology and family labor or relatively small amounts of hired labor. However, large numbers of seasonal farm workers are required to perform such operations as harvesting apples, thinning beets, and chopping cotton. The need for seasonal farm workers is being met by about 400,000 domestic migratory farm workers, accompanied by about 150,000 dependents, and by about 450,000 foreign agricultural workers chiefly from Mexico, but also from the British West Indies, Canada, the Philippines, and Japan.

During 1959 approximately 1,402,900 seasonal hired agricultural workers were employed in the peak month of October in major producing areas covered by Bureau of Employment Security reports, compared with only 331,800 workers in January.[24] In recent years there has been a slight increase in the proportion of seasonal farm workers who are local workers and a reduction in the proportion who are intrastate workers.

*Technological change has given many farm people an opportunity to add to their income by working off the farm:* The Bureau of the Census reports that the number of farm operators working off their farms 100 days or more has increased steadily from about 700,000 in 1930 to 1,334,000 in 1954. In 1958, 34 per cent of the employed men and 61 per cent of the employed women living on farms were engaged in nonagricultural work. Corresponding percentages for 1940 were 17 for men and 52 for women.

*Contract farming and vertical integration are increasing:* Contract farming is now one of the major developments in agriculture.[25] Accord-

[23] Alvin L. Bertrand (ed.), *Rural Sociology* (New York: McGraw-Hill, 1958), 405.

[24] Bureau of Employment Security, U. S. Dept. of Labor, inseason farm labor report for major agricultural areas.

[25] *Contract Farming and Vertical Integration in Agriculture* (Agriculture Information Bulletin No. 198 [Washington: USDA, July, 1958]).

ing to Scoville, the main forces that are responsible for the growth of agriculture-business integration include the following:

a. Efforts of firms having expensive processing equipment to assure themselves of an adequate and stable supply of farm produce of acceptable quality.

b. Efforts of processors to extend the seasonal use of their plants.

c. Efforts of processors and marketers to improve quality of product.

d. Efforts of farmers to spread or reduce risk in the production of a commodity.

e. Efforts of farmers to improve prices or create a market.

f. Efforts of farmers to reduce costs.

g. Efforts of farm suppliers to expand the market for farm supplies.

h. Efforts of either farmers or business firms to improve efficiency of resource use in farm production.[26]

Studies indicate that, under proper guidance, contract farming and vertical integration will not impair the tenure status of farm people. Apparently vertical integration would not result from technological change if the economic system were functioning smoothly. However, integrating arrangements can become important factors influencing land tenure.

A summary of major changes in farm production indicates that total acreage of cropland has not changed greatly. Crop production per acre has increased. Man-hours of labor used for farm work have decreased. The number of tractors, a general measure of advance in technology, has substantially increased. Farms have increased in size but decreased in number. The number of commercial farms has de-

[26] See the following references: O. J. Scoville, " Where to in Agriculture-Business Integration? " *Proceedings: Agricultural Economics and Rural Sociology Section, Association of Southern Agricultural Workers* (1958), 6–7. Maier, Maitland, and Bowles, *The Tenure Status of Farmworkers in the United States*, 68. Marshall Harris, " Discussion: Tenure Innovations and Tenure Problems Associated with Vertical Integration," *Journal of Farm Economics*, Vol. 40 (December, 1958), 1390–92; W. G. Miller, " Farm Tenure Perspective of Vertical Integration," *Journal of Farm Economics*, Vol. 42 (May, 1960), 307–16.

creased while the number of part-time and residential farms has increased.

## The Impact of Technology on Specific Tenure Systems and Type-farming Areas

The 1956 report of the Subcommittee on Technology, Southwestern Land Tenure Research Committee, points out that in the Southwest the relationship of machines and tenancy varies among type-of-farming areas and by stages in the mechanization process. Between 1940 and 1950 tenancy tended to decrease more rapidly in the family-farming areas of low levels of mechanization than in areas of relatively high levels of mechanization. In the western grain area, where the peak of the combine harvester stage of mechanization had passed, the rate of tenancy decrease was diminishing. The Rolling and High Plains cotton areas, in which mechanical cotton harvesting was advanced, had low tenancy decreases, while the Rio Grande Plain, which was less advanced but active in adoption of the cotton stripper, registered the greatest decrease in tenancy. The western livestock area, which had no sharp seasonal peaks of labor needs and no major mechanical improvements, had a low rate of tenancy.[27]

Technological changes that increase the land area operated by one man will cause changes in tenure arrangements and labor relations. In plantation areas, for example, the old cropper system is not readily adaptable to the use of large-scale tractor-drawn equipment. Mechanization has influenced a shift from cropper to wage labor and a decrease in status differences between croppers and laborers. On many cotton plantations a large proportion of the work that was formerly done by a cropper with mules is now done by tractor drivers who receive an hourly, weekly, or monthly wage. The cropper chops his cotton and handpicks the part of the crop that is not harvested by machines. In the Mississippi Delta this type of cropper-wage arrangement began

[27] Alvin L. Bertrand, J. L. Charlton, Harald A. Pedersen, R. L. Skrabanek, and James D. Tarver, *Factors Associated with Agricultural Mechanization in the Southwest Region* (Ark. Agr. Exp. Sta. Bul. 567, [Fayetteville: A. E. S., University of Arkansas, 1956]), 28–29. For additional studies of the relation of technology to tenure see: Harold Hoffsomer (ed.), *The Social and Economic Significance of Land Tenure in the Southwestern States* (Chapel Hill: The University of North Carolina Press, 1950), 115–16; and Alvin L. Bertrand, *Agricultural Mechanization and Social Change in Louisiana* (La. Agr. Exp. Sta. Bul. No. 458 [Baton Rouge: A. E. S., Louisiana State University, 1951]).

to develop during the 1930's. Cropper families were given small share-crops that were inadequate to support a family. They were dependent on wage employment on the plantation for additional income.[28] This type of arrangement provides the employer with a stable labor supply without obligating him to provide full employment for wage laborers.

Mechanization and increased cotton yields have been important factors in reducing the number of sharecroppers in the Cotton Belt. A 1951 case study of two plantations in Bolivar County, Miss., one of which was in an advanced state of mechanization and the other relatively unmechanized, gives an indication of the effect of agricultural technology, coupled with opportunities for nonfarm employment, on tenure arrangements.[29] "Mule Plantation," where only limited use was made of tractors, was operated almost entirely with sharecroppers who worked the crop with mule power and hand labor. "Tractor Plantation," which was extensively mechanized, was mainly a "day crop" operation. On Mule Plantation, the cropper tract was the unit of operation, and housing was dispersed on the plantation. On Tractor Plantation, the field was the unit of operation, and dwelling units were no longer associated with specific fields but were moved to new locations along the main roads. All workers on Mule Plantation were tenants—the cropper system predominated. On Tractor Plantation, tenure rights to a crop were assigned to a worker or his wife when necessary to secure services as a hoe hand, tractor driver, or mechanic. Of the ninety occupied dwellings on Tractor Plantation, twenty-nine contained full-time cropper families, thirty-seven cropper wage families and twenty-four wage families. All except two of the sharecrops were worked through.

By 1957 a number of different arrangements had been developed as adjustments to the increase in the relative importance of machinery in cotton production. Many plantation operators prepared the land, planted the seed, machine-cultivated, irrigated, defoliated, and machine-picked the cropper cotton and charged their croppers fees for these services. The cropper was responsible for chopping his crop and hand-picking the part not harvested by machine. Many croppers were

[28] Frank J. Welch, *The Plantation Land Tenure System in Mississippi* (Miss. Agr. Exp. Sta. Bul. 385 [Starkville: A. E. S., Mississippi State University, June, 1943]), 49.
[29] Harald A. Pedersen and Arthur F. Raper, *The Cotton Plantation in Transition* (Miss. Agr. Exp. Sta. Bul. 508 [Starkville: A. E. S., Mississippi State University, 1954]).

employed as farm wage workers when not working in their own crops. The importance of the resident labor force in hand-picking and chopping cotton had decreased, while greater dependence had been placed on nonresident laborers.[30]

The number of workers displaced by technology depends not only on the type of technology but also on the type of farm. Displacement is not necessarily in proportion to the amount of labor saved. On large farms labor may be easily replaced by machines, but on family farms the labor force may not be quickly reduced by labor-saving equipment. If farm enlargement is present, there will be a decrease in number of farms and hence a decrease in the number of farm families. The amount of family labor used may increase with the increase in size of farms.

Nelson LeRay and Grady Crowe point out that there is no direct correlation between a reduction in labor requirements and a reduction in numbers in the labor force.[31] In the Delta the main economic reasons why the resident labor force did not decline in proportion to the reduction in labor requirements were: (1) cotton production operation with peak labor requirements had not been completely mechanized and (2) plantation operators do not like to depend upon seasonal off-farm labor for picking and chopping.

T. Lynn Smith lists the mechanization of agriculture along with the commercialization of agriculture as the more important forces undermining the family-farm system. He contends that the dependence of the farm family on industry, which resulted from the replacement of home-grown workstock and feed, means less security for the farm family.[32] M. L. Wilson holds that the completely mechanized commercial farm represents complete surrender of agriculture to economic and technological forces.[33]

However, Welch and Miley remind that:

Even though society will gain little or nothing in the short run from technological advancement in agriculture if displaced

[30] LeRay and Crowe, *Labor and Technology on Selected Cotton Plantations in the Delta Area of Mississippi*, 19–23.

[31] *Ibid.*, 19.

[32] T. Lynn Smith, *The Sociology of Rural Life* (3d ed.; New York: Harper & Bros., 1953), 321.

[33] M. L. Wilson, "Economic Agriculture and the Rural and General Social Welfare," *Proceedings: the Fifth International Conference of Agricultural Economists* (London: Oxford University Press, 1939), 44.

labor go to swell the relief rolls or are forced to find employment on made-work projects, such a contingency does not justify the discouragement of more efficient techniques of production. To do so would hamper or prevent economic progress and the gradual improvement in standards of living for everyone. However, inasmuch as society benefits from such progress in the long run, society should contribute to cushioning the shock of technological unemployment and general economic and social dislocations that result from such progress.[34]

## Broad Consequences to Tenure of Technology

Self-sufficient farmers use technology to satisfy the direct needs of their family for food and shelter. The costs and returns of technology are measured, not in terms of money, but in terms of available resources and the suitability of the products for family consumption.[35]

Money profit is the determinant of economic organization for commercial farms. After discussing the trend toward larger operating units and mechanized operations and a reduction in tenancy on plantations in Mississippi, Welch comments:

> Finally, it may be safely assumed that, unless public policy decrees otherwise, the organization and operation of the plantation system in the future as in the past will be determined largely by whatever appears to be economically advantageous. The broader social implications of the system, whether in the abstract or in the form of immediate concrete problems, will be of secondary importance as casual factors in shaping the future course of the plantation system. The profit motive is still the basis for its existence. On the other hand, continued government subsidy and support of agriculture by the Federal Government is likely to be accompanied by increasing interest in the incidence of such programs on land tenure, tenancy arrangements, and relationships.[36]

[34] Frank J. Welch and D. Gray Miley, *Mechanization of the Cotton Harvest* (Miss. Agr. Exp. Sta. Bul. No. 420 [Starkville: A. E. S., Mississippi State University, 1945]), 22.

[35] Bertrand, *Rural Sociology*, 391.

[36] Welch, *The Plantation Land Tenure System in Mississippi*, 54.

Farming has changed from a subsistence to a commercial operation. The farm family now consumes only a small part of what it produces. The commercial farmer is a specialist who produces a few types of crops and livestock for sale. He has transferred the storing, processing, and distribution of food and fiber to nonfarm entrepreneurs.

In this connection Davis and Goldberg note that between 1947 and 1954 the total working force of agribusiness remained almost unchanged at about twenty-four million persons.[37] However, considerable change occurred among the aggregates. In 1947, 20.4 per cent of the total agribusiness working force was in farm supplies, 40.8 per cent in farming, and 38.8 per cent in processing distribution, compared with 25.0, 33.3 and 41.7 per cent, respectively, in 1954.[38]

Farming has become more specialized. It now depends more on others for supplies and for storage, processing, and distributing of farm production than was formerly the case.

Technology has brought about revolutionary changes in American agriculture. The agriculture that Jefferson knew and the visions that he had for an agricultural America are only memories. The problems of economic and social adjustment that are associated with the revolution in agriculture are as complex as those associated with any revolution fought on the battlefield. And the revolution is far from over. New technology that will increase productivity and efficiency will be developed and adopted. Changes will continue to take place in the American economic system and in agriculture's place in this system.

The value of orientation of both farm and nonfarm people affects the pattern of asset control and the framework of decision-making in agriculture. Changing economic forces now require society to choose between deep-seated values with respect to the structure of agriculture and the levels of income of farm families.[39]

[37] Agribusiness is defined as " the sum total of all operations involved in the manufacture and distribution of farm supplies; production operations on the farm; and the storage, processing, and distribution of farm commodities and items made from them." John H. Davis and Ray A. Goldberg, *A Concept of Agribusiness* (Boston: Harvard University, 1957), 2.

[38] *Ibid.*, 14.

[39] C. E. Bishop and K. L. Bachman, " Structure of Agriculture," *Some Selected Papers on Goals and Values in Agricultural Policy* (Washington: F. E. S., USDA, 1960), 72–82. For additional statements of these and related value principles in American agriculture, see J. M. Brewster, " The Impact of Technical Advance and Migration on Agricultural Society and Policy,"

Some persons may hold technology responsible for social and economic problems arising from adoption of technology. In the opinion of the writer, the responsibility does not lie with technology but with the failure of society to make necessary adjustments in its economic and social systems. Technology is socially neutral. The influence of technology on society depends on the use society makes of it.

*Journal of Farm Economics*, Vol. 41 (December, 1959), 1169–84; J. M. Brewster, " Society's Values and Goals in Respect to Agricultural Policy," *ibid.*, 18–38; G. L. Johnson and Joel Smith, " Social Costs of Agricultural Adjustments," *Problems and Policies of American Agriculture* (Ames: Iowa State College Press, 1959); and William H. Metzler, " Socioeconomic Aspects of Manpower Adjustments: Low-Income Rural Areas," *Rural Sociology*, Vol. 24 (September, 1959), 226–35.

# CHAPTER FOURTEEN

# Changing Interpersonal Relations in Land Tenure Systems

THE VAST CHANGES in our ways of living which have been wrought by the revolutions in agriculture and industry, in science and technology, in transportation and communication, in education and the arts are well known. Preceding chapters have already noted the impact of these changes on land tenure in the United States. One of the major changes in American society has been the shift from an essentially rural and agricultural society to an urban and industrial society. For those who remain in farming these sweeping and basic changes have powerful social implications. This chapter proposes to review the changing nature of interpersonal relations in given tenure systems.

## The Trend from Gemeinschaft to Gesellschaft in Tenure Situations

The terms *Gesellschaft* and *Gemeinschaft* are defined and explained in Chapters 1 and 2. By way of review, *Gesellschaft* relations are those where behavior is marked by what Ferdinand Toennies called " rational will." Relations are viewed by the actors in a *Gesellschaft* system as means to attain other objectives. Obligations and duties become specific, relationships impersonal and contractual, and social status achieved rather than ascribed. In contrast, a system of *Gemeinschaft* relations is based on " natural will." Personal relations are ends in and of themselves and are intimate, spontaneous, emotional, and traditional. Obligations and duties are diffuse and general, and social status is ascribed.[1]

---

[1] For a fuller discussion of *Gemeinschaft* and *Gesellshaft*, see Charles P. Loomis and J. Allan Beegle, *Rural Social Systems* (New York: Prentice-Hall, 1950), Chap. 1 and Appendix A; and Charles P. Loomis, *Social System* (Princeton: D. Van Nostrand, 1960), 59–61.

The *Gesellschaft* trend in land tenure relations is the major thesis of this chapter. This trend involves relationships which are becoming increasingly rational, specific, limited in responsibility, and integrated outside the system of land tenure. Three major aspects of the broad trend serve as a focus for the following discussion. (1) Land tenure status-role changes have generally been in the direction of *Gesellschaft*. (2) Facilities and sanctions, especially social and economic rewards and punishments, are becoming increasingly *Gesellschaft*. (3) Attitudes, values, and goals of tenure groups also are becoming increasingly *Gesellschaft*. More specific hypotheses about changes in land tenure systems can be developed from these three broad propositions.

## Status-role Shifts in Land Tenure and the Trend to Gesellschaft Relations

Changes in interpersonal relations are manifest in shifts in statuses and roles within a given system.[2] The types of status-role changes which have or are taking place in United States tenure system are discussed in this section.

### The Decline of Tenants

Preceding chapters have shown the decease in tenancy in the United States. The status-role structure of land tenure is bound to change with the general decrease in tenancy. Tenants whose status-role most resembles that of landowners have a considerable say in their farming operations. They plan, arrange financing, produce and dispose of their crops. By the terms of their tenancy they usually have "ownership" control of the land for a specified period of time. Their relationship to the owner is therefore limited and specific. As long as they pay their rent and do not otherwise violate the terms of their lease or contract, they are free to use the land as they see fit. Although these tenants are often related by kinship to their landlords, the fact that a tenancy agreement exists is evidence of *Gesellschaft* quality in their relationships.

Sharecroppers, on the other hand, occupy a status more nearly like farm wage workers than tenants. They have limited control of land and farming operations. Many sharecroppers do not live on the farm they operate, and without exception sharecroppers have low incomes. They provide only their labor—and often that of their family as well

[2] Status, role, and social system are defined in Chapter 3 of this volume.

—and in return receive part of the proceeds from the sale of the products. Sharecroppers wait till the end of the season to settle with the landlord, who takes his share and deducts for the " furnish " before paying the sharecropper.

## Growth in Part-time Farming

The increase in part-time farming also reflects movement toward *Gesellschaft* patterns. Part-time farming is not only a means of supplementing income from agricultural pursuits for permanent farmers, but it is also an intermediate step between full-time farming and full-time nonfarm employment.

The definition of a part-time farm for census purposes is based on the amount of money from farming as opposed to family income from other sources. In 1959 part-time farms were " those with value of farm sales of $50 to $2499, provided the farm operator was under 65 years of age and reported 100 or more days of work off the farm and/or the nonfarm income received by him and the members of his family was greater than the total value of farm products sold." [3]

In addition there are part-retirement farms in census tabulations where operators sixty-five-years-old or over sold farm products with a value of $50.00 to $2499. Many of these had nonfarm income greater than farm income. Others are residential, subsistence, or marginal farms.

The integration of agricultural and land tenure social systems with urban, industrial systems has continued through the years. In 1930 about 700,000 farm operators worked one hundred or more days off their farms. In 1959 the number had increased to 1,115,914. Under the new definition of part-time farms, there were 882,371 part-time farms with operators under sixty-five years of age and 403,696 classified as part-retirement farms where the operator was 65 years of age or over.

Part-time farms are relatively lacking in work power, including horses and mules as well as tractors and other kinds of mechanical equipment. Consequently mechanization of middle-sized income farms should help increase part-time farming by making more time available for off-farm work.

The combination of agricultural and nonagricultural work roles

[3] *1959 Census of Agriculture-Preliminary*, summary for the 48 states (Washington: Bureau of the Census, USDC, January, 1961), 10.

embodied in part-time farming is evidence of *Gesellschaft* rationality. Although part-time farming has existed in the United States since the days of the American Revolution, it now assumes major proportions. A likely hypothesis is that part-time farmers regard farming as a means to some other end. For those in process of moving either into or out of agriculture, it is a means of some security during the transition. For those who plan to make part-time farming a perma-

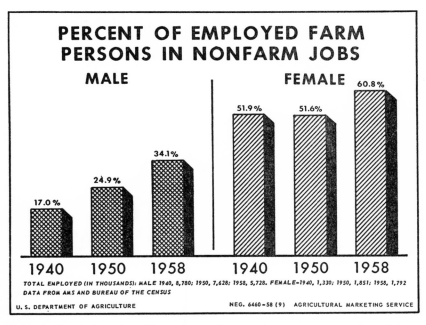

Fig. 14. One index of social change is the ever increasing proportion of farm people employed in nonfarm jobs.

nent operation, it is a means of augmenting low income from farming to enable a higher level of living.

The rational, farming-as-a-means nature of part-time farming is illustrated by suitcase and sidewalk farmers, as Carl C. Taylor points out.[4] Suitcase farmers own or rent land and come into an area from the outside during seeding and harvest seasons. They are often con-

[4] Carl C. Taylor *et al.*, " The Wheat Areas," *Rural Life in the United States* (New York:  Alfred A. Knopf, 1949), Chap. 22.

sidered by local residents as pure speculators. Sidewalk farmers live in towns of the area in which they own land and may or may not have an occupation other than farming. Since wheat farming requires attention only during two short seasons of the year, sidewalk farmers are able to enjoy the convenience of schools, churches, and other phases of modern town living despite their farming roles.

Both of these cases of " part-time " farming involve substantial role shifts. Urban life is substituted for the daily routine of farming and for life in the rural community for a major part of the year, especially for the suitcase farmer. Farming becomes a means of acquiring wealth and living standards in keeping with urban society. When the suitcase farmer hires workers or combines, his relationships are clearly contractual.

### Increase in Number of Farmers of Retirement Age

The general aging of a population is bound to result in various status-role changes. In the United States increased life expectancy accompanied by norms encouraging retirement has led to a larger number of " retired " farmers. The average age of farmer operators increased from 45 years in 1900 to 50.5 years in 1959. Among all farm operators in 1959, 17 per cent were 65 years of age or over.

Although half of the present number of farmers will have reached retirement age of sixty-five years, if they live another fifteen years, evidence indicates that many of them may continue as active farmers beyond that time. This may be taken as a traditional or *Gemeinschaft* tendency, or it may be interpreted to mean that older farmers who continue to farm lack the financial means to retire. If the financial reasons are paramount, inclusion of farmers in our social security program should speed retirement for farmers.

With older farmers leaving agriculture, through either retirement or death, ownership and use of land should undergo changes. In those cases where sons or other relatives inherit the land, traditional patterns are likely to be maintained. However, where sons may already have established themselves in nonagricultural occupations, ownership or operation of the farm may pass into other hands. In any case, ownership status in the tenure system will remain fluid over the next few decades as those in the upper age brackets reach the point of retirement.

## Changes in Status of Laborers

Both labor and residential mobility characterize a society that is highly urban and industrial, such as the United States. The farm population as a whole is vitally involved in residential shifts. Migrants from farms are typically young adults, persons who have not yet established their roots in farming. Many migrants from farms act rationally by searching primarily for greater economic opportunities. Evidence of this, however, is mainly indirect. It is known that migration losses are greater in low-income farming areas and that departures from farms increase when urban-industrial employment opportunities are greatest.

In their rational or *Gesellschaft* tendencies, migrants from farms resemble urbanites, who are widely known for being highly mobile and who often give " getting a better job " as their reason for moving. Persons who migrate from rural areas break the traditional attachments to farm, home, and community. In a more nearly *Gemeinschaft* society such attachments would assume priority over desires for economic improvement of the individual.

Migratory farm workers, though neither owners nor tenants, play a vital role in agricultural production as well as in the rationality and specificity of the land tenure system. Their compensation is primarily in the form of wages, and their work obligations are specific. Migratory workers are important because of the seasonal nature of farm labor requirements. Their part in agricultural production is based more on rationality than tradition. For the migrant workers themselves farm work is a means of livelihood. From the standpoint of employers they are necessary " tools " of production, especially in cases like the Mexican " wetbacks " or Puerto Ricans where the whole process, from recruitment to termination of services, is handled in an impersonal manner.

Farm wage workers who live in town and commute to work occupy much the same position in agriculture as the migratory workers. Residentially they are more stable than migratory workers and their employment may be less insecure. These day-haul workers play an important part in the economy of agriculture, especially in areas such as the cotton-producing Mississippi Delta. But like the migrants they have no legal claims on farm land. Moreover, they appear in many cases to occupy a transition status in their movement from full-time agricultural work to nonagricultural work.

All the above situations involve status changes in tenure systems which are oriented toward *Gesellschaft* relations.

## Changes in Socio-economic Factors and Gesellschaft Orientation

Two basic trends in social and economic aspects of agriculture and land tenure include changing facilities and sanctions. *Facilities* are means within the system for attaining ends; things such as land and equipment are both a facility and a possession, if these are used as a means of production and also held as a matter of ownership rights. *Sanctions,* on the other hand, are the rewards and penalties in a system that induce conformity to ends and norms. Rewards are potentially satisfying mechanisms, or positive sanctions, whereas penalties are deprivations, or negative sanctions. In a land tenure social system rewards might include wages, rent, profits, and prestige, privileges or rights deriving from tenure status. Penalties would be simply the deprivations of such rewards.

### Trend Toward Large-Scale Farming

In this section the changes in facilities and sanctions of tenure systems toward a *Gesellschaft* orientation are discussed.

The trend toward larger-sized farms and farming on a grand scale is the result of various technological and economic changes. Large-scale farming, however, represents a facility for maintenance of the land tenure system. Whether the ends involved are greater production, greater profits, greater prestige as a farmer, or some combination of these and other objectives, large-scale farming is a rationally applied means, a facility. Large-scale farming serves also as a positive sanction in the land tenure system by providing for the satisfaction of desires for production, profits, prestige and so on. Whether the particular land tenure system is like the feudal system of medieval Europe or the corporate farm in California, farming on the grand scale is a rewarding facility.

The extent to which farming has become large-scale is both familiar and phenomenal. Farms grew in size tremendously during the fifty years from 1900 to 1950. From an average acreage of 146 in 1900 farms reached an average of 215 acres in 1950 and 302 by 1959.

*The Impact of Social Security*

The deluge of federal government programs over the past generation or two has had widespread effects on our social and economic life. In the main, such programs are related to land tenure only indirectly, although rural electrification, soil conservation, or welfare and social security programs are obviously important to everyone in agriculture. (See Chapters 4, 5, and 6.)

Development of the federal social security program provides an excellent example of the *Gesellschaft* drift. Farmers were not included in the original Social Security Act of 1935. But with amendments to the law in 1950 some hired farm workers became eligible for Old Age and Survivors' Insurance (OASI), and by 1954 additional hired farm workers and self-employed farmers were included in the insurance program. An estimated 3.5 million farm operators and 2 million hired farm workers were brought into the program for the first time in 1955. OASI thus is a facility in the land tenure system, even though it is superimposed from the outside.

The traditional way of caring for older folks in American society was for children and relatives to attend the needs of the aged. This tradition has been dwindling for years, especially in cities. Now farmers, having been brought into the social insurance fold, follow the precedent set by their urban fellows, and social security helps solve the problem of financial need among the aged. However slight the inducement to remain in farming because of OASI, the program nevertheless constitutes a potentially satisfaction-giving mechanism. Prior to 1950, on the other hand, farmers were denied this protection by their exclusion from the social security program.

Most farmers lack the financial means or facility for retirement without endangering their level of living and sometimes their very existence. In a summary of four studies done before the expansion of social security coverage in 1955, the inability of farmers to meet their financial needs in retirement was clearly established.[5] Most of the farm operators surveyed did not have enough money to provide for themselves in old age. Over half had less than $10,000 net worth in three of the five farming areas, and most of their assets were in farms, livestock, and equipment. Less than half of them had health or accident insurance. Farm workers were even less well prepared for retirement than farm operators.

[5] I. M. Baill, *The Farmer and Old-Age Security* (Agricultural Information Bulletin No. 151 [Washington: AMS, USDA, December, 1955]).

Thus the inclusion of people in agriculture in the federal social security program provides a reward and at the same time a means of preparing for retirement while remaining in agriculture. So far, however, low-income operators and farm wage workers, those who might benefit the most, have not participated fully in the program.

Other federal programs, such as the Soil Bank, Farm Credit, and Farmers' Home Administration, also represent facilities and sanctions. (See Chapters 4, 5, and 6.) The *Gesellschaft* tendencies are clear. Such programs are rationally oriented with a heavy emphasis on efficiency, security, and protection for the various tenure classes. They are also functionally specific rather than diffuse because they establish rights and impose duties and obligations on both farmers and government agencies. Responsibilities of farmers and government agencies are spelled out by legislative provisions and restricted to what is defined and required by law. And finally, programs like OASI help integrate land tenure and agriculture as a whole with nonagricultural social systems, especially with the urban-industrial social system.

### The Trend Toward Urbanization

Among the major characteristics of an urban-industrial society are the *Gesellschaft* qualities we have been discussing. There is an abundant literature on the many aspects and implications of an urban-industrial society. David Reisman, for example, has portrayed eloquently the departure from traditional norms of behavior in modern urban society. Wilbert Moore and many others have carefully analyzed the rational, bureaucratic nature of an industrial society. W. F. Whyte has popularized the "organization man," as the epitome of modern society, one who would be extremely *Gesellschaft* oriented in our terminology.

Urban-industrial growth has meant higher levels of living, more and bigger schools, better housing facilities, higher wages and salaries, and a great variety of occupational opportunities. It has also meant poverty, slums, inequalities, and unemployment. Many colorful and exciting adjectives have been used either to praise or condemn industrial cities. Whatever one's personal judgment, however, the all-pervading influence of one of the most basic trends in modern times cannot be ignored. Certainly the effects of urban-industrial growth are felt throughout our entire society.

Land tenure units as social systems are no exception to this influence. The rationality of decision-making in a cash economy carries over to owners and tenants in agriculture. The functionally specific nature of assignments and obligations in a business or industrial organization can be seen in the corporate farm and in many landlord-tenant leases. Through most of the tenure status groups the thread of limited and functionally specific responsibility weaves its way. Movement of workers between agriculture and industry, farm and city, is extremely instrumental in helping spread urban-industrial ways of living. Modern means of transportation and communication speed the diffusion process. The impact of urbanism and industrialism is so far-reaching as to suggest that even the most isolated rural areas will someday come into the *Gesellschaft* fold. Perhaps the critical turning point in the transition comes when attitudes and values become predominantly *Gesellschaft*, a point to which we shall return shortly.

## Improvements in Transportation and Communication

The many ingredients that make up our transportation and communication systems have changed tremendously since the turn of the century. These changes affect land tenure relationships. Highways, railroads, and airlanes provide the avenues for movements of people and materials to and from rural areas. Radio, television, telephone, and the general extension of electricity into rural areas brought vast changes in communication and have had profound effects on rural life. School enrollments and attendance have also grown greatly, thereby elevating the general know-how of all classes of tenants.

Vast changes in transportation and communication have taken place on farms in the United States. Almost all farms, 93 per cent, reported having electricity in 1954 as compared with only 7 per cent in 1920. Within the space of about one decade over a third of all farms were able to acquire television sets, and two-thirds had telephones by 1959. Most farms, 80 per cent, reported an automobile and more than half had a truck by 1959. The growth of transportation is evidenced further by the fact that surfaced rural roads covered only 387,000 miles in 1921 and 2,083,000 miles, or 71 per cent of all rural roads in 1958.[6]

A major consequence of this generalized expansion of transportation and communication facilities in rural areas is the greater ease with which rural people are able to acquire *Gesellschaft* characteristics. Paralleling the growth of these expanded facilities has been a strong emphasis on speed, efficiency, and know-how in farming operations

[6] *Statistical Abstract of the United States, 1960* (Washington, USDC, 1960).

or, in short, an increase in the rationality-orientation of behavior. Increases in agricultural production combined with ever larger market areas represent rewards within the land tenure system. And these rewards may be traced to the development of transportation and communication facilities.

Movements of workers between agriculture and industry and within agriculture have obviously been encouraged by knowledge about, and easier access to, different opportunities. The great migration from farms to cities might never have reached the proportions it has in the twentieth century, if our transportation and communication systems had not grown. Migratory farm workers certainly move more easily and with better knowledge of opportunities and destinations because of available facilities. Absentee ownership, part-time farming, and all kinds of off-farm work have similarly been encouraged by the development of our transportation and communication systems. However, not all the consequences of expanded transportation and communication systems have been in the direction of encouraging movement of farmers. Farm life, in fact, has become more attractive by *Gesellschaft* standards. Rural people are more rapidly acquiring modern facilities for transportation and communication and, therefore, have many of the rewards that might otherwise prompt a move to the city.

## Changes in Attitudes and Values Tending Toward Gesellschaft Orientation

Farmers are traditionally attached to land, neighbors, community, and the many tasks that make up the farming operation. But owners and tenants are departing from traditional ways of acting and thinking and are becoming more *Gesellschaft*-like. Once very tradition-minded, farmers are becoming increasingly rational in their outlook. Obligations and duties of farming, once diffused over the whole of agricultural and rural life, now are more specific, as already noted. This greater specificity of personal relationships is accompanied by less general responsibilities. Now responsibilities are becoming limited to specific persons under rather narrowly defined circumstances. Farmers no longer are oriented to agriculture and rural life as strongly as in times past. Farmers have shifted their orientation gradually to industrial and urban systems and standards of behavior. So much so in fact that agriculture is no longer a way of life for many farmers.

Evidence of the more *Gesellschaft* pattern of attitudes and values is mainly indirect. By their abstract nature, attitudes and values must be observed indirectly. No one can " see " an attitude or a value. Conclusions on changing attitudes and values are made more difficult too because of the relative scarcity of attitude-value research among tenure groups. Nevertheless, it is possible to infer changes in attitudes and values from various trends in the behavior of farmers in socio-economic life as a whole.

### Changing Attitudes Toward Farming as a Way of Life and as an Occupation

The familiar urban-industrial-bureaucratic pattern of behavior emerging in America—and in many other places around the world—goes far toward explaining changing attitudes and values. At least there appears to be a relationship between behavior and attitudes, whether changes in behavior precede changes in attitudes or vice versa. Ascendance of this typically *Gesellschaft* pattern outside of agriculture has many implications for farming and tenancy in general. As has been noted, departures from farming have reached sizable numbers, and many more persons straddle agricultural and industrial pursuits by part-time farming. Bigness and efficiency are important to farmers as well as to businessmen and industrialists. Individual farmers value high income and the acquisition of material possessions much in the same way as their urban-industrial counterparts. Large-scale farms employ ever larger numbers of hired hands and more and more resemble the bureaucratically organized industrial plant, with all the specialization, division of labor, lines of authority, and impersonality of relationships. Efficient production has become a major goal in both agriculture and industry to the extent that all else seems to be judged according to standards of efficiency.

With changes of this kind many farmers have come to view farming more as an occupation rather than an entire way of life. If farmers at any tenure level view farming primarily as a job or a way to make money, it is much easier for them to make the switch into part-time farming or to leave farming entirely. On the other hand, if farmers view farming as a way of life, relatively few would move into other pursuits. Thus the very fact that millions have left farming supports the contention that increased numbers of farmers view farming primarily as an occupation and source of income, a rationally applied means to an end.

Tenants, managers, and wage workers are especially likely to think of farming as a job, since they lack ownership rights in land. At the same time one can find many instances of farm owners who cling to the traditional view of farming as a way of life and who continue in agriculture despite greatly depressed economic conditions. Eventually economic distress may force many of these more tradition-minded persons out of farming. Nonowners in agriculture, of course, are less likely than owners to continue farming when the going gets tough. Lacking ownership rights, facing insecurity and low income, already conditioned to *Gesellschaft* ways, and perhaps enticed by opportunities outside of agriculture, the rationally minded landless can reach but one decision: to leave agriculture.

Young folks also tend to make their decisions on a rational basis when they contemplate the prospects of a career in agriculture. Conditioned considerably throughout their early years with the importance of higher levels of living, it becomes easy for young folks to recognize that the income necessary to acquire desired material possessions can more easily be obtained outside of agriculture. They see also the great difficulties in acquiring sufficient land and equipment to start farming as an owner and to make enough money quickly to meet their demands. The easy and rational conclusion then is to seek the goals of income and level of living much earlier in life by choosing a nonfarm job. In this manner many young adults assess their prospects in farming against the alternatives—a line of reasoning that has relatively little to do with the sacred and traditional values of farming.

### Changes in Levels of Living and in Attitudes Toward Security and Retirement

Rationality, specificity of relationships, and limited responsibility characterize attitudes and values toward levels of living, security, and retirement just as they are prominent features of the changing system as a whole.

Rural levels of living have increased steadily since 1930.[7] The farm-operator level-of-living index (1945 = 100) rose from 75 in 1930 to 145 by 1956. Level of living varies, of course, by age, education, and location of the farm operator, but in general owners have a higher level of living than renters.

[7] See A. L. Bertrand, *Trends and Patterns in Levels of Living of Farm Families in the U. S.* (Agricultural Information Bulletin No. 181 [Washington: AMS, USDA, February, 1958]), 8–9.

The rapidly increasing level of living is indicative of desires among farmers, regardless of whatever else may be inferred. The fact that migration to other regions and a general exodus from agriculture occurs in regions such as the South, where relatively low levels of living prevail, strengthens the notion of a relationship between desire for a higher level of living and an existing low level.

Rural people have traditionally stressed thrift and hard work, but since the depression of the 1930's have gradually, sometimes reluctantly, come to accept dependence as a legitimate condition. As many as one in four rural families were dependent on relief of some kind during the lean years of the 1930's. Coupled with the growth of public insurance and relief programs is the great variety of government programs in agriculture, many of which have been resisted by farmers. Despite such resistance, however, government-aid programs of one kind or another have become fairly well established. It certainly is unlikely that programs such as federal social security will pass from existence in the foreseeable future.

Empirical data are lacking as to precisely how and to what extent attitudes and values have changed among various status groups. However, it may be inferred from the development of social insurance that farmers are now more favorably inclined toward government-sponsored social insurance than was the case a generation ago. Also, those who stand to benefit most from a social security program in agriculture—low-income tenants and wage workers—are tenure groups likely to have the most favorable orientation toward social security. Many in agriculture are now covered by social insurance. Even prior to the extension of social insurance to those in agriculture, many were covered by the program by virtue of having been in covered employment outside of agriculture—either as part-time farmers or as a result of having shifted between employment in covered industry and agriculture.

The federal social insurance program includes, of course, provisions for retirement benefits, as well as death and other benefits. A major objective of retirement programs is to enable older persons to cease working for a living by providing a guaranteed income—income to which the recipient has a right rather than income in the form of charity. In theory at least a retirement pension provides a family with sufficient income to maintain itself at approximately the pre-retirement level.

Thus the attitude has grown that farm workers as well as city workers should retire at about age 65 with an income from the OASI

program, plus whatever private insurance they may have, sufficient
to maintain a " respectable " level of living. Retired people should be
financially independent, it is felt. They should not have to rely on
their children or on private charity for financial support. Children
and other relatives are no longer responsible for their aging parents
since " social security " will take care of their needs. In these respects
the attitudes, values, and goals of agricultural workers are becoming
more and more like those of their city brethren.

### Changing Attitudes Toward Size, Technology, and Efficiency

The trend toward larger, more highly mechanized and more productive farms promises to continue indefinitely. Despite this general
trend we find a large number of small-sized, low-production farms
operated as family enterprises even here in the United States. This
situation has led to much controversy as to the ideal kind of farm and
land tenure system. Should farms be large, profit-making enterprises
operated by professional managers who are devoted to the principles
of bureaucratic efficiency? Or, should farms, ideally, be relatively
small, family-owned and operated enterprises governed primarily by
values of " farming as a way of life "? The first alternative represents
an essentially *Gesellschaft* point of view and the latter a *Gemeinschaft*
position. Both kinds of values have considerable support despite the
very pronounced trend in *Gesellschaft* direction.

In the face of the many changes in agriculture itself and attitudes
and values, the ideal type and size of farm is highly elusive. Improved
farming practices and mechanization have already greatly increased
the optimum size of a workable profitable farm. Some have suggested
that " family farms " should incorporate. The future thus may bring
an increase in incorporated farms, not to mention agricultural auto-
mation. The movement to maintain or revitalize the traditional style
family farm appears more a matter of nostalgia than agricultural
reality. The traditional family farm cannot survive economically without some modification. More and more farm families, for example,
may own and operate a relatively large acreage with the help of auto-
mated planting and picking machines on land that is held through
incorporation.

Under the norms of high production, efficiency, and profit-making
the large, mechanized farm becomes an ideal. Such values are derived
in part from the spread of urban-industrial techniques of production,
bureaucratic organization, standards of efficiency, and desires for

profits. Many owners of farms already have been quick to recognize that the way to higher profits was through enlargement and mechanization of their operation. In this way, they could see, costs per unit of production might be lowered. In all such cases values governing the farmer's decision are rational, and his aim is to expand his farming operation for the sake of making more money and not simply to maintain the old family farm and a rural way of life. Some critics see a danger in this change of attitudes and values. Bigness and efficiency, they say, may become ends rather than means and thereby replace traditional goals of farmers.

### Changing Attitudes Toward Conservation and Development of Resources

Encouragement to conserve and develop agricultural resources comes from both public and private sources. Government programs for soil conservation illustrate the publicly derived incentive, while a number of private groups and individuals have been greatly concerned over agricultural resources. In the broadest sense " resources " should be defined to include both the human and nonhuman. Attitudes and values toward resources therefore constitute a highly complex maze in which any consensus is difficult to locate. Although conservation and development of human resources are ostensibly central concerns of most persons, specific programs focus on such nonhuman resources as soil, minerals, and water.

When it comes to more specific considerations, such as the adoption of soil conservation practices on farms, further evidence of *Gesellschaft* attitudes can often, though not always, be detected. In a study of western Iowa, for example, obstacles to the adoption of soil conservation practices were found to include uncertainty of tenure, inadequate financial resources, a reluctance to assume risk, and lack of confidence in practices already tried.[8] Adopters of conservation practices realized that erosion losses could reduce farm income and that certain practices would enhance their chances for higher farm incomes over the long run. The emphasis on economic gain as a justification for adopting soil conservation practices is quite apparent.

---

[8] R. B. Held and J. F. Timmons, *Soil Erosion Control in Process in Western Iowa* (Iowa Agr. and Home Econ. Exp. Sta. Research Bulletin 460 [Ames: Iowa State College, August, 1958]), 315.

## Attitudes Related to Tenure Differentials

Attitudes and values are also related to tenure status. That not all people engaged in agriculture adhere to the same principles is evident in examining soil conservation practices. A study of the North Central states indicated that conservation is more commonly practiced on owner-operated land than on renter-operated land.[9] Authors in this study submit some interesting evidence in support of a *Gesellschaft* trend by suggesting that leases contain provisions specifying responsibilities and obligations of landlords and tenants. To the extent that these suggestions are followed, leases will show extreme rationality toward money matters, the specific nature of landlord-tenant relationships, and the clearly defined and limited responsibilities of both parties to the agreement.

Part-time farmers and others who shift or alternate between farming and nonfarming have attitudes and values oriented both to agriculture and to nonagricultural activities. More than any other tenure group perhaps, the part-time farmers are oriented away from agriculture.

Farm managers and owners of large farms are more likely than other tenure groups to place great importance on technological improvements and efficiency in farming. This is to be expected since it is the large enterprise where these considerations are felt to be most appropriate. By a kind of " trickle down " process, workers employed on the larger farms also become impressed with the advantages of technology and efficient farming procedures. Wage workers and croppers, however, may quickly recognize the threat of their pending technological displacement and therefore resist technological change. They also display a rather weak concern over conservation and development of resources, in contrast to a more immediate and powerful interest in an improved level of living.

Along with such tenure status differences we find a more or less generalized resistance to *Gesellschaft* tendencies stemming from traditions. The " family farm " may be idealized most among older farmers who own and operate relatively small acreages, but the strength of this ideal is so deeply rooted that it tends to manifest itself in many agricultural quarters.

---

[9] W. H. Pine *et al.*, *Conservation on Rented Land in the Midwest* (Kan. Agr. Exp. Sta. Bul. 377 [Manhattan: A. E. S., Kansas State College, February, 1956]), 2.

## Outlook for the Future

Basic societal trends permeate the whole of agriculture, including land tenure relationships. The processes of urbanization and industrialization have centered in urban areas, but there are many indications that rural areas are coming under the same kinds of influences. Land tenure relationships have become increasingly *Gesellschaft* in the terminology used here. Evidence of this *Gesellschaft* movement may be found in the changing status-role pattern, socio-economic changes, and changing attitudes and values, as shown. At least part of the outcome of the many changes taking place can be seen as an extension of changes in past and present conditions.

The role of farm owners will become even more *Gesellschaft*-like, if present trends continue. The increase of incorporated farms, vertical integration, use of machinery for custom work, and the greater size of farming operations all point in this direction. The continued expansion of transportation and communication facilities will increase the exposure to urban ways of life. Daily movement between farms and farm and city has already become commonplace. At home the farmer has most of the material advantages found in cities—electricity, running water, and so on.

In planning and decision-making the farmer will act much like an urban industrialist. Decisions on the size of his farming operation, management of his crops and livestock, and the marketing of his produce will be just as rational as those of any businessman. Decisions to substitute machines for hand labor, initiate or expand irrigation and fertilizer use, or to combine his farming with nonfarm work will also be based on rationality rather than sentiment. Even his decisions on retirement and disposition of his farm are likely to be rational-oriented. Coverage by a retirement program, public or private, for example, will undoubtedly influence the time and the conditions of his retirement, and upon retirement, control of his farm will not go " automatically to his children in the traditional manner. By the time of retirement, his children may no longer be interested in the farm, except for the money its sale might bring.

The size of the farming enterprise will have some bearing on degree and kind of *Gesellschaft* role characteristics of farm owners. Small-size operations are more likely to impede the shift to *Gesellschaft* behavior. Farmers with farms large enough to employ a number of workers, for example, will find themselves serving as " general managers," planning, budgeting, overseeing production and marketing, and also as "personnel managers," hiring, keeping employment records, and even negotiating with labor organizations.

While the role of farm owners, especially of large farms, is apt to become more rational, functionally specific, and with more limited and formally defined responsibilities, tenants too will be caught up in the trend. Leases will be more formalized and specific, calling for specific obligations from the tenant. Tenants on larger and more prosperous farms will find themselves in much the same role as owners, while tenants on smaller and marginal farms may not assume so many and such specific contractual obligations. But tenants in general are likely to experience the impact of urbanization in all its aspects. Off-farm employment may be expected to increase most rapidly among the lower-income tenants. Tenants, more than owners, are likely to regard farming as a job rather than a way of life.

# CHAPTER FIFTEEN

# Changing Ecology of Land Tenure Systems

## Introduction

THE ECOLOGY OF land tenure systems refers to the relationship between land tenure systems and the environment in which they appear. In a broad sense environment includes both physical and cultural settings. This chapter shows how tenure patterns and forms vary in response to environmental conditions found in the different regions of the nation.

The large ranch-type farms in the West are in direct contrast to the small family-type farms in the Appalachian region of the East. Likewise, the arid and semiarid conditions of the West prescribe special moisture conserving farm practices far different from farming techniques observed in the more humid sections of the nation. The daily routine associated with the popular dairy enterprise in the Northeast is noticeably absent in the highly seasonal farming of the wheat belt, and cotton culture in the South varies appreciably from the farming patterns observed in the corn belt.

Farms in the United States, whether operated by owners or by tenants, vary greatly in character from one section of the country to another. In fact, neighboring farms can differ appreciably in size, type of farming, resource use, and profitability. Despite these variations, however, there appears to be a definite relationship between the rate of farm tenancy and type of farming. Areas of high tenancy are found to predominate in areas of specialized cash-crop production, namely in the South and North Central areas.

Although specialized farming areas do not conform exactly to the geographic divisions used in reporting agricultural census data, it is surprising how well the specialized farming regions conform to the major geographic divisions.

The four major geographic divisions, namely Northeast, North Central, South, and West, embrace major types of farming areas.[1]

The Northeast region is characteristically a dairy producing section. The North Central area is more diverse in that it includes the corn belt, a large part of the wheat and small grains area, and a part of the general farming area in the Allegheny Mountains. The South consists primarily of the cotton belt but also includes that part of the range and livestock area found in west Texas and the general farming area of the Piedmont Plateau. The West is essentially range and livestock country.

Spottily scattered among the major geographic regions are the fruit, truck, and special crops areas. These are relatively small within a given region because they rely on some unique feature to provide a particular advantage to special crop production; for example, air drainage for grapes, muck soils for vegetables, nearness to market for truck crops, or water-tempered climate for fruits.

## Geographic Distribution of Farms

### Number

According to the 1954 Agricultural Census there were about 4,783,000 farm operators in the United States. About 339,000 of these were in the Northeast, 1,704,000 were in the North Central region, 2,317,000 in the South, and only 423,000 in the West.[2]

The Northeast region today ranks fourth in number of farms, but prior to 1925 it ranked third. The West continued to add new farms

---

[1] The Northeast includes the New England and North Atlantic states (Maine, New Hampshire, Vermont, Massachusetts, Rhode Island, Connecticut, New York, New Jersey, and Pennsylvania). The North Central states are Ohio, Indiana, Michigan, Wisconsin, Illinois, Missouri, Iowa, Minnesota, North Dakota, South Dakota, Nebraska, and Kansas. The South includes the South Atlantic, and East and West South Central states (District of Columbia, Delaware, Maryland, Virginia, West Virginia, North Carolina, South Carolina, Georgia, Florida, Kentucky, Tennessee, Alabama, Mississippi, Arkansas, Louisiana, Oklahoma, and Texas). The West includes the Mountain and Pacific Coast states (New Mexico, Colorado, Wyoming, Montana, Idaho, Utah, Arizona, Washington, Oregon, and California). The eight major types of farming areas are portrayed in Map Negative 47424-X published by the U. S. Department of Agriculture.

[2] *A Statistical Summary of Farm Tenure, 1954* (Agricultural Information Bulletin No. 200 [Washington: Agricultural Research Service, USDA, 1954]), 10–11.

during the period 1900 to 1935, while the number in the Northeast was declining. By 1954 the number in the Northeast had been reduced to 339,000, or about one-half the 678,000 that existed in 1900.

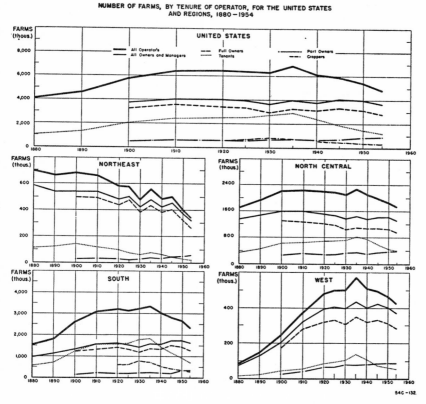

NUMBER OF FARMS, BY TENURE OF OPERATOR, FOR THE UNITED STATES AND REGIONS, 1880–1954

FIG. 15. The emerging tenure picture in the United States depicts an average of tenure trends for the major regions of the nation.

### Size

In the past fifty years the average size of farms in the Northeast increased from 92 to 121 acres. In the South the average has increased from 105 to 167 acres. In the North Central region the average farm has been generally twice as large as the average for the Northeast, increasing from 144 acres in 1900 to 232 acres in 1954. In the western states the average acreage per farm exceeds that of any other region.

In fact, during the past fifty years the average size in the West has always been four to six times larger than the average size in the Northeast; an average of 297 acres in 1910 increased to 800 acres in 1954.

## Value

The average value of land and buildings per farm has fluctuated in accord with general business trends. From 1900 to 1920 the trend was upward. From 1920 to 1930 the values moved downward irregularly with a very decided decline from 1930 to 1935. Since 1935 farm values have been consistently climbing but have recently indicated a tendency to level out.

In the United States average values have increased from about $5,000 in 1935 to $33,000 in 1959, an increase of more than six and one-half times. Preliminary data from the 1959 census of agriculture indicate similar increases within the major geographic regions.[3] In the Northeast the average value of land and buildings per farm increased from about $5,000 in 1935 to about $27,000 in 1959. The increase for the North Central states was equally impressive in that the average farm value jumped from $7,000 in 1935 to about $39,000 in 1959.

The average value of a western farm increased from about $9,000 in 1935 to about $75,000 in 1959, an increase of more than eight times. A similar increase was evident in the South where the average farm value in 1959 was about $24,000, as compared to the $3,000 average value in 1935.

Although one might be inclined to associate a high rate of tenancy with areas of high capital value, this does not appear to be the case. In fact, the reverse seems to be more evident. Whereas, the average farm values are highest in the West, followed in order by the North Central, Northeast, and the South, the proportion of tenancy is highest in the South followed by the North Central, the West, and Northeast regions. Thus, the rate of tenancy cannot be said to be the direct result of the high capital investment required to become an owner-operator. The high rate of tenancy in the South may be attributed not so much to the capital requirements but rather to the traditional plantation system of farming, which evolved from the days of slavery. Furthermore, contrary to popular belief, there are more white tenant operators in the South than there are nonwhite tenants.

[3] Preliminary data from the 1959 Census of Agriculture, *Farm Real Estate Market* (Washington: E. R. S., USDA, May, 1961), 2.

## Land Tenure Systems in the United States

For our purpose the tenure systems to be discussed will be identified by the relationship of the farm operator to the land, as reported in the Agricultural Censuses.

### Types of Tenure

As indicated in Chapter 7, farm operators may be divided into two broad tenure groups; that is, farmers who own the land they operate and those who farm the land they do not own. In the owner-operator group there are two types, the full-owners and the part-owners. The full-owners own all the land they operate. The part-owners operate leased land in addition to what they themselves own.

In the farm tenant group there are four major types of tenancy—namely, cash, share, share-cash, and croppers.

The proportion of farm operators who owned all of the land they operated in 1954 varied only from 55 to 77 per cent among the four major geographic regions. The highest ratio was found in the Northeast where 77 out of 100 were full owners, followed by 66 out of 100 in the West and 55 out of 100 in both the North Central and Southern regions. The full-owners and part-owners together account for three-fourths of all the farm operators according to the 1954 Census of Agriculture.[4] Tenants and managers make up the other one-fourth, with the managers accounting for less than one per cent of the total.

## Trends in Ownership

Although the proportion of full-owner operators appears to be declining in three of the four regions, the proportion of part-owner operators is increasing. Combining the two types of ownership more aptly reflects the true ownership trends. With this grouping in mind, the proportion of owner-operators in 1954 amounted to 93 per cent in the Northeast, 87 per cent in the West, 77 per cent in the North Central region, and 70 per cent in the South.

### The Northeast

The proportion of farm ownership in the Northeast consisted of a series of continuous increases and ranged from 77 per cent in 1900

[4] *Ibid.*, 6.

to 93 per cent in 1954. In each of the other three regions there was a general decline in rate of ownership from 1900 to about 1935 and then a gradual increase for the remainder of the period.

The continued high proportion of ownership in the Northeast is indicative of the early agricultural development in that area. The farms are typically small and indicative of early settlement patterns. The proximity to heavily populated areas has provided economic support for the small, family-type, dairy farm characteristic of that region. The daily routine of dairying, the regularity of income through monthly milk checks, and the certainty in living patterns provides a stability in this area that favors ownership of farms. Not only is tenancy low in this area, but the existing tenancy is usually of the cash-rent type—one of the most independent types of tenancy.

The rural population of the Northeast contains the remnants of a hodgepodge of nationalities indicative of the diverse immigrant groups that established early settlements in the area. Northern Europeans were among the first settlers and included groups from England, Ireland, Scotland, the Scandinavian countries, Poland, and Germany. The French Canadians, Italians, Swiss and other immigrant groups came into the area a little later, mostly after 1870. The early immigrants who took up farming in this country were by tradition hardworking and frugal. They were obsessed with the desire to have their own properties and to enjoy personal freedoms previously denied them. These historical, economic, and cultural characteristics undoubtedly explain the relatively high rate of ownership that has continued in this section of the country for the past half century.

### North Central Region

A large part of the North Central region is today owned and farmed by descendants of immigrants from northern Europe, with much the same cultural background that existed earlier in the Northeast. Nevertheless, a decline in rate of ownership was evident during the first thirty years of this century because of adverse influences such as drouths and widely fluctuating prices in a grain oriented economy. The proportion of ownership in 1900 was 71 per cent. By 1935 it had declined to 63 per cent and then increased to 77 per cent in 1954.

The corn belt has historically been subject to booms and busts associated with long-time price cycles. At the peak of the price cycles the farmers' financial problems are minimized while at the trough of the cycle those who are heavily mortgaged, or have large investments in operating equipment, find they are unable to carry the financial burdens. One such period of economic bust occurred at the end of World War I and another in the early 1930's.

Another factor contributing to the slight rise in tenancy from 1900 to 1930 was that, at this time, the early homesteaders, who had gained possession of the farms in pioneer days, were dying or retiring in increasing numbers. Frequently those retiring retained ownership and leased the farms to tenants.

## The South

Farm tenancy has been historically more prevalent in the South than in any other region. The percentage of ownership was 52 per cent in 1900, decreased to 44 per cent in 1930, and increased to 70 per cent in 1954. The South also has the highest proportion of its total population living on farms, and the highest proportion of non-whites in its population. The people, white as well as Negro, are almost all native born. In 1940 less than one per cent were foreign born.

Early migrants into the Cotton Belt came from northern Europe, especially the British Isles. Smaller numbers came from France and Germany. English backgrounds predominate among the white people, except in southern and central Louisiana where French ancestry prevails. A few small cultural islands of Germans, Czechs, and Italians resulted from sporadic migration into Texas, Oklahoma, and Louisiana.

The foreign influence on tenancy in the South has been relatively insignificant in comparison to its effect in the North Central and Northeast regions. The relatively high rate of tenancy is attributed to the presence of the Negro. The Negro is closely identified with cotton-plantation farming. In fact, the vast majority of all the Negro farm operators in the country live in the South. Slightly more than one-third of them are landowners, the balance are tenants, and half of these are croppers. The trends toward mechanization and larger farm units have already had important influences on tenure and population adjustments in the South. Since 1930 there has been a sharp decline in number of tenants and a steady out-migration of Negroes.

## The West

The proportion of ownership in the West has been slightly higher than in the South. It was 80 per cent in 1900, decreased to 74 per cent in 1935, and then increased to 87 per cent in 1954. Settlers to the

West came chiefly from the midwestern states and from north European countries. Those from other states migrated westward from the corn belt, some farther east and a lesser number from the South. Those who came from Europe were chiefly from Germany, Austria-Hungary, and Russia. In the Southwest the influence of the Spanish and the Indians is still much in evidence.

Throughout the West there are many large ranch operations. The average farm operation in 1954 consisted of about 800 acres, with part-owners operating an average of slightly more than 2,000 acres per unit.[5]

## Trends in Tenancy

In 1935 the number of farms in the United States reached the highest number ever reported, a total of 6.8 million farms. During the next twenty-five years there was a gradual decline and reclassification of farms so that the 1959 census reports 3.7 million. The number of farms operated by tenants followed a similar pattern of growth and subsequent decline. The peak in number of tenant-operated farms, reached in 1935, was about 2.9 million, or 42 per cent of all farms. In 1959 the rate of tenancy in the United States had dropped to an all-time low of 20 per cent.

### The South

A comparison of the number of farms and the rate of tenancy by major geographic regions reveals that, historically, the South has always had the largest number of farms and also the highest rate of farm tenancy. There was a continual increase in number of farms from the 2.6 million in 1900 to 3.4 million in 1935 and a subsequent decline to 1.6 million, as reported in the 1959 Census of Agriculture. Since the South contains about one-half of all the farms and almost two-thirds of all the tenant operators, it determines to a large degree the overall farm-tenure trends for the United States. Thus it will be noted that the trends for number of farms and rate of tenancy in the South parallel those for the United States.

Tenancy in the South included 1.2 million tenant operators in 1900. The number continually increased to a peak of 1.8 million in 1935 and then continued to decline until a low of 381,000 was reached in the latest Agricultural Census of 1959. Percentagewise, it can be stated that 47 per cent of the farms in the South were tenant operated in

[5] *A Statistical Summary of Farm Tenure, 1954,* 39.

1900; by 1930 the proportion had increased to 55 per cent, but since that time there has been a very rapid decline to about 23 per cent in 1959.

Share tenancy is the predominant type of tenancy in the South, and practically all of this is crop share rather than livestock share. At the turn of the century about one-half of the tenants were share-tenants, but the proportion has been dwindling so that now slightly more than a third are share-tenants.

Since croppers are distinguished from share-tenants only for the South, it is noted that in 1930 almost one-fourth of the farm operators were classified as croppers, and by 1954 the proportion had dropped to about 12 per cent.

Another differentiation made for the South is that nonwhite operators are distinguished from white operators. Tenure characteristics between the two groups are decidedly different. Whereas, during the peak tenancy period of the 1930's about 46 per cent of the white operators were tenants, among the nonwhites the rate of tenancy was about 80 per cent. By 1954 white tenancy was down to 22 per cent and nonwhite tenancy was 61 per cent.

### The North Central Region

The North Central region runs a close second to the South in number of farms, but because farms are larger in size, the total farm acreage in the North Central region exceeds that of the South by about five million acres. The number of tenant operators in the North Central region has consistently been about one-half the number in the South. In 1900 there was about 613,000 tenant operators. By 1935 the number had increased to 821,000. This increase was indicative of the back-to-the-farm movement during the depression years. With the improvement of general economic conditions there followed a gradual exodus of farm people so that by 1954 the number of tenant operators had dropped to 396,000. Here again it is necessary to point out that, although the number of tenant operators in the North Central region is only half the number found in the South, the tenant operated acreage exceeds that for the South by about thirty-one million acres.

Despite the secular rise and fall in tenancy it is evident that the fluctuation was very moderate when compared to changes which had occurred in the South during the past fifty years.

The percentage of tenancy within the region increased from 28 per cent in 1900 to 36 per cent in 1935 and then began a gradual decline to a low of 23 per cent in 1954. Share tenancy in general accounted for about one-half of the tenant operations, and this was again almost equally divided among livestock-share and crop-share tenancies. Cash-share tenancy seems to be declining in popularity. Although it represented 9 per cent of the tenancy in 1930, it now accounts for less than 3 per cent.

### The Northeast

In the Northeast the trend in tenancy was downward just as for the trend in number of farms, but the rate of decline was much more rapid, so that the 141,000 tenant operators in 1900 declined to only 20,000 in 1954. This represented a change from 21 per cent tenancy in 1900 to only 6 per cent in 1954, and one-third of these were cash-rent tenants.

### The West

As indicated previously, since 1925 the number of farms in the West closely approximates the number in the Northeast. Nevertheless, the number operated by tenants in the West has recently been more than double the number of tenant operations in the Northeast. Despite this, however, the combined tenants of the Northeast and West still would be only one-fifth as many as there are in the North Central region, and slightly less than one-tenth the number found in the South.

The percentage of tenancy in the West increased from 14 per cent in 1910 to a peak of 24 per cent in 1935 and then declined gradually, so that by 1954 it had dropped to about 12 per cent. Only about one-fourth of the tenants operate on a cash-tenant basis.

The proportion of land under tenancy in the West follows a trend similar to that for the South and North Central regions. There was a gradual increase in tenant-operated acreage from 1900 to 1935 and then a sharp decline, with the result that the Census of Agriculture reports a tripling of tenant-operated acreage from 1900 to 1935, but a 36 per cent decline from 1935 to 1954.

## The Influence of Soils and Metropolitan Centers on Tenure

According to agricultural location [6] and metropolitan dominance theories,[7] the size of the metropolitan center, the distance from it,

---

[6] Johann H. von Thunen, *Der Isolierte Staat in Beziehung auf Landwirtschaft and Nationalokonomie* (Berlin: Hempel and Parey, 1895); August

the soil, and other physiographic resources are major factors in creating differentials in the composition and distribution of the farm population and agricultural land uses.

Johann Von Thunen was perhaps the first to detail systematically the influence of market centers and geographical location (distance from an urban center) upon agricultural land-use patterns. Assuming one vast self-sufficient, isolated state having but one large city—the manufacturing and processing site for all nonagricultural commodities —with a uniform physical plain stretching outward to a broad wilderness separating it from the rest of the world and with prevailing modes of technology and land travel, von Thunen described the specific land utilization patterns which are found in each successive concentric farming " zone " from the city.

Then, to show that the unit cost of shipment of farm products was really the basic economic factor rather than distance, per se, in determining land-use patterns, he observed that, when a navigable river bisected the isolated state and shipping costs of farm commodities were cut to one-tenth that of conventional modes of land movement, the limits of the farming zones along the navigable stream were extended ten times the distance of those in areas unaffected by navigation. Similarly, he indicated that modifications in existing land transport systems altered the shape of farming zones, thereby changing the economic rent margins for competing crops and land uses. Various writers have amplified von Thunen's original concepts, making them somewhat more realistic as analytical tools for a greatly altered agricultural system, indicating that variations in natural resources, soil

Losch, *The Economics of Location* (New Haven: Yale University Press, 1954); Edgar S. Dunn, *The Location of Agricultural Production* (Gainesville: University of Florida Press, 1954); E. T. Benedict *et al.*, *Theodor Brinkman's Economics of the Farm Business* (Berkeley: University of California Press, 1935); Walter Isard, *Location and Space-Economy* (New York: The Technology Press and John Wiley & Sons, Inc., 1956); Edgar M. Hoover, *The Location of Economic Activity* (New York: McGraw-Hill Book Co., 1948).

[7] Roderick Ducan McKenzie, *The Metropolitan Community* (New York: McGraw-Hill Book Co., 1933); Amos H. Hawley, *Human Ecology* (New York: The Ronald Press, 1950); Edmund de S. Brunner and J. H. Kolb, *Rural Social Trends* (New York: McGraw-Hill Co., 1933), Chap. 5, Appendix D; Warren S. Thompson and Nelle E. Jackson, " Fertility in Rural Areas in Relation to Their Distance from Cities," *Rural Sociology*, Vol. 5 (June, 1940), 143–62; Otis Dudley Duncan, " Gradients of Urban Influence on the Rural Population," *The Midwest Sociologist*, Vol. 18 (Winter, 1956), 27–30.

characteristics, climate, settlement patterns, transportation routes, cultural values, physical barriers, historical accidents, and other factors affect land-use patterns.

Still others have employed the ecological concepts of dominance and subdominance to characterize metropolitan and regional communities, to delineate their vast networks of interrelationships, and to determine their ties of economic, social, and political integration and interdependence. Using these analytical tools, many have explored various demographic, economic, and social gradients of metropolitan and/or urban influence over outlying areas.

Theoretically, urban influence increases as cities grow in size. Moreover, urban influence increases as distance decreases, irrespective of city size. This also signifies that, with an increase in distance from urban areas, one finds more extensive land uses, larger farm units, a relative decline in farm tenancy, and a corresponding decline in the density of the farm population. Oddly enough, with increased distance from metropolitan centers there is an apparent increase in number of males to females and an increase in the birth rate among the farm population.

Conversely, as one moves from rural areas toward large market centers, land uses progressively intensify, farm units decrease in size, farm lands increase in value per acre, farm population density rises, and the birth rate falls. With nearness to urban centers, the level of adult education of the farm population improves, the proportion of females in the labor force increases, the level of living of the farm-operator's family is elevated, intensive crops make up a greater proportion of farm income, and the proportion of operators working off their farms one hundred days or more per year continues to increase.

Economists, ecologists, geographers, and sociologists continue to explore man's production and social activities, trying to ascertain precisely their spatial arrangements. Because of the large number of relevant variables, their complexity and diversity, and the rapidity of technological changes in agriculture, research findings are rather inconclusive on many points. No one has, as yet, conclusively established whether farm land uses and population characteristics differ because of climate, soil, nationality, nearness to cities, varying sizes of the metropolitan areas, or because of historical accident. On one thing they will agree, however, and that is the possibility that all of these factors are important and interrelated considerations in explaining farm tenure arrangements and rural population characteristics.

# Part 5: Research Approaches, Needs, Methods, and Concepts

PART V IS an effort to pull together what might be termed the philosophy and working tools of land tenure study. Before seriously embarking on a research project, one needs to conceive the overall "problem" of land tenure in the United States. This is the purpose of Chapter 16. Chapter 17, in a logical sequence, appraises the current tenure research trends and needs in the nation. After this, in Chapter 18 the reader is given a general review of methods and techniques which might be used in a tenure research project.

# CHAPTER SIXTEEN

# The Land Tenure Problem in National Perspective

In the United States it is customary to speak of the " farm problem " in an overall or generic sense. The " land tenure " problem may be spoken of in the same way. As a matter of fact, the " farm problem " and the " land tenure problem " are so closely related that it is impossible to disassociate the two, except in an abstract way. The former has received much attention by scholars, with many articles, workshops, symposiums, and books devoted to this theme. Robin Williams has summarized its several crucial points as follows:

1. We have a market-oriented agricultural economy into which technological innovations are rapidly and continuously introduced.

2. The net effect is to increase greatly productivity per unit of land and labor.

3. But the inelastic demand for agricultural products, in the face of greater production and lower costs among the more efficient commercial producers, leads to " surpluses "—production in excess of population growth and hence of effective demand.

4. Even with a rapid decrease in the number of farmers, the transfer of farm workers to other employment does not proceed rapidly enough to equalize agricultural returns with those which would result from alternative employment of factors of production.

5. The resulting " hidden underemployment " and comparatively low returns leads to:
   a) very low returns to the less efficient producers;
   b) an incessant race even on the part of the more efficient producers to stay ahead of the " price-cost squeeze ";
   c) under past and current political conditions, special aid

and supports to commercial farmers have been established to meet this situation;

d) considerable public dissatisfaction with the existing
modes of coping with a chronic farm problem is present,
and may be growing.[1]

The important consideration for this discussion is that low income,
rural-urban migration, and other aspects of the farm problem are
related to or have ramifications for tenure arrangements. This chapter
proposes to focus attention on the overall nature of the "tenure
problem" and to describe its various facets.

## The Nature of the Tenure Problem

For the purposes of the present discussion the overall tenure problem may be posed as having three major facets. The first is manifest
in the fact that farm business units cannot fall below a minimum
income level if equitable income (compared to national per capita
incomes) is to be maintained. The second is found in the difficulties
associated with achieving "equitable" income for all tenure status
groups under certain tenure conditions. The last facet is a function
of change. It is the dilemma faced in trying to maintain adequate
and efficient social organization when advancing technology and resultant changes in tenure arrangements serve to reduce the number
of people to such an extent that schools, churches, etc., cannot survive.
Each of these aspects of the overall tenure problem will be elaborated
and illustrated in the discussion which follows.

### The Persistence of Large Numbers of Uneconomic Farm Units

The problem of low income in agriculture is partly due to the
farmer's lack of access to land resources. Evidence of this fact is
found in the studies made of homogeneous agricultural regions. These

[1] Robin M. Williams, *Rural Sociology in a Changing Society: Future Prob-
lems and Prospects* (Seminar proceedings of a North Central Rural Sociology
Committee, NCR–5 [Columbus: Ohio Agr. Ext. Ser., Ohio State University,
November 11, 1959]), 2–3. For a comprehensive summary of the farm problem
see Earl Heady and Joseph Ackerman, "Farm Adjustment Problems: Their
Cause and Nature and Their Importance to Sociologists," *Rural Sociology in
a Changing Economy* (Seminar proceedings of North Central Rural Sociology
Committee [Urbana: Dept. of Agri. Econ., University of Illinois, November
13, 1958]), 2–14.

studies have clearly shown that income derived from farming is closely correlated with the amount of land and other capital applied to the individual farm operation. Despite the trend toward consolidation of farms (see Chapter 6) the number of extremely small farms remains large. It may be noted that the average size of farms in the United States now exceeds 300 acres, but that 80 per cent of all farms fall below 260 acres. Farms of less than fifty acres make up more than one-third of the farms in the nation.[2] The latter are generally insufficient to maintain an adequate income, not to mention level of living, as measured by national standards.

Several factors account for the persistence of small farms in certain regions of the nation. The first may be identified as the fixed nature of land and the fact that farm lands are customarily sold in units. The presence of a dwelling and other buildings add to the sale price of farm land but may be of little value to the buyer who already has such facilities.

A second factor complicating the process of adding land resources is the usual wish or desire to keep farm holdings contiguous. If fragmentation of holdings is to be avoided, the farmer must purchase land that borders his acreage. Neighboring farmers are generally not interested in selling but rather in buying. When such acreage is put on the market, sellers are aware of the demand for land close by and inflate the price of land they hold next to a prospective buyer. This practice represents a problem which is difficult both to detect and to cope with.

A third factor which militates to keep small farms small is the difficulty of obtaining credit. One might think that available credit sources should be ample for farmers interested in expanding. However, in a practical sense, the farmer who is on a small farm and has a low income is in an unfavorable position to compete for credit in the commercial market. Government loan programs may help, but to date have not served to alleviate this problem to a great extent. In some areas of low income, vertical integration has been tried as a way

---

[2] For 1959 the preliminary census report shows that farms of less than fifty acres comprised 28 per cent of all farms. However, if farms are defined according to the less restricted definition used in 1949, approximately 35 per cent of all farms are in the less than fifty-acre class. The change in definition of farm from 1950 to 1960 and the consequent drop in the number of share-croppers accounted for about 60 per cent of the decrease in "farms" of less than fifty acres.

of obtaining operating credit. However, this type of arrangement is
limited to enterprises in which relatively few farmers are employed.
In addition, initial capital outlay requirements quite frequently represent insurmountable barriers.

A fourth factor which serves to retard the increase of farm size may
be identified as cultural lag. This is the situation when traditional
patterns of operation and income are considered satisfactory, and

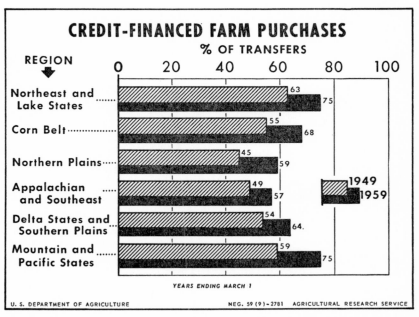

FIG. 16. Credit continues to be an important aid in facilitating farm purchases.

efforts to better one's self are not felt necessary. In other words, while
the practices of certain farmers are outdated and their income low
by national standards, they do not have a feeling of insufficiency.
Thus, they make no effort to acquire the size of unit necessary for
what might be considered an acceptable level of living. Many operators
of so-called subsistence farms fall in this class.

In studying the problem of small-sized farms, we find that the
southern region of the United States has a disproportionate number
of units falling into this category. Nearly two-thirds of the farms in
the South have operations including less than thirty acres of crop

land and a similar percentage of southern farms has less than fifty acres of total farm land. While the farms of all sizes in the region comprise about two-fifths of the number of farms in the nation, southern small farms comprise about two-thirds of all the small farms in the nation.

The Ozark and Appalachian regions in the South serve as an excellent illustration of areas which have a problem of small-sized farms. In certain subregions of these regions more than 90 per cent of all farms are operated by the owners of the land. Tenancy is thus virtually unknown and could not be said to be a cause of low income in these areas. According to the 1954 Census of Agriculture, gross farm income (value of farm products sold) fell below $1,300 per farm for most of the counties of these regions. Studies made in connection with the Rural Development and Rural Area Development programs determined that many counties in this so-called " General and Self-Sufficing " region [3] were in the serious low income bracket for one of the following reasons: (1) a large percentage of farms had less than $1,000 residual farm income for the operator and his family; farm operator level-of-living indexes fell below the regional average, and 25 per cent or more of all commercial farms were classified as low production; or (2) the county farm operator level-of-living index was in the lowest fifth in the nation; or (3) 50 per cent or more of the commercial farms were classified as low production farms.[4]

While this is not the place to go into a detailed analysis of low income in the Appalachian and Ozark regions, it may be pointed out that lack of land resources is one of the most important factors in keeping farms small. The natural or physiographical features of these areas do not lend themselves to easy farming. Farmers are located in the small, fertile, well-watered coves and valleys, but the steep hillsides which rim the valleys prevent expansion. At the same time there has not been too great an inclination on the part of local farmers to expand their operations. Until recently most of them have appeared content to live a life more or less in isolation from the outside world.[5] At the present time there is an apparent recognition of the opportunity presented by a more efficient operation, but little can be done. The

[3] See Carl C. Taylor et al., *Rural Life in the United States* (New York: Alfred A. Knopf, Inc., 1949) , Part 4.

[4] *1954 Census of Agriculture, Annual Report, Statistics by Subject* (Washington: USDA, 1954) , 909, Map No. A54–326.

[5] *Ibid.*

limited amount of land, low income, and low capital accumulation form a vicious circle deterring man-land adjustments toward higher income.

### The Continuing Problem of Tenancy

The tenure classes found in the United States were discussed in Chapter 7. In this discussion it was noted that tenancy was decreasing in the nation as a whole. Despite the fact that the percentage of tenancy in the United States has dropped drastically since the 1930's, in some areas of the South a sizable percentage of the farm people still have the low tenure status of sharecropper. A " cropper " or " sharecropper " is a crop-share tenant who furnishes his labor and little else and who works under the close supervision of his landlord. The land worked by a sharecropper is often a small part of a larger enterprise operated as a single unit.[6] The latest census (1959) reports about 121,000 sharecroppers, the majority of whom are located in the Mississippi Delta and in the specialized tobacco and cotton growing areas of the southern Piedmont region. In these areas the number of sharecroppers exceeds the number of all other tenants. For the South as a whole the number of sharecroppers now equals about one-half the number of other tenants, although they make up only 10 per cent of all farm operators.

Many writers have shown that the economic and social status of sharecroppers is exceedingly low. Within other tenant classes there is a wide variation in the amount of land cultivated and in the productive resources employed by the operators. This is generally not true for sharecroppers. The average size of farm operated by the latter group was reported to be twenty acres in 1954. However, the actual amount of land in cultivation was apparently much below that figure. In a survey of farmers in the Arkansas Delta, it was found that 30 per cent of the sharecroppers interviewed were cultivating less than ten acres and 80 per cent had less than twenty acres. Only one per cent of the families reported a net income of more than $3,000 for the year.[7]

The sharecropper system usually does not provide for advancement

---

[6] There is a continuing debate as to whether sharecroppers should be classified as laborers or tenants. (See Chapter 7.)

[7] " Rural Development Survey " (unpublished; State Employment Security Division, Agr. Ext. Ser. and Exp. Sta., University of Arkansas, Fayetteville, 1957).

in terms of the agricultural ladder. For illustration, the study mentioned above discovered that there was no significant difference in the net income of age classes up to sixty-five years among sharecroppers. Normally the farm operators' incomes would gradually increase with age.

It is rare, even today, to find that the husband and wife in a sharecropper family have more than an elementary school education. These families generally hold attitudes and values toward education which are, to say the least, not favorable. Consequently, their children tend to have poor school attendance records and to drop out of school at an early age.[8]

There is no attempt here to discuss sharecropping per se but to show that this type of tenancy remains a major facet of the overall land tenure problem in the United States. In this regard, it must be remembered that, from the point of view of the landlord, the farm is not unlike any other business. The sharecroppers' function is to supply labor, and since the landlord is concerned with the entire farm operation, the tenant is called on to supply labor to the landlord as well as on the land nominally rented in. A conflict of interest, therefore, lies in the landlord's desire to avoid the risk of extending the harvest season and the sharecropper's need for work beyond the requirements of the land assigned to him. The result is a chronic oversupply of labor, which is reflected in the low income of sharecroppers. Interestingly, in areas where sharecropping is a predominant practice, resident wage labor, migratory labor, and sharecropper families have similar net incomes. The findings of recent studies indicate that Arkansas Delta Negro sharecropper families had an average income of $1,300, that Mississippi Delta Negro farm laborer households averaged an income of $845, that Negro farm households averaged $1,177, and that white migratory laborer households averaged an annual income of $1,893.[9] As long as substantial portions of the rural popula-

---

[8] The relation between high school drop-outs and tenure status is shown in Alvin L. Bertrand and Marion B. Smith, *Environmental Factors and School Attendance* (La. Agr. Exp. Sta. Bul. No. 533 [Baton Rouge: A. E. S., Louisiana State University, 1960]).

[9] " Rural Development Survey "; Nelson LeRay, " Negro Farm Labor in the Delta Area of Mississippi," (Abstracts of papers, 58th Annual Convention, Assoc. of Southern Agri. Workers), p. 15; and Melvin S. Brooks, *The Social Problems of Migrant Farm Laborers* (Carbondale, Ill.: Southern Illinois University, 1960), 63.

tion tend to remain in this low tenure class, there will be a " tenure problem," which will contribute to the " farm problem " of low income.

### Depopulation of Rural Areas

The third facet of the land tenure problem in this country is not readily recognized as related to tenure. It is the continued migration of persons from rural areas to urban areas. Although the social implications of migration out of rural areas were discussed in Part Four, certain pertinent facts are appropriate to review at this time. This trend is, of course, related to technology and other factors, but it has serious implications, which stem from a change in man-land relations as technology takes over and certain rural dwellers become displaced. The problem may be stated somewhat as follows:  The proportion of farmers who reside on the land cultivated by them has tended to approximate 93 per cent for several decades. However, the total number of families on farms has been reduced by nearly one-half since 1935, because of migration from farms to towns and cities. At present the average number of families residing on farms is about two per square mile, and indications are that there will be even fewer farm families in the future. Since the typical pattern in this country is for each family to reside on its holdings, rather than in a village, it can be seen that social organization stands to be affected. As a matter of fact, evidence is at hand which shows that some community centers or villages whose economy was based primarily on trade or other services supplied to farm people have suffered a population drop. With the decay of community centers, social institutions such as churches, schools, government, etc., begin to lose strength and virility. Indeed, adjustments in terms of social organization must be made if the community is to survive. The ruralite whose community is on the downgrade has two choices—increased isolation or increased participation in more remote communities. In either event, his interaction patterns likely will change and include more group contacts of a secondary nature. He also will probably resort more frequently to mass media type of communication. Studies have shown that changes of the above nature may result in a psycho-social isolation, with possibilities of deleterious effects on personality, among other things.

The weakening of rural neighborhoods and communities has other implications as well as the ones reviewed above. Folkways and mores undoubtedly will change as will rural values generally. What implications these have for the greater society is hard to say. However, one can anticipate a drastic change in the rural way of life as it has traditionally been known. These changes may or may not compound the tenure problem.

## The Land Tenure Problem in Perspective

The above discussion was designed to show the concrete aspects of the land tenure problem. In this section a more theoretical approach is made, to show the basic nature of the problem. If the concrete manifestation of the tenure problem is low income, then its more abstract implications may be seen in the resultant disparity between farmers' levels and standards of living. In sociological terminology levels of living represent actual consumption—that is, the goods, services, and conveniences actually owned or available. Standards of living, by contrast, have reference to the cognitive level of goods and services. In other words, level of living is what one has, while standard of living is what one knows about and would like to have.

In certain areas, then, because of the tenure problems previously discussed, there are serious gaps between farmers' consumption level for family living and for agricultural production and their wants in these regards. This discrepancy is partly a function of mass media of communication and of increasing contacts with outside persons and groups. The increased wants of persons in relatively low income situations are manifestly varied and cover such things as health and recreational services, as well as material goods for use on the farms or in the home.

The problem may be restated as one of standards of living continuing to rise at a time when the farmer's capacity to consume remains fixed or decreases. It may be generally illustrated by the fact that the gross income from the sales of products has decreased during the latter half of the 1950 decade. In 1959 the per capita income of farm people was only 44 per cent of the per capita net income of nonfarm people.

Farmers, in their endeavor to increase their income, compete with their fellow farmers and others for land. The result is that land values rise more rapidly than net returns from farming and there is a tendency to overproduce as an attempt is made to maintain and increase income levels.[10] The resulting surpluses present the nation with a dilemma.

[10] *Farm Production* (Agricultural Information Bulletin No. 239 [Washington: Agricultural Research Service, USDA, 1960]), 91.

Students of the farm problem have advocated two recourses for resolving the problem of oversupply of food and fiber. The first is shifting people out of agriculture, and the second is shifting land out of agricultural production. Obviously, these two suggestions are inter-related and must be done simultaneously in order to be effective.

Past experience indicates that the movement of people from farms in sufficient numbers to curtail farm production is an extremely com-plicated endeavor. For one thing, the population replacement in agri-culture for twenty years following World War II has been about double that necessary to maintain a constant number of people on farms. It may be noted that the rural birth rate rose between 1940 and 1947 and has been on a high plateau since that time. Thus, despite the excess of out- to in-migration in rural areas the number of people residing on farms has only been reduced by one-third since 1940.

In spite of the fact that opportunity for income is considered more promising in nonfarm occupations, the rate of migration of farm families is apt to diminish in the future. This is expected because migration has been selected for tenants. Tenants now comprise only a relatively small percentage of all farm operators.

The problem of shifting land out of agriculture is also a complicated one. In spite of policies and programs which have aimed at this goal, the acreage of land in farms continued to increase until recently. In 1954 the census reported more land in agriculture than ever before and in 1959, after extensive experiments with the " Soil Bank " and other programs, the amount of land in agriculture had only decreased by 3 per cent. Cropland did decrease by 10 per cent, however.

The tenure problem, then, is a serious one of adjusting man-land relations in such a way as to provide adequate and equitable incomes for ruralities, at the same time that national food and fiber needs are met.

# CHAPTER SEVENTEEN

# Tenure Research Trends and Needs in the United States

RURAL SOCIAL SCIENTISTS in the United States are continuously striving to discover ways and means of solving tenure problems. Currently the subjects under investigation by researchers include a variety of topics associated with recent trends in agricultural technology, population shifts, and agricultural programs. The topics listed in this chapter represent some of the more important areas which are being looked into or need looking into. Most of the topics treated here were reviewed in a recent publication issued by the Interregional Land Tenure Research Committee.[1]

## The Difficulty of Getting Started in Farming

Preceding discussions made it clear that the scarcity of land and the high costs of capital investment in machinery, livestock, etc., have made it difficult for the young person to get started in farming in the United States. This condition is considered one of the more serious tenure problems of today by many persons. The baffling question is, how can agriculture attract, acquire, and maintain its proportionate share of the qualified youths of the nation. Attempts to find answers to this question occupy the energies of many rural social scientists. The goal is to overcome institutional barriers to farm ownership by encouraging family-sized farms and making capital available for purchase or operation of economical units.

## The Relative Efficiency of Alternative Tenure Arrangements

The various types of tenure arrangements found in this country and abroad have been discussed in preceding chapters. Many questions

[1] *A Report Prepared by the Interregional Land Tenure Research Committee, Agricultural Land Tenure Research, Scope Nature: Reappraisal, 1955* (Chicago: Farm Foundation, 1955).

still persist regarding which type of arrangement presents the greatest efficiency in terms of agricultural production and social relationships. Although tenure researchers have learned much regarding the most efficient production methods, they have not determined how to bring about the necessary changes under certain tenure systems. In other

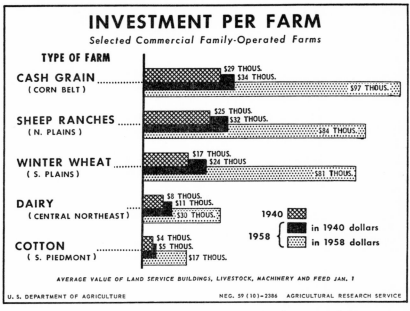

FIG. 17. Note the wide range in investment by type of farm.

words, while the economists may point out the farm management procedures and the combinations of capital and other inputs which make for maximum production efficiency, these practices may not be put into effect because they are not considered compatible to the tenure arrangements worked out by individual farmers. So the problems which continue to hold the interest of researchers relate both to the determination of the most efficient tenure system and of getting acceptance of certain procedures where particular tenure systems are apparent.

## The Impact of Federal Action Programs on Land Tenure

Each new Congress passes laws intended to help farmers. However, it is difficult to write a law which applies equally well to all regions, and it is even more difficult to administer these laws equitably. In the past, tenure legislation has invariably tended to favor certain groups over others. Tenure researchers are thus concerned with the differential impacts of each new program upon tenure groups, whether it be concerned with credit, conservation, subsidy, or market controls. They also have a continuing concern over how these programs might be administered equitably throughout the nation and for different size farm units.

## The Effect of Leasing Arrangements on Tenure

In a preceding chapter is was pointed out that a good lease was important to tenure efficiency. One of the characteristics of a good lease was the provision for maximum security and protection of the tenant's investment as well as that of the landlord. The research which continues along this line is devoted to finding out more about the type of leases best suited to particular types of farming areas and to particular types of production enterprises. Rapid technological changes in agriculture continue to alter the risks and uncertainties faced by different tenure groups, thus requiring continuing research to achieve equitable leasing arrangements.

## The Impact of Migration Patterns on Farm Tenure

Much has been written about migration patterns in the United States. Two types of migration especially affect tenure. One is the continuing stream of migrants from the rural areas of the nation to urban places. The second is the seasonal movement of laborers from one farm area to another. To date, few studies have been made which presume to assess the impact of these migrations on tenure arrangements generally. More study is also needed regarding the impact of migratory workers on housing, health, and other aspects of farm and community life.

## The Impact of Mineral Development on Land Tenure

It has already been pointed out in an earlier chapter that wherever minerals have been discovered in commercial quantities agricultural production has been affected. The impact of mineral activity on tenure relationships was also covered in detail. The purpose here is simply to remind the reader that this type of development has many implications for tenure and that research along this line is a matter of continuing concern.

## The Tenure Aspects of the Use of Water Resources

Tenure rights to water resources have been treated in a previous chapter. These problems magnify as the competition for limited water supplies continues to increase. In order not to belabor the obvious, it may be simply pointed out here that the many-faceted problems of water rights in tenure continue to represent an increasing share of the tenure research performed in this country.

## The Impact of Mechanization on Farm Tenure Arrangements

Farm mechanization, one aspect of technology, has proceeded at a very rapid pace throughout the nation. Some regions, especially, have been revolutionized by the introduction of machinery within the past few years. Machines displace laborers, create a need for more skillful workers, and alter cost structures which have far reaching implications for tenure. These matters are continually being studied and in many ways represent a genuine frontier in tenure research.

## The Impact of the OASI Amendments on Land Tenure

The Federal Social Security Program in 1954 enlarged its coverage to include farmers. As was noted in preceding discussions, the Social Security provisions will have a tremendous impact on farmers. The nature of this impact, however, is not yet fully known. Although some farmers will retire, the question remains as to how many. This and like questions are under study at the present time.

## The Land Tenure Problems of Minority Groups

One of the least studied areas of tenure is that associated with minority group problems. These problems stem from cultural conditioning and affect such groups as Negroes, American Indians, Mexicans, and Orientals. The nature of these problems is found in the fact that many of these groups have to expect lower pay, farm with less capital, use poorer land, and face a certain amount of discrimination of other kinds as well. Social scientists are interested in examining the factors related to this kind of tenure problem.

## The Question of Rural Zoning

The people of the United States have become so accustomed to a plentiful supply of land that many persons tend to play down the need for studying rural zoning. However, it is an undisputable fact that we have about reached the limit in the supply of arable land. In addition, cities, super highways and other structures keep taking some of our best lands out of production. The first problem which needs attention then is how should land be classified and then what restrictions should be imposed on its use.

Another question relating to zoning which needs further investigation is the esthetic factor. The English and others have recognized that " green belts " have such value. Also, it may be that lands should be zoned for sale to persons for only a particular predesignated use, so that this land might not remain idle or be used inefficiently. These and many other questions relating directly to zoning need more attention by tenure researchers.

## Changing Emphasis to Short Term Credit Needs

Prior to World War II farm mortgage credit received considerable attention. Following the war increasing emphasis was placed on the use of short-term or operating credit. There is every indication that short-term credit will continue to gain in importance because of the increased use of off-farm supplies in agricultural production. Tenure researchers are not only concerned with credit availability for farm purchases but also with marginal analysis in the use of credit for various farm enterprises. Their goal is to determine the proper application of capital and use of credit so that an individual may be spared financial distress and, in the aggregate, lessen the burden to society.

## The Influence of Taxes on Tenure

The taxes most closely related to land tenure are property taxes. In this country property taxes have been levied primarily to provide public revenues, but they have been used in other countries in a regulatory capacity to either encourage or discourage certain land uses. Past research has been concerned primarily with evaluating tax loads and assessment procedures. One facet of taxation that needs further exploration is how land taxes can be used to help a given tenure system fulfill a role compatible with the overall social goals of the nation.

Additional research is needed to determine the consequences of various exemptions, such as veterans and homestead benefits upon land values.

Another area of tax inquiry relates to the question of how estate, inheritance, and gift taxes affect the efficient use of resources and the access to these resources under various tenure systems.

## Risk and Uncertainty Related to Tenure

Ideally, a tenure system should eliminate the basic causes of risk and uncertainty.

Studies have shown that risk can be reduced to some extent through insurance coverage. Insurance for crops, livestock, farm mortgage, and even life insurance is available to most farmers. Technological developments such as rust resistant wheat and drought resistant corn will also help reduce risk. Uncertainty, however, continues to plague farmers.

Tenure decisions are influenced by risk and uncertainty. An operator faced with a cash-rent lease recognizes his vulnerable position in the event of a crop failure. The crop-share tenant, on the other hand, is in a better position to survive a crop failure. However, the short-term lease, usually one year with a renewable clause, adds to a tenant's uncertainty. The objective of research in this regard is to determine to what extent the various tenure forms are affected by risk and uncertainty.

## Legal Aspects and Land Tenure

The relationships among people regarding ownership, use, and occupancy of farm land has given rise to a large body of land tenure law. Ownership rights, inheritance, transfers, leases, contracts, taxes, and credit are some of the legal areas which have received research attention.

Since land tenure law is legislated at local and state levels, there is justification for each state to have its own legal studies without fear of unnecessary duplication.

Legal research is needed to (1) clearly interpret provisions of existing laws and to call attention to defects and inconsistencies, (2) evaluate legal provisions relative to benefits and goals of society, and (3) relate legal provisions to people's attitudes and current administrative and enforcement problems.

There is a continuing need for studies to evaluate the functional efficiency of specific programs in light of restrictions imposed by legal institutions. Does the law discourage business decisions which would otherwise bring about desirable economic changes and improved performance?

## Impact of Recreation on Tenure

The shorter work day, shorter work week, paid vacations, forced retirement, and high-speed transportation have all increased the time available for recreational activities. Demands for these facilities have increased accordingly.

Fortunately, there are many areas not fit for agricultural use that can be utilized for recreational purposes; but where this is not the case, there is a growing conflict for use of the land. The basic problem is to determine the income or benefits derived from recreational use versus agricultural use. Some research on this matter has been done, but more is needed to provide a basis for decisions regarding the most efficient use of the above resources. Sometimes it is possible to arrange for multiple use of the land whereby, during certain seasons or with certain controls, agricultural lands can be opened to recreational use such as hunting, fishing, hiking, skiing, camping, etc. Nevertheless, more research is needed to determine: (1) the demand for recreational lands, (2) the availability and location of land resources suitable for recreational purposes, (3) the feasibility of putting recreation on a pay-as-you-go plan so that costs are really allocated in proportion to individual benefits, and (4) the management techniques required for effective administrative and utilizaton of recreational areas.

## World Problems and Land Tenure

The United States, as a relatively young nation, has been blessed with a tenure system that reflects the philosophy and wisdom of its founders. Agricultural progress in terms of efficiency, stability, and opportunity has been unequaled in any other country. The successes, however, have not been achieved in isolation from the rest of the world but rather in a spirit of cooperation and helpfulness.

The foundation for our whole system rests upon the knowledge and experiences brought to this country by migrants from foreign lands. In like manner, the American people today are willing and anxious to share their prosperity, knowledge, and experiences with those less fortunate. Our agricultural development and technical assistance programs continue to be an important part of our foreign policy. Resources devoted to this effort provide mutual benefit to members of the world community.

In light of emerging agrarian reform movements in many parts of the world, even to the point of confiscation and redistribution of lands, there is a need for more research to bring into focus the land tenure problems so often contributing to land reform movements. The research would necessarily encompass the broad spectrum of tenure institutions including ownership patterns, tenancy, leasing arrangements, land rents, servitudes, land taxes, income taxes, inheritance taxes, agricultural credit, marketing provisions, conservation, and education.

Any comprehensive study for tenure improvement would necessarily consider changes to tenure institutions with the ultimate aim of achieving more efficient use of resources, more economic and social stability, and a more equitable sharing of agricultural benefits among the land workers.

## The Increasing Public Interest in Private Lands and Vice Versa

Conflicts between public and private interests have prevailed ever since the two institutions were recognized as having separate and distinct rights. The increasing public demand upon private lands is indicative of the broader role assumed by the government. The constantly expanding demand for land for public use, whether it be for highways, parks, military reservations, or easements for public utilities, conflicts with private rights of land ownership and use. The government, by virtue of its right of eminent domain and also its police power, can insist on private lands being used in a manner consistent with public welfare.

More research is needed to evaluate controversial private and public use of resources from the standpoint of costs and benefits. Group tenure arrangements need to be explored whereby the group's motives can be analyzed and tax burdens properly allocated among those receiving the benefits. A more definitive analysis of public and private interests in private land is needed to reveal whether these interests are complementary or conflicting. Findings will help guide citizens and their legislators in establishing policy.

In the reverse situation, there is considerable private interest in publicly owned agricultural land, particularly as to rights of use. Tenure arrangements usually consist of lease contracts which are quite varied as to length of term, rental rates, maintenance and upkeep provisions, and restrictions on land use. The direction of research in this context should focus on methods of transferring use rights and the evaluation of efficiency of resource use under government negotiation. Further emphasis should be directed to analyzing regulations governing the use of public lands, their effect on agricultural stability in a given area, and the opportunity for potential users to gain access to these lands.

Incidental to the methods of acquiring tenure rights, leasing arrangements deserve analysis to determine whether they contribute to resource development and conservation. Furthermore, what are the enforcement problems and to what extent does the presence of public lands affect the values of adjacent properties?

## Impact of Industrialization on Tenure

Over one-third of the farmers in the United States are classified as part-time or residential farmers. This proportion is expected to increase as industrialization extends more and more into rural areas. Industrialization is rather unique in that it can either help farmers to start up the agricultural ladder or to step off the ladder and move from farming into nonfarm pursuits.

Future research in this area is needed to determine: (1) how industrialization in rural sectors affects the efficient use of land and labor resources, (2) how economic and social stability are affected, (3) to what extent industrialization and part-time farming have fostered capital accumulation and family farm ownership, (4) whether part-time farming provides an adequate social and economic adjustment for low income farms, and (5) to what extent out-migration has been encouraged by off-farm opportunities.

The tenure patterns in industrialized areas differ appreciably from those in typically agricultural areas, but little research has been conducted to evaluate adequately these patterns in terms of conservation and efficient use of resouces. Farms near industrial areas are frequently idle, dotted with unused buildings and creased by rivulets. In other areas mushrooming structures and the need for utilities and public services places an undue burden on the taxpayer, particularly the landowner. In this respect, studies are needed to determine the proper allocation of costs for providing public services to emerging rural residential areas.

## The Influence of Farm Management Services on Tenure

The astounding growth in number of " gentlemen " and absentee farmers, particularly near metropolitan areas, is related to the increased use of farm management services. The availability of these services has undoubtedly influenced many nonfarm businessmen to purchase farms with the assurance that the farm would be skillfully managed.

Very little if any research has been directed to this type of tenure arrangement. Research in this area should determine: (1) to what extent the availability of farm management services influences nonfarmers to buy farms, (2) the impact of this third party on landlord-tenant relationships and resource allocation, (3) the effect of this arrangement on distribution of income, (4) the social and political implications in light of agricultural adjustments frequently leading to land reform movements, and (5) the feasibility of utilizing professional and technical services to improve income on low income farms.

## The Relation of Land Values to Tenure

Market values frequently shroud in mystery the true productive value of the land. Nonfarm forces tend to bid up land prices in excess of prices warranted by the productive or income producing ability of the land, thus creating insurmountable obstacles to those who wish to buy a farm and pay for it through normal farm operations. Apparently there is a need for capitalized value data to identify and quantify adequately the nonfarm factors which add to the productive value of the land.

Furthermore, as nonfarm factors add to the market price, it is conceivable that farm ownership will tend to deviate from owner-operator status toward absentee landlordism and increased tenancy.

More research is needed on problems of land pricing and the evaluation of land as a factor of production in the farm firm. The importance of land changes through time, as a result of technology and changes in factor combinations and prices.

In view of existing patterns of land values and within the framework of our tenure system, it is increasingly essential that research be directed to determining land rental rates in conformance with variations in factor productivity and with full recognition given to recent farm programs which dictate, to a limited extent, the use of the land.

# CHAPTER EIGHTEEN

# Methods and Techniques for Tenure Research

> " *Problems are solved not through vague generalities, or picturesque descriptions of the relations between man and the world, but through technical work.*"—*Hans Reichenbach,* The Rise of Philosophy.
>
> " *It has long been an axiom of mine that the little things are infinitely the most important.*"—*Sir Arthur Conan Doyle,* Adventures of Sherlock Holmes.

BRILLIANT INSIGHT IS sometimes credited with the solution of a problem but, more often than not, the success of a research undertaking depends on painstaking attention to the details of methodology. Research on the problems of land tenure is no exception. As this book approaches the subject of land tenure from the viewpoint of economics and sociology, it is useful to examine the concern for research methods which is common to both these disciplines of social science.

Successful research is constantly introspective. So this chapter begins self-consciously with some concepts of what research is. These concepts are followed by a description of how research is done and what research results show.

The research methods in this chapter are not unique to tenure; they are applicable to all fields of study. However, when possible, the examples in the text are directed more specifically toward illustrations in tenure.

The objective of this chapter is to give the beginning researcher guides to evaluation of research literature that he will encounter in tenure and other social sciences and an overview of scientific method that may be helpful to him in thinking through his own research problem.

A theory of inquiry is the way in which questions are asked and answered. As questions are put in a form capable of answer, the need for research emerges. Research, then, is a systematic means of, first, stating and, second, answering questions.

From the standpoint of research, what is a question? A " question " —or " problem "—is a framework for identifying the information needed to explain a situation or thing. The main difference, if any, between a question or problem in research and a question or problems in everyday language is that the former is so precisely stated that it has an answer which can be validly related to experience. The skill with which questions are asked often determines the relevancy and usefulness of the answers.

An answer or solution is the objective of a research effort. The answer therefore becomes (1) the guide for the scope and precise expression of its questions and (2) the object for a test of its adequacy. An answer, then, must be determinable and in such a form that its adequacy can be tested. From this definition it may be seen that a question (more exactly, the *form* of the question) is determined by the answer sought.

In a philosophical sense, answers, as objects of research, need not suggest some universal truth. Answers are always tentative; they are valid only in relation to their corresponding questions.

### Positive and Normative Approaches

The approach to research has a strong bearing on the methods used. The method of research employed in modern science and emphasized in this chapter is associated philosophically with the so-called *positive* approach. The difference between the positive and the *normative* approaches is that the former is concerned with *what is* and the latter with *what ought to be*.

" Ought to be " in this context does not necessarily imply good and evil but connotes the gap between some desired goal (or norm) with an existing situation. The narrowing of this gap becomes the objective of normative research.

In general, studies in the methodology of economics and sociology have made this distinction in order to: (1) evaluate the kind of inferences produced from research, (2) separate the type of results sought from research produced from each of the two approaches, and (3) differentiate the role of the research worker as a scientist from the role of the policymaker. The first reason is chiefly the subject of this chapter. The second and third reasons were demonstrated more fully in earlier chapters dealing with various policies and programs.

According to Milton Friedman,[1] who has explained the positive approach to economics research as succinctly as anyone, " the ultimate goal of a positive science is the development of a ' theory ' or ' hypothesis ' that yields valid and meaningful predictions about phenomena not yet observed." Studies aimed strictly at predictions are concerned with the development of appropriate models to explain what is, without attempting to say what ought to be. Thus land tenure problems, which are frequently related to policies and programs, present an excellent exercise in analytical surgery to separate the positive " is " elements from the normative " ought to be " elements. When this separation is made, the footings have been poured for the structure of scientific method applied to tenure problems.

### The Scientific Method

Although origins of the scientific approach to economic and social problems can easily be traced as far back as the early nineteenth century,[2] the full acceptance of social science is relatively recent. Until a generation ago the usefulness of scientific method to the study of social problems was still doubted by some researchers in the field. Today the occasional critic of the method of social science is usually outside the field. He is found among those who consider science a subject matter rather than a method of answering questions. The scientific method has been accepted almost universally by researchers on social and economic problems.

Since the scientific method was developed and accepted so slowly, it may seem an oversimplification to say that research is merely a systematic way of answering questions. The basic principles of the scientific method are, in fact, neither difficult nor mysterious. T. H. Huxley, for example, said about the scientific method:

[1] Milton Friedman, *Essays in Positive Economics* (Chicago: University of Chicago Press, 1953), 7.

[2] The works of John Stuart Mill, particularly *A System of Logic, Ratiocinative and Inductive, Being a Connected View of the Principles of Evidence and Methods of Scientific Investigation* (New York: Harper & Bros., 1900), and Auguste Comte, " Plan des travaux scientifiques nécessaires pour réorganiser la societé," *Système de Politique Positive* (Paris: chez Carilian—Goeury et Vor Dalmont, 1854), Chap. 3, were pioneer efforts toward the scientific organization of research into social problems.

The method of scientific investigation is nothing but the expression of the necessary mode of working of the human mind.
It is simply the mode at which all phenomena are reasoned
about, rendered precise and exact. . . .

There is a well-known incident in one of Moliere's plays, where
the author makes the hero express unbounded delight on being
told he had been talking prose during the whole of his life. In
the same way, I trust, that you will take comfort, and be de-
lighted with yourselves, on the discovery that you have been
acting on the principles of inductive and deductive reasoning." [3]

The essence of the scientific method is the formulation of hypotheses.
These hypotheses are no more than tentative answers so stated that
they are subject to confirmation or rejection when tested in experience. The questions or problems that precede these answers, of course,
must have been constructed in such a way that the hypotheses are
relevant. Thus, the researcher who employs the scientific process first
identifies the problem; second, he isolates its relevant components in
order to determine the question to be answered; third, he formulates
tentative answers—hypotheses—and specifies the tests necessary to
confirm or reject; and, fourth, he implements the test and confirms or
rejects the hypotheses.

A good researcher, like a good billiards player, keeps his eye on the
ball, which in this instance is the hypothesis. Most fuzzy thinking
and inconclusive research are due to failure either to form a useful
hypothesis or to use it as a guide in collecting and organizing facts.

## How Research Is Done

To some extent each research undertaking is unique, so it is not
possible to formulate a single, mechanical procedure for getting correct
answers to all questions. What follows, then, are some generalizations
about the research process which are common enough to be found in
one form or another in most inquiries in which the scientific method
is used.

The scientific method is a framework or procedure for organizing
information so that it bears most directly on the question under study.
In the course of building upon this framework, the scientific method

---

[3] T. H. Huxley, " We are All Scientists," *Treasury of Science*, ed. by Shopley,
Rapport and Wright (4th ed.; New York: Harper & Bros., 1958).

follows what has been called "the road of systematic doubt." That is, the scientific method does not doubt everything but directs inquiry toward certain specific questions while accepting other information as given. The device used to direct the inquiry is called a model.

A model is used to represent the design of an inquiry in a single, precise statement. In a narrow sense, the model is a hypothesis. In a broader sense, the model includes the problem, the assumptions, the hypotheses, and the tests of the inquiry. In scientific research, the model is similar to a blueprint in engineering.

Should the model take a mathematical form? The answer to this question depends, of course, on the study undertaken. For example, it is unlikely that, in a study in which mathematics is not used in the later phases, much would be gained by constructing a mathematical model. This is not always true, however, and even such a study might be improved by a precise symbolic statement in its earlier stage. There are two advantages of mathematics: (1) precision and (2) economy. The enforced exactness of defining a symbol can have the desirable effect of eliminating obscurities in an analysis. Manipulation of symbols is less likely to lead the researcher astray with shades of meanings than in manipulation of words. Symbols, of course, can have no more precision than the concepts they represent, and the researcher should not expect mathematical form to improve on an inadequate concept. The economy of symbols comes, first, from their abbreviated character and, second, from their reduction of redundancy.

Perhaps the chief advantage of symbols is that they can be manipulated with less chance of interpretative errors. It is possible that restatements of, and solutions to, problems are often suggested by a mathematical form.

### The Research Process

Analysis by way of the scientific method consists of a number (stated as four here) of separable but interconnected steps: (1) realization of the problem, (2) observation and isolation of the problem. (3) formulation of the hypotheses, and (4) analysis or test. Actual research projects may contain all or only some of these steps of the research process. Some researchers prefer to add a fifth step, recommendation. but in economics and sociology such a step frequently involves projections beyond the scope of inquiry and should not be included in the research process.

Not all of what researchers do is research as it is described in this chapter. Although it is useful and even necessary, much of the talking and writing of economists and sociologists is not analytical.[4] A complete program of research calls for outlining new problems, appraising present research, building broad conceptual frameworks,[5] developing measurement and testing devices,[6] offering policy adjustments, developing programs, and preparing materials for public use.[7] The four steps that follow describe only the analytical aspects of research.

*(1) Realization of the problem:* The awareness of a problem or of an unanswered question may arise through the interaction of a combination of individuals or in the mind of a single individual. Some problems are brought to the scientist, but probably most questions are conceived by him in his constant contact with the subject matter. In an overall sense the problem realization phase of research is nothing more than a vague expression of a phenomenon that is not clearly understood. It is the discovery that information about a situation or thing is complete. The scientist moves very quickly into the next step.

*(2) Observation and isolation of the problem:* A large volume of the work in a research undertaking is done in this phase. Here, the exact nature of the problem or question under study is specified. The problem is placed in its perspective, and all available information is reviewed. Standards for valid evidence are determined, and relevant and irrelevant facts are separated. The end product of this phase of the research is a clear statement of the question or questions in a way capable of answer.

*(3) Formulation of the hypothesis:* Tentative answers in a form capable of test are the objectives of this step. Frequently there is a

---

[4] A review of items of tenure literature in economics and sociology published between 1955 and 1960 showed very little fresh research. The rest consisted of situational and historical description, policy and program statements, data summaries, and extension-type " how-to-do-its."

[5] Walter E. Chryst, " Some General Considerations of Theoretical Foundations of Legal-Economic Research," *Legal-Economic Research*, ed. by Marshall Harris and John C. O'Byrne (Monograph No. 1 [Ames, Iowa: Agr. Law Center, 1959]).

[6] Alvin L. Bertrand, J. L. Charlton, Harald A. Pedersen, R. L. Skrabanek, and James D. Tarver, *Factors Associated with Agricultural Mechanization in the Southwest Region* (Southwestern Regional Bulletin No. 6, Ark. Agr. Exp. Sta. Bul. No. 567 [Fayetteville: A. E. S., University of Arkansas, 1956]).

[7] John F. Timmons and William G. Murray, *Land Problems and Policies* (Ames: Iowa State Press, 1950).

great deal of interaction between the last stages of Step 2 and the first stages of this step. It is here that a model is constructed in a mathematical form, if useful. Required evidence is specified so exactly that only the facts needed to test the hypothesis are used.

When fully stated, the hypothesis is not only a tentative answer; it is a framework of tests needed for acceptance or rejection of the answer. As such, the hypothesis forms the basis for the collection, organization, and analysis of data. The hypothesis also sets the limits of certainty required for its acceptance or, more correctly, to avoid its rejection.

It is the hypothesis that separates the scientific method from " common sense." Because the answers proposed by scientific hypothesis are hypothetical rather than categorical, they are subject to empirical test and thus require more than internal consistency. The hypotheses of empirical science require verification from outside the scheme from which they are developed.

(4) *Empirical test:* The final stage of the scientific process is subjection of the hypothesis to empirical test. Facts from the real world are arranged and compared with the hypothesis. The test is an integral part of the hypothesis itself for, unless it can be compared with experience, the hypothesis as such does not exist. Implicit in the construction of the hypothesis are the conditions for its acceptance or rejection.

An empirical test is diametrical; that is, it is the basis for either acceptance or rejection of the hypothesis—not for a little of each.

The conditions for acceptance or rejection of a hypothesis are determined before testing. Such conditions often include limits of tolerance for error.

Before turning to the practical problems of finding and using facts, a philosophic note of caution should be injected. Acceptance or rejection of a hypothesis neither proves nor disproves the truth of the proposition from which the hypothesis was derived. Empirical research concerns itself with the relation of hypotheses to experience, not with problems of determining truth.

## Evidence: the Selection and Use of Facts

The function of the scientific method is the relating of theory to the real world. The earlier steps of the research process are the development of models and hypotheses. The last step is testing the adequacy of the hypothesis; that is, how well does the hypothesis explain what we experience in the real world. An adequate test of the hypothesis requires valid evidence. Thus, the means for collecting, screening, and assembling evidence are crucial to the success of the research undertaking.

*Choosing facts:* Facts—the raw materials of research—are unrelated observations or experiences that are sufficiently definite for the researcher to accept. Facts are not necessarily true; they are simply accepted as true. As such, they are confirmed and verified to the satisfaction of the researcher, even though he realizes that, in a sense, the acceptance of a fact is an assumption.

Obviously in research one neither collects all facts nor collects facts at random. The person who says, "Let's get all the facts first," is talking nonsense. In all observations the selecting and ordering process is at least implicit. Research makes this process explicit. First, the population [8] is defined, and the portion of the population to be observed is specified. Second, groups of facts are examined in terms of their relevance to the research question. Third, each fact or group of facts is examined in terms of its accuracy (acceptability).

Of each bit of data, of each fact, two questions should be asked: Is it relevant? Is it right, i. e., acceptable?

*Finding facts:* Sources of information for research may be " primary," meaning direct observation or interview of the persons or things studied, or " secondary," meaning indirect evidence obtained from sources other than the persons or things studied. Most research undertakings will use both of these sources. Although specific sources of information are suggested by the particular research problem, there are general sources that are helpful to researches in land tenure. The following are suggested.

### A. THE LIBRARY.

A review of literature on the subject studied is necessary background. Usually the library is the first stop on a research route.

*(1) Journals.* Many articles containing pertinent information, as well as major papers presented at economic, statistical, legal, sociological, and other association meetings, appear in professional journals. See, for example, *Journal of Farm Economics; Land Economics; Rural*

---

[8] The population is *the entire group* about which the researcher will be making statements, not just the group he observes.

*Sociology; Journal of Political Economy; American Journal of Sociology; American Economic Review*; Law Reviews of the relevant states; *Journal of Law and Economics*; and *Journal of Farm Managers and Rural Appraisers.*

(*2*) *Bibliographies.* Innumerable bibliographies on specific subjects, including bibliographies of bibliographies, are available, but the general researcher in land tenure would do well to consult the *Agricultural Index* in which items covering books, journals, bulletins, periodicals, etc., are arranged by subject matter, and references to the particular area of study can be readily located. Another excellent source, although slower to use, is the monthly publication of the United States Department of Agriculture, *Bibliography of Agriculture*, wherein items are arranged under general subject heads and a yearly index is given by both subject matter and author. Other bibliographies that should be consulted are: *FAO Bibliography of Land Tenure*; United States Department of Agriculture list of available publications; United States Department of Agriculture Bibliographical Bulletin *22—Land Ownership; Cumulative Book Index; Readers Guide to Periodical Literature;* Eldridge: *The Materials of Demography*; and *Public Affairs Information Service.*

(*3*) *Books.* Only a few of the many books pertaining to land tenure can be listed here. Two publications that contain excellent references to additional publications are: *Origin of the Land Tenure System in the United States*, by Marshall Harris, and *Land Problems and Policies*, by V. Webster Johnson and Raleigh Barlowe. Other books the researcher may want to examine are: *Land Tenure and Land Taxation in America*, by Aaron Sakolski (1957); *Land Economics*, by Roland R. Renne (1958); *Rural Sociology*, by Lowry Nelson (1953); *Land Resource Economics*, by Raleigh Barlowe (1958); *Land Tenure* (world problems), edited by Parsons, Penn, and Raup (1956); *Rural Sociology*, by Alvin L. Bertrand (1958); *Land Title Origins*, by Alfred N. Chandler (1945); *Land Problems and Policies*, by John Timmons and William Murray (1950); and *Yearbooks of Agriculture*: especially *Land* (1958), *Farmers in a Changing World* (1940), and *Power to Produce* (1960).

(*4*) *State lists of bulletins and pamphlets.* Checklists of state, experiment station, and extension service publications are issued periodically. In addition, many universities publish lists of their publications. See for example: *Agricultural Publication*, California Agricultural Experiment Station and Extension Service, Division of Agricultural Sciences, University of California; and *List of Publications, Agricultural Experiment Station and Agricultural Extension Service, Iowa State University.*

### B. Sources of Published Data.

*(1) International.* Publications of the United Nations are listed in *The International Reporter,* issued bimonthly by the Columbia University Press. Attention is directed particularly to the Food and Agricultural Organization publication, *Monthly Bulletin of Agricultural Economics and Statistics.* Data and information are available from various other United Nations agencies also.

*(2) Federal Government.* Statistical data relating to agriculture abound in government publications. Some of the relevant sources are: *Statistical Abstract of the United States; Historical Statistics of the United States; Agricultural Statistics; Major Statistical Series of the USDA* (Agr. Handbook 118, especially vols. 2, 3, 6, and 7); *Graphic Summary of Farm Tenure; Statistical Summary of Farm Tenure; GSA Inventory of Federal Land; Census of Agriculture—General Report; Census of Agriculture—Special Reports* (especially multiple-unit operations, farm-mortgage debt, irrigation, size of operation by type of farm); *Current Developments in the Farm Real Estate Market; The Balance Sheet of Agriculture; Farm Costs and Returns; Commercial Farms by Type, Size, and Location;* and *Population and Rural Life Statistics.*

*(3) State reports.* In most states, various agencies prepare reports on subjects within their jurisdiction. These reports usually contain some data on subjects such as vital statistics, state lands, agriculture, health, and education.

### C. Unpublished Government Records and Reports.

A great deal more information is available in various public agencies than is published. Some of this information may be obtained for research purposes if suitable cooperative arrangements are worked out. A few examples of sources are:

*(1) Federal.* Agricultural Stabilization and Conservation Service, Soil Conservation Service, Forest Service, Public Health Service, Bureau of the Census, Economic Research Service, and the Information Service of any federal agency.

(*2*) *State*. Department of Agriculture, Land Board, Statistician's Office, and Office of Vital Statistics.

(*3*) *County*. Register of Deeds, County Clerk, Superintendent of Schools, and Assessor.

## D. FIELD STUDIES.

When desired information cannot be obtained from available sources, a " field " survey may be necessary. The techniques for mail and personal interview are discussed in detail in *Research Methods in the Behavioral Sciences*, by Leon Festinger and Daniel Katz (New York: Dryden Press, 1953); and *Surveys, Polls and Samples*, by Mildred Parten (New York: Harper and Brothers, 1950).

The foregoing should be regarded only as very general, preliminary leads. For a particular project, the researcher must locate facts wherever he can find them. Within this brief chapter, it is necessary to concentrate on what to do with facts rather than where to find them.[9]

*Using facts: Descriptive studies* consist of collections of unscreened information about a subject. These studies may be historical or situational, or some combination of both. The historical study attempts to show how conditions change through time. The situational study shows how conditions vary among groups of people, geographic areas, or other classes at one time. Descriptive studies may contain elegant classifications and typologies but, in general, they do not provide explanations, expose relationships, or permit tests. Although helpful in presenting the circumstances within which a research problem is found, a description alone has little analytical value. Descriptive studies are not designed to predict.

As a preliminary to research, acquaintance with the general nature of the subject to be studied may be gained through description. Too frequently, however, many research projects do not get beyond description. Facts cannot speak for themselves. They must be selected and interpreted. Description should be regarded only as the background for research.

[9] Methods of presenting facts is another subject that can receive only a nod in this chapter. We refer the reader to *Graphic Analysis* (Agriculture Handbook 128 [Washington: USDA, July, 1957]); Palmer O. Johnson and Robert W. B. Jackson, *Introduction to Statistical Methods* (New York: Prentice-Hall, 1953); and Willard C. Brinton, *Graphic Methods for Presenting Facts* (New York: The Engineering Magazine Co., 1914).

The *case study* is a means of collecting many facts about each unit of observation and of preserving the individuality of the unit throughout the analysis. This device is useful when little is known about the phenomenon in question. The case study can provide useful insight into general problems and can yield hypotheses for testing within a conventional scientific framework.[10]

The basic implication of the case method is that the case studied is representative of some broader universe. Selection of the case (usually a matter of the researcher's judgment), therefore, is very important, and indiscriminate use of this method can be more misleading than helpful.

As a distinct method of research, the case study has gone the way of the touring car and the bustle. However, like the touring car or the bustle, the case study appears now and then in some new form, in some new place.

Much empirical research involves the selection or collection of numerical data. Broadly speaking, these data are called " statistics." But to the extent that such data merely quantify a description without explaining or predicting, they are better termed " assembled numbers " to avoid confusion. Assembled numbers are not numerical counterparts of what were called descriptive studies above.

Assembled numbers may appear as background information for specific studies or as basic data for fields of inquiry. As background for a specific study, assembled numbers are needed to judge the relative importance of the various relationships to be tested. Basic data for a field of inquiry—say, land tenure—are needed to suggest problems, assess the importance of various problems, and broaden the inferences of specific studies.

Many compilations of data are important sources of information for research. The basic data supplied, for example, by the Censuses of Population and Agriculture, federal and state departments of agriculture and the United Nations, often are the only practical means of testing hypotheses about large populations. When readymade data must be used, it is sometimes necessary to adapt a hypothesis or adjust the data so that the facts available are valid for the test. When data are collected for a specific study, such adjustments should not be necessary.

---

[10] Marie Jahoda, Morton Deutsch, and Stuart W. Cook, in fact, use the term " insight-stimulating " study rather than " case method." *Research Methods in Social Relations* (New York: Dryden Press, Inc., 1951), 42–47.

*Analytical statistics* is a body of research techniques used in making valid inferences from quantifiable information. In general, statistics are used to make inferences about a larger population from a limited number of observations. Some of the advantages of statistics are economy over complete enumeration, precision over literal description, and validity over inference by judgment.

The social sciences particularly must depend on statistical methods for experimental control. A test of a hypothesis in physical science can often be accomplished with laboratory equipment. Experiments in a social environment must rely more heavily on control by mathematical manipulation. Therefore, statistics, as applied in either econometrics or sociometrics, is the principal basis for relating fact to theory in tenure research.

## What Do Research Results Show?

In the scientific process the assumptions of an inquiry and basic data determine the conclusions. Scientific methods and techniques are largely mechanical in the sense that they are devices for analysis; they cannot produce results better than the raw material to which they are applied. Methods are like automobiles. At best, they are effective in conveying the researcher down the road of inquiry. Given the road and the direction by the assumptions, the arrival at the destination is simply a matter of how fast and how skillfully the researcher applies the methods.

This interpretation of the scientific method means that the researcher must be familiar with the general theory and the subject matter of his inquiry, as well as skilled in methods and techniques of research. A responsible researcher devotes considerable attention to the assumptions that underlie the solution of his problem. The assumptions of a study should be stated explicitly at the beginning of the inquiry and perhaps next to the conclusions as well.

In scientific inquiry, the acceptance of a hypothesis indicates that necessary, not sufficient, conditions have been satisfied. *Research results show a measured weight of evidence—never proof.* But if the assumptions of an inquiry are clearly stated and the right research technique is properly used, the scientific method will provide valid statements rather than unsupported assertions.

The scientific method, rigorously applied, is man's only known protection from " accepting the plausible as true and rejecting the uncongenial as false." Strict adherence to mechanical, albeit unglamorous, methods separates scientific thinking from unfounded judgments. Even the most scientifically motivated researcher must continuously scrutinize his procedures for logical errors.

A scientific inquiry is subject to two forms of logical error. The first is the unwarranted conclusion or inference. This type of logical error is internal to the inquiry. It results from incorrect reasoning about the relation of the problem to hypothesis and the relation of hypothesis to test. The second type of logical error is the unwarranted extension or the projection of inference beyond the scope of the inquiry. Such errors are made when conclusions about one population or situation are projected to another or larger population. Both types of errors are to be avoided.

Statistical errors are often called Type 1 (rejecting a hypothesis when, in fact, it is true) and Type 2 (accepting a hypothesis when, in fact, it is false). No statistical procedure can protect the researcher completely from making these errors, but the likelihood of making the first type of error can be reduced by rejecting a hypothesis only if there is small probability that an estimate outside the range of acceptance could occur if the hypothesis is true. For the latter type of error, this writer recommends sympathy.

## Diagnosis and Remedy [11]

The function of the researcher is to describe, analyze, and predict. However, he may be called on to make recommendations for an appropriate action to accomplish some objective. Under such circumstances, it is important that he separate clearly his diagnosis from his remedy. This was stated earlier as the separation of *what is* from *what ought to be*. To the extent that the researcher is facile in the methods of science, he may claim some special competence in the value-free process of determining *what is*. Whether he could claim any special competence to prescribe *what ought to be* is doubtful. With the researcher equipped only with the tools of analysis, how does he contribute to the selection of an appropriate action?

It is sometimes possible for the researcher to analyze a set of actions so that their outcome may be predicted on an " if A, then B " basis.

[11] For an excellent treatment of this subject see " Proceedings of a symposium: ' Applied Social Research in Policy Formation '," *Philosophy of Science*, Vol. 16 (1949).

Such an approach confines the researcher to analysis only, yet yields results that may be useful in social engineering. If the array so analyzed includes all relevant actions, it may seem that analysis is tantamount to recommendation. But this is not the case, as recommendation usually involves assumptions, particularly as to values that are outside the scope of the analysis. The research scientist may predict the consequences of actions, but it does not follow that he is then in position to recommend action. In the world of practical research the subtle distinction between the diagnosis and the remedy is easily forgotten. For this reason, the objective researcher from time to time must appraise himself as well as his problems.

## Some Techniques for Empirical Research

A technique of empirical research refers to the way in which experience or fact is related to a conceptual model. Just as it is important to form tentative answers in a way that can be tested (hence hypotheses), it is important to choose an empirical test that is valid and efficient.

Validity means that the organized facts actually test the hypothesis, and efficiency means that best use is made of the facts.

Techniques of research vary as to popularity for more reasons than their inherent qualities. The following techniques are described largely in terms of how they might be used efficiently in tenure research without reference to any particular order of importance or usefulness.

### Regression and Correlation

Regression and correlation techniques are used to identify and measure the relationship between two or more variables. In regression analysis, some dependent variable, Y, is said to have some functional relationship with an independent variable, X. This relationship is called the regression of Y on X. Stated another way, values of X are used to " predict " values of Y. Regression is designed to answer the question: What amount of Y can we expect for a given amount of X?

Prediction in regression means estimation. It does not necessarily mean forecast, although some models may be developed to associate a variable in one time period with a variable in another time period. Neither does regression imply any cause-effect relationship between the variables X and Y.

Mathematically and intuitively, correlation is a combination of the regression of Y on X and the regression of X on Y. It is a measure of the *degree* of association of two variables, in contrast to regression, which describes the *form* of the relationship of two variables. Correlation is designed to answer the question: How closely are amounts of X associated with amounts of Y?

In the economic aspects of tenure research, regression analysis is particularly useful in describing production relationships, such as input-output, factor substitution, and product transformation functions.

In practice, regression and correlation problems frequently include more than two variables.[12] Until the relatively recent development of high-speed electronic computers, multiple regression and multiple correlation problems involving more than five or six variables were too laborious to compute. The number of variables is now limited mainly by the analytical capacity of the research worker, and the need for a simple solution.

### Analysis of Variance and Covariance

Analysis of variance (ANOVA) and its modification, covariance, are two empirical techniques which may also be used effectively in tenure research. They are used to determine whether one group of a population distinguishes itself from other groups in the population to a degree greater than could be attributed to chance. Analysis of variance, as described by its title, is based on comparisons of the variances of respective classes of a population with the variance of the population itself.

Essentially, it is the same as comparing the averages of several classes of a sample with the average of the whole sample except that use of the variance permits the researcher to see whether the differences obtained between classes might occur by any random grouping (in which case the differences in his chosen classes are not significant).

Suppose, for example, a sample of farmers whose overall average size of farm is 156 acres was classified into three groups—full owners,

[12] For examples of regression analysis in tenure research, see Walter G. Miller's, " Comparative Efficiency of Farm Tenure Classes in the Combination of Resources," *Agriculture Economic Research*, Vol. 11 (January, 1959) ; and Frank H. Maier, James L. Hedrick, and W. L. Gibson, *Sale Value of Flue-Cured Tobacco Allotments* (Va. Exp. Sta. Tech. Bul. No. 148 (Blacksburg: A. E. S., Virginia Polytechnic Institute, 1960) .

part-owners, and tenants—and their respective average sizes of farms were 155, 160, and 150 acres. Do these averages differ sufficiently so that, except for a small chance, such averages will not occur by throwing any three groups of operators together and computing their average acreage? ANOVA provides a simple, accurate test to see whether the groups under observation differ significantly.

A special modification of ANOVA, covariance, is used in analyzing the relation of two or more variables when some additional information is available on an associated variable that could not or was not included in the statistical design. Suppose in the ANOVA problem above, for example, the age of the operator is suspected to have an important associated effect on the length of lease. Analysis of covariance will permit the elimination of this age effect, so that the pure effects of residence on length of lease may be measured.

The tests of hypotheses in analysis of variance and regression depend on the rather rigid assumptions that (1) the characteristic to be measured is normally distributed in the population from which the sample is drawn and (2) the errors in sampling are also normally distributed. There are other techniques that do not depend on the assumption of a particular distribution and do not require the use of parameters of the distribution, such as the mean and variance, in calculating the statistics for test. Two of several such *nonparametric* techniques are discussed below. The *parametric* devices described above are more efficient statistically when a normal distribution can be assumed, but when a normal distribution cannot be assumed, the *nonparametric* techniques may be helpful.

### Enumeration Statistics

The regression and ANOVA techniques briefly described above are based on the measurement of some characteristic. Another group of techniques is based on *enumeration*, or counts, of cases occurring in various discrete categories. The statistical techniques, chi-square and rank correlation, described below, are illustrated by such enumeration data.

The relative ease of its computation and its flexibility often make *chi-square*, ($\chi^2$), a useful research tool, particularly for exploratory comparisons before more elaborate methods are undertaken. Chi-square, in one or more of its many variations, can be used in several different ways. One of these ways is to test whether two classifications of an observed group are independent or related.

As an example of how $\chi^2$ may be used to test the independence of two discrete variables, consider a simple tenure problem: The researcher is asked whether tenure status of young farm operators is related to family assistance. A group of twenty-seven owners is compared with a group of thirty-one tenants, according to whether they receive family assistance, with the following results:

OPERATORS 40 YEARS OF AGE OR LESS

|  | *Owners* | *Tenants* |  |
|---|---|---|---|
| Family assistance | 16 | 8 | 24 |
|  | (a) | (b) |  |
|  | (c) | (d) |  |
| No family assistance | 11 | 23 | 34 |
|  | 27 | 31 | 58 = N |

The hypothesis to be tested is that young operators who have had some family assistance are more likely to own their farms. The null hypothesis, of course, is that family assistance and tenure status are unrelated. To test the hypothesis, the value of $\chi^2$ calculated in the family assistance problem is compared with the appropriate value in a $\chi^2.95$ table (the .95 probability was chosen arbitrarily for this example). The value in the $\chi^2.95$ table is the largest value of $\chi^2$ one could expect if these two classifications—tenure and family assistance —were independent. The appropriate value of $\chi^2.95$ was found to be 3.8. The calculated value of $\chi^2$ was 6.99. Thus the first hypothesis was accepted and the null hypothesis rejected.

It may be useful to restate the hypothesis, test, and conclusion in this way: There seems to be some relationship between tenure status of young operators and family assistance because 95 per cent of a very large number of samples of independent items would have values of $\chi^2$ of 3.8 or smaller, and the sample chosen had a $\chi^2$ of 6.99. Or, stated more loosely, there is only a 5 per cent chance that variables in a sample of this size with $\chi^2$ greater than 3.8 are not related.

*Rank correlation* may be used to test the independence of two evaluations when the items to be evaluated cannot be measured but can be placed in order of importance. Suppose a test of harmony of landlord-tenant relationships requires a comparison of landlord and tenant attitudes about the relative importance of various components of the lease. The items in the lease can be ranked in importance by landlord and by tenant in the following order:

| Lease provision | Landlord | Tenant | $d_i$ |
|---|---|---|---|
| a. Term of lease | 3 | 1 | 2 |
| b. Repair of buildings | 2 | 4 | 2 |
| c. Rental rate | 1 | 2 | 1 |
| d. Expense sharing | 4 | 3 | 1 |
| e. Improvements | 5 | 5 | 0 |
| f. Management | 6 | 7 | 1 |
| g. Custom work | 7 | 6 | 1 |

The test of harmony (there may be many other tests) is that the rankings of importance of the lease provisions are similar; that is, the rankings are not independent.

The correlation calculated from the illustration above is .786, the maximum level of $r_{s.95}$ for independent rankings is .714, and so the null hypothesis, that the rankings by landlord and tenant are independent, is rejected. The $H_1$ hypothesis, that landlord and tenant similarly rank the lease provisions, is accepted.

Rank correlation may be of value in tenure research when (1) a measurement value cannot be assigned to the observations, (2) more information about relationships is required than a simple enumeration, and (3) the observations can be ranked under two or more classes.[13]

### Activity Analysis

Activity analysis as a research tool should be mentioned, if only because of its rapid development and increased use during and since World War II. One aspect of activity analysis, linear programming, has vastly expanded the scope of budgeting while using essentially the same assumptions.

Linear programming is a decision-making device. Its function is to determine a proper course of action, given stated objectives, measur-

[13] For treatment of nonparametric tests, enumeration statistics, and other statistical methods that are useful in tenure research, see Helen M. Walker and Joseph Lev, *Statistical Inference* (New York: Henry Holt & Co., 1953); Wilfred J. Dixon and Frank J. Massey, *Introduction to Statistical Analysis* (New York: McGraw-Hill, 1951); and for more intensive discussion, Leo A. Goodman and William A. Kruskal, "Measures of Association for Cross Classifications," *Journal of American Statistical Association*, Vol. 49 (1954), 732–64.

able consequences resulting from measurable actions taken, and limited means (usually " resources " in economics). As a decision-making device, programming is principally that of determining *what ought to be done*. Thus, it is *normative* in character. The statistical techniques briefly described in this chapter are designed to test hypotheses about " *what is*," i. e., with a positive approach. In keeping with the scope of the chapter, therefore, linear programming can receive only passing attention.[14]

Another aspect of activity analysis, input-output analysis, is more closely related to *positive* research. Originally conceived as a device for identifying and measuring the interdependence of sectors of the economy,[15] input-output analysis has been used on some broader economic problems in agriculture, particularly in problems of interregional specialization and product flows.[16] The input-output table is a scheme of coefficients that describes the relationships between various segments of specifically defined geographic or functional areas. Because it does describe, it may be used, in a sense, to predict. The use of input-output techniques in the analysis of tenure problems has not yet been appraised adequately, but in its broad sense, tenure is the relationship between resource owners and resource users. To the extent that interdependence of the owner and user groups and the subgroups within them can be expressed in coefficients, some modification of input-output analysis may be helpful in describing the tenure structure of an area.

[14] The potentialities of linear programming in providing recommendations for the solution of tenure problems should not be ignored. The researcher who works on tenure problems will profit by familiarity with at least the basic concepts and elementary computational methods of linear programming. Two excellent readings to start with are: Robert Dorfman, " Mathematical or ' linear ' programming: a nonmathematical exposition," *American Economic Review*, Vol. 43 (December, 1953); and Earl Heady and Wilfred Candler, *Linear Programming Methods* (Ames: Iowa State College Press, 1958).

[15] W. W. Leontief, *Structure of the American Economy, 1919–1929* (New York: Oxford University Press, 1951).

[16] See, for example, G. C. Judge and T. D. Wallace, " Estimation of Spatial Price Equilibrium Models," *Journal of Farm Economics*, Vol. 40 (November, 1958), 801; and Earl O. Heady and John A. Schnittker, " Application of Input-Output Models to Agriculture," *Journal of Farm Economics*, Vol. 39 (August 1957), 745; or Heady and Candler, *Linear Programming Methods*. For a general evaluation of input-output analysis, see National Bureau of Economic Research, *Input-Output Analysis: An Appraisal* (Princeton: Princeton University Press, 1955).

## Game Theory

Models developed to explain the strategies of persons involved in various tenure arrangements constitute a promising field of socioeconomic research. These game theory models [17] contain the attributes of both sociology and economics. Most " games " (especially in tenure) involve behavior patterns dependent on the interpersonal relations of two or more persons and thus are social in nature. Games also are based on maximizing principles and thus are economic in nature.

Game theory is a formal means of explaining behavior of a person (or persons) when the attainment of his objective is in competition with the attainment of the objective of another player (who is usually, but not always, thought of as another person). From the standpoint of farm tenure, landlord-tenant relations seem to be a natural for the illustration of game theory.

For practical purposes, the history of formal game theory covers less than two decades, [18] but advances in this field have exceeded what economists and sociologists have adequately digested and applied. Study of strategies of landlord and tenant may be a fruitful venture for researchers interested in tenure problems.

[17] Game theory methods are sufficiently unique to warrant a section apart from the techniques described. Considering the scope of this chapter, however, the relation of game theory to tenure research is thrown in more or less as an afterthought. The reader is referred to Duncan R. Luce and Howard Raiffa, *Games and Decisions: Introduction and Critical Survey* (New York: John Wiley & Sons, 1957). A helpful thumbnail treatment of games may be found in Heady and Candler, *Linear Programming Methods*, 449–527.

[18] J. Von Neumann and Oskar Morgenstern, *Theory of Games and Economic Behavior* (Rev. ed.; Princeton: Princeton University Press, 1955).

# Name Index

# Subject Index